BENT'S
LIFE HISTORIES OF
NORTH AMERICAN BIRDS

BENT'S
LIFE HISTORIES OF
NORTH AMERICAN BIRDS

VOLUME I *Water Birds*

EDITED AND ABRIDGED BY
Henry Hill Collins, Jr.

HARPER & BROTHERS, PUBLISHERS, NEW YORK

CONTENTS

INTRODUCTION

Arthur Cleveland Bent was one of the great bird students of North America. His *Life Histories of North American Birds* (1919-1958) is an ornithological masterpiece. Its twenty volumes are wide-ranging in scope, comprehensive in content, and filled with the pulsating enthusiasm of a man whose scientific life work must have been one of his life's most sustained pleasures. In the field of zoology, the *Life Histories* constitute a literary landmark of a magnitude not equalled hitherto in America or the world.

Wendell Taber, who knew Bent, tells in the In Memoriam that follows of his life and activities and how he decided to become the biographer of the birds. I never knew Bent myself, but I grew up in the pleasant shade cast by the monument of his books. For forty years the appearance of each new volume has been an ornithological milestone. Those who possessed the entire set, lovingly increased by each new volume as it appeared, represented to lesser eyes the privileged group of American birders. Any volume of Bent was a prized possession, and the earlier ones, as they went out of print, were special treasures. To quote Bent on any species was to quote, in almost every instance, the most thoroughgoing available authority. At the end of the field trip, doubtful points, or doubtful species, were checked in Bent, if the relevant volume were at hand.

Alas, as the need for more copies increased with the great increase in the number of birdwatchers, available copies of the *Life Histories* virtually disappeared, or were held for such prices as to put them out of ordinary reach. Despite verbatim reprints of four issues and an increase in the initial order of recent volumes at the Government Printing Office, most of them today are out of print. The complete set of the twenty bulletins (as they are modestly called by the Smithsonian Institution, the publisher) so far issued is sold for as much as $250.

To make Bent more accessible to the present-day birdwatcher is the purpose of this abridgment into two volumes—Water Birds and

Land Birds. But it is an abridgment using full excerpts, not condensations—for such would have killed the spirit of the author, whose strong, free style, fresh with wind and sea, would not have survived the imprisonment of a digest.

Bent, it seems to me, tries to give in each life history the personality of the bird, or its place in the world of man; or, sometimes, its place in history. Certain birds are famous for their flight, others for their courtship. The nests of some are remarkable, as are the eggs of others. The plumages of many excite admiration, the peculiar habits of a number may be especially noteworthy. Various ones are renowned for their extensive migrations, certain others for their colonial nesting habits. Contact with man has hurt some birds, helped others. A number have provided man with sport, with food, or with vexation. The history of several, since European settlement of the continent, is fraught with special romance, and sometimes with tragedy. These are some of the subjects with which the *Life Histories* deal.

Bent's interests include both the mother's down and the downy young; the location of the species on the taxonomist's chart and the location of the duck hunter's blind in the Massachusetts marsh. These and many other facets of the bird and its place in the world, Bent discusses. If he knows the species or the facts himself he takes us along with him in the comfortable and secure sweep of his own prose. If others know the species or the facts better, he lets them tell us what they know.

I have attempted in these two volumes to select excerpts of the *Life Histories* that would illustrate these characteristics of the original. Omitted almost completely, therefore, are the data on plumages, distribution, field marks, eggs, and technical details. These are well covered in various books already possessed by most bird men. I have rather chosen passages that show the bird in other aspects of its life, or that discuss the place of the bird in the world in which it lived at the time that Bent, or Bent's sources, wrote. These selections in many cases show conditions as they once were; not as they necessarily are now. Where conditions in recent years differ widely from those described in the *Life Histories* a footnote is appended.

These books are designed for the field man and the student of birds. They are meant to supplement (obviously not to replace) the standard field guides. He who reads these passages will, I hope, acquire a richer, fuller understanding of the world of North American birds, birdwatchers, and bird hunters.

Bent's writing and his interests reflect naturally enough the times in which he lived. The collecting of birds' nests and eggs was at its height in his early years and when many of the authorities he quotes were writing. So were market hunting, spring shooting, and live decoys. Bent decries with vehemence the massacre of millions of birds for the millinery trade and the commercial food market. Yet he sheds a sportsman's tear at the outlawing of spring shooting for brant; and he reserves some of his most colorful paragraphs for the joys of the duck hunter.

Bent lived in an era—not totally vanished—when emphasis was placed on which birds were beneficial and which were supposedly harmful to man's interest. The broader, overriding effect of the existence and activities of a species on the balance of nature as a whole was then less often realized or stressed. The day of the birdman as ecologist had not arrived. Like a good reporter, Bent describes the temper of his times—and as the times changed during the forty-four years he spent at his task, he changed, too. Yet I doubt that he ever outlived the memory, or the anticipation, of a roast brant and a bottle of Burgundy; and the sight of a rare or beautiful clutch of eggs must have made his eye as a collector gleam long after the theft of a bird's nest and eggs was outlawed by statute and public opinion.

Like a philosopher and humanitarian Bent deplores the slaughter and cruelty of the early days. Mournfully he predicts the extinction of certain species that enlightened conservation in our day may still bring back from the verge of annihilation. But he did not live to see the new and deadly menaces of widespread spraying of insecticides and of nuclear radiation from fall-out. His attitude toward these, had he lived to know of them, may well be imagined.

As time passed Bent began to doubt that he would live to see the end of his stupendous project. One day he turned to Wendell Taber and asked him if he and the Nuttall Ornithological Club, of which both were members, would take up the work when Bent laid it down. Taber accepted. Bent finished the manuscript for the twentieth volume in 1949. It was published in 1958, four years after his death. The two volumes of the *Life Histories* (on the *Fringillidae*) still to be published will come out in time under the aegis of the Arthur Cleveland Bent Life History Committee of the Nuttall Ornithological Club. Wendell Taber, Chairman of this Committee, has graciously agreed to the use in this abridgment of his In Memoriam of Bent which appeared in *The Auk* of October 1955.

I shall be pleased if, from this abridgment, new generations of birdwatchers can be introduced to Bent's *Life Histories*. Perhaps it will please Bent himself, from beyond the sunset, to know that in this way many another, who otherwise could not do so, will be able to share some of his choicest experiences—to feel the fog closing in on him on an Aleutian island; to see the avian multitudes and witness the avian tumult about Bird Rock; to hear the lapping of the waves on the shores of Florida Bay; or to welcome back to a Massachusetts garden the returning hosts of spring.

Henry Hill Collins, Jr.

Scarsdale, New York
December 1, 1959

NOTES

Each species Bent treated that occurs or occurred annually in North America north of Mexico, i.e., the area of the American Ornithologists' Union (A. O. U.) Check-List except Lower California, is included in this abridgment. Casuals and accidentals are not included, nor are species of annual occurrence only since Bent's day such as the Cattle Egret, Ringed Turtle Dove, Spotted Dove, and Spotbreasted Oriole. Bent also did not treat two introduced species, namely, the Mute Swan and the Rock Dove. Sometimes in this abridgment excerpts from two or more subspecies accounts are given under one species. In such cases the scientific trinomial appears as a subtitle together with the former official English name in parentheses.

The common and scientific names of species and subspecies in the titles, and the order of the species in this abridgment, follow the 1957 Check-List of the A.O.U. (These names and order often differ from those in the 1910 and 1931 Check-Lists used in Bent's original.) Common and scientific names in the body of the text, however, are those used in the original, with a reference to the 1957 Check-List name, where helpful.

On the title line a name in parentheses indicates the contributor of the text on that species. The texts of all other species were written by Bent himself. At the end of each species is given the year when the volume containing it was published, or the year when the original manuscript was completed, if Bent gave this information. The years in parentheses following an author's name refer to the year of publication of his work from which Bent quoted. These references are cited in the Bibliography, p. 329. Brief biographies of most of these authors are given at the end of the companion volume on Land Birds.

The sequence of paragraphs under each species has occasionally been changed, and an editorial privilege of running together selected sentences and paragraphs has been used to promote smoother reading. Otherwise, except for footnotes and editorial insertions in brackets the original text is preserved throughout.

THE SMITHSONIAN INSTITUTION BULLETIN NUMBERS, TITLES, AND DATES OF PUBLICATION OF THE TWENTY ORIGINAL VOLUMES ARE AS FOLLOWS:

107. Life Histories of North American Diving Birds, August 1, 1919
113. Life Histories of North American Gulls and Terns, August 27, 1921
121. Life Histories of North American Petrels and Pelicans and Their Allies, October 19, 1922
126. Life Histories of North American Wild Fowl (part), May 25, 1923
130. Life Histories of North American Wild Fowl (part), June 27, 1925
135. Life Histories of North American Marsh Birds, March 11, 1927
142. Life Histories of North American Shore Birds (pt. 1), December 31, 1927
146. Life Histories of North American Shore Birds (pt. 2), March 24, 1929
162. Life Histories of North American Gallinaceous Birds, May 25, 1932
167. Life Histories of North American Birds of Prey (pt. 1), May 3, 1937
170. Life Histories of North American Birds of Prey (pt. 2), August 8, 1938
174. Life Histories of North American Woodpeckers, May 23, 1939
176. Life Histories of North American Cuckoos, Goatsuckers, Hummingbirds, and Their Allies, July 20, 1940
179. Life Histories of North American Flycatchers, Larks, Swallows, and Their Allies, May 8, 1942
191. Life Histories of North American Jays, Crows, and Titmice, January 27, 1947
195. Life Histories of North American Nuthatches, Wrens, Thrashers, and Their Allies, July 7, 1948
196. Life Histories of North American Thrushes, Kinglets, and Their Allies, June 28, 1949

ACKNOWLEDGMENTS

The publishers and the author wish to thank the authors and copyright owners listed below for their permission to quote in this abridgment extracts from these works:

"Report on the Parasitic Jaeger" by R. M. Anderson in *My Life with the Eskimo*, by Vilhjalmur Stefansson, The Macmillan Co., 1918.

Birds of Washington, by John H. Bowles and W. Leon Dawson, Cooper Ornithological Society, Los Angeles, Calif., 1909.

Camps and Cruises of an Ornithologist, by Frank M. Chapman, D. Appleton and Co., 1908.

Birds of California, by W. Leon Dawson, Cooper Ornithological Society, Los Angeles, Calif., 1923.

Hill Birds of Scotland, by Seton Paul Gordon, Edward Arnold (Publishers) Ltd., 1915.

Game Birds of California, by Joseph Grinnell, Harold Child Bryant, and Tracy Irwin Storer, University of California Press, 1918.

The Flight of Birds, by Frederick Webb Headley, H. F. & G. Witherby Ltd., 1912.

Birds of La Plata and *A Hind in Richmond Park*, by W. H. Hudson, E. P. Dutton & Co., Inc., 1920, 1922 respectively.

British Bird Book, ed. by F. B. Kirkman, Thomas Nelson & Sons, Ltd., 1910.

The Hawks of North America, by John B. May, National Audubon Society, 1935.

British Diving Ducks, by John G. Millais, Longman's, Green & Co., Inc., 1913.

Feathered Game of the Northeast, by Walter H. Rich, Thomas Y. Crowell Co., 1907.

"Kings of Winter" by Herbert R. Sass, *Good Housekeeping*, Curtis Publishing Co., February, 1930.

IN MEMORIAM: ARTHUR CLEVELAND BENT

BY WENDELL TABER

ARTHUR CLEVELAND BENT, President of the American Ornithologists' Union from 1935 to 1937, died in his home on December 30, 1954. Born on November 25, 1866, the son of William Henry Bent and Harriet Fellowes Hendee Bent, he had lived for many years at 140 High Street in Taunton, Massachusetts, diagonally across the street from the home of his childhood days. Bishop Cleveland, for whom he was named, was a favorite friend of the family.

His mother died when he was about six years old. Not many years later his father, watching a frail and delicate child growing up, embarked him on an invigorating outdoor life to promote physical development. Father and son would amble off together on long walks into the woods and country so easily accessible around Taunton in those days. Came the bicycle at first, that one-huge-wheel affair with trailer-wheel, and carriage drives to exercise the family horse. Not until many years later, when he was in middle life, did the era of the automobile arrive. Much of the time he was alone, simply because of inability to arouse interest among his companions. With the limited transportation facilities of the era, bird trips were necessarily of a type that would now be considered local. Rarely did they extend beyond the neighboring townships of Rehoboth and Fall River. Ultimately, he became acquainted with and frequently joined forces with Owen Durfee of Fall River, only a few years his senior. In these boyhood days, too, came the beginnings of specimen and egg collections. Carried on throughout years of travel all over North America, the specimen collection ultimately attained a size which warranted presentation to Harvard University. Similarly, the United States National Museum in Washington received a 30,000-unit egg collection. The trips were health-maintaining, and ornithologically constructive. At home, the use of an ax later in life was a daily delight. At night came setting-up exercises with dumbbells. His major long-distance trips ceased when he was sixty: the ax and dumbbells he kept using until he was over eighty.

Primary education in the local public schools instilled in him a lasting spirit of democracy. After seven years of secondary education at Bristol Academy, he entered Harvard College. He graduated, with Honorable Mention, and an A.B. degree, in 1889. A broken nose from boxing reflected his athletic career.

In the fall of 1889, he commenced work with the Massachusetts National Bank at a salary of $15 a month. Early in 1890, however, he went to Fall River to learn the cotton mill business, working in the Crescent Mills. In the fall of 1891, he took charge of the Seamless Pocket Mill in Plymouth, a position he retained for four years, drawing a monthly salary of $50. He was able to augment his income by acting, also, as manager of the Atlantic Covering Co., which manufactured magnet wire. Here he obtained a yearly salary of $1000. He invested $1000 in the business—and lost it when the company failed in the Panic of 1893. In the fall of 1892, he and a certain John Scott purchased the Plymouth Electric Light Co. from the General Electric Co. for $87,500—in notes with company bonds as collateral. He writes:

"In the Panic of 1893 the Electric Light Company defaulted on its bonds and was bankrupt and so was I, as I could not meet my notes. John Scott died bankrupt and I had to buy out his interest in the company and assume his debt. But I persuaded the General Electric Company to let me work out the situation, which I finally did."

One sees, here, the beginning of the successful business man, inspiring confidence and trust, overcoming tremendous obstacles, forging ahead. In his sixties, "After the sale of Plymouth interests, (I) retired from all business, to live on income from what was left, and devote my time to ornithology."

On October 23, 1895, he married Rosalba Peale Smith, daughter of Professor Clement L. Smith, a former dean of Harvard College. After a few months the Bents moved from Plymouth to Taunton and Bent became associated with the Mason Machine Works as superintendent's assistant. Ultimately he became general manager, a position held before him by his father and brother. He moved the Seamless Pocket Co. to Lowell in connection with the Whittier Cotton Mills there, and was able to reduce his time with that company to one day a week. Childless, the couple was divorced in 1911.

In 1914, he married Madeleine Vincent Godfrey, who survives as do three married daughters, six grandchildren, two great granddaughters, and a great grandson. The family is noted in Taunton for its almost Scottish clannishness and unity. On Thanksgiving Day in 1954 the assembled family, eighteen of them, took turns going upstairs to see the patriarch.

One can but be awe-struck by the dynamic energy and vitality displayed by this former "frail youth." In his initial three jobs, he worked from 6:30 A.M. to 10:00 P.M daily. Success came from all directions—business, civic affairs, charities, ornithology. He was president and treasurer of the Plymouth Electric Light Co. from 1900 to 1931, and general manager of the Mason Machine Works from 1900 to 1914. He also served as treasurer and director of this company. At one time or another he acted as vice president and manager of the Campbell Printing Press and Manufacturing Co., New York, vice president of the Autoplate Co. of America, director of the Jager Engine Co., and director of the Corr Manufacturing Co. He preferred that limited success which he could derive operating from his own home city to the greater glitter of a business career in a large metropolis. Envisioning the future of the then infant public utility field, he organized and developed a number of small, local utilities. He was president of the Provincetown Light and Power Co.; president of the Old Colony Light and Power Association; director of the Plymouth Gas Co. and the Southeastern Massachusetts Power and Electric Co.; and trustee of the Massachusetts Utilities Associates.

Civic duties he took seriously, entering wholeheartedly into the life of his community. He was an alderman of Taunton in 1906 and one of the nine members of the first Municipal Council set up in 1910 under the new city charter. He also held a three-year term on the School Committee. During the First World War this prominent business executive and municipal leader, a corporal in the State Guard, drilled in the armory, on rifle range, on parade, under regular army discipline, and did a tour of duty in camp each summer. He also acted as escort for the governor on the latter's public appearances. He still found time to become farm agent for the Food Administration Board, urging Bristol County farmers to produce more food, and he worked closely with the Exemption Board to secure exemption from military service for those farmers who were producing satisfactorily. He was a member of the local committee on public safety, and a "Four Minute Speaker." He organized and served as president of the Bristol County Academy of Sciences, acted as president of the Taunton Chamber of Commerce and a trustee of the Taunton Savings Bank. Many were the other committees of which he was chairman or a member, undertaking to raise funds for various civic purposes.

Along charitable lines he was vice president of the Associated

Charities of Taunton. Came the depression of the 1930s and he acted
as chairman of the so-called "Rochester Plan" which raised over
$300,000 in promised employment for improvements. He took special
interest in youth and for his services as Scout Commissioner for
Anawan Council, Boy Scouts of America, he received the Silver
Beaver with citation. He also took an interest in the John Burroughs
Association in New York and was a recipient of the John Burroughs
Medal. He served as president of the Massachusetts Society for the
Prevention of Cruelty to Children, and the Social Welfare League.

Devoutly religious, he took an active part throughout his adult life
as vestryman, clerk, or senior warden of the St. Thomas Episcopal
Church in Taunton.

Indicative of the extraordinary breadth of mind and character of
the man was his club membership. He organized, became president
of, and moved a few times, the Segregansett Country Club as it is
now called. He was a member of organizations such as the Taunton
Yacht Club, the Taunton Rod and Gun Club, the Bristol Branting
Club—and in sharp contrast, organizations such as the Massachusetts
Audubon Society where his name appeared in the lengthy list of
honorary vice presidents, the Massachusetts Fish and Game Protective Association, the Massachusetts Forestry Association, the
American Forestry Association, and the National Association of
Audubon Societies. Other clubs included the Old Colony Club in
Plymouth, the Harvard Clubs in Taunton, Fall River, and Boston,
the University Club in Boston, the Cosmos Club in Washington, and
the Explorers Club (honorary) in New York.

In spite of the pressure of business, civic, and charitable interests,
he somehow found time, too, to keep up an interest in birds and to
publish numerous minor ornithological papers. Until about twenty-five
years ago the Bents maintained a summer home in Harwich on Cape
Cod. Thence it was but a short motor trip to Chatham and Monomoy.
The latter area was a favorite haunt. In later life he looked forward
annually to a day's outing counting osprey nests in the late spring
in southeastern Rhode Island and adjoining parts of Massachusetts.
Many were the different ornithologists who partook in this memorable
event. Not infrequently the group would record, also, the Carolina
Wren and the White-eyed Vireo.

The childhood joys of exploring the great unknown found reflection
in the adult on a grand scale. And this in spite of an episode which
might well have caused a less confident, strong-willed man to relax
into a life of comparative ease! Right at the peak of his young man-

hood, in 1896, alone, he shinned without climbers up the trunk of a large dead oak in a tract of swampy, mixed woods in North Middleboro, near Taunton. While attempting to reach into a wide, deep cavity for the eggs of a Barred Owl, he slipped and fell. He jerked to a stop with his arm tightly wedged in the narrow slit at the lower end of the opening. For twenty-five minutes by the village clock, visible in the distance (he would take note of that) he struggled hopelessly, calling in vain for help. How, he never knew: he tore his arm loose. The fall should have killed him. On the ground, he rested for some time in a state of collapse and exhaustion. For the rest of his life he carried the reminder—a trembling hand. With the passage of time the other hand developed a sympathetic reaction.

The great unknown called him. Without premeditation, he prepared himself by travel and exploration for greater things to come. Later, as part of his self-preparation for writing life histories, he methodically set about the task of seeing North America. The chronology of his trips is:

1901. North Dakota with H. K. Job and C. G. Day
1902. Florida, east coast, with Job and Day
1903. Florida Keys, with Job and Day
1904. Magdalen Islands and Nova Scotia with Job, M. L. Church, and an eager youth named James Lee Peters
1905. Assiniboia, Saskatchewan, with Job and Day; L. B. Bishop joined them later
1906. Saskatchewan, with Bishop; later, Jonathan Dwight joined them
1907. Cobbs Island, Virginia, and Nova Scotia, both with Bishop
1908. Florida Keys with F. M. Chapman and L. A. Fuertes
1909. Labrador, southern, with C. W. Townsend
1910. Louisiana coast
1911. Aleutian Islands and Alaskan points with A. Wetmore, R. H. Beck, and F. B. McKechrue
1912. Newfoundland and eastern Labrador with D. B. MacMillan
1913. Manitoba with Job and F. S. Hersey
1914. California and the Canadian Rockies with Madeleine V. Bent
1915. South Carolina with his family and A. T. Wayne; also alone to the Magdalen Islands
1916. Virginia with H. H. Bailey
1917. Northern Saskatchewan alone
1918-19. Remained at home on war work

1920. Percé, Province of Quebec, with family
1922. Arizona with F. C. Willard
1923. Texas with G. F. Simmons and others
1924-25. Central Florida with family
1926. Central Florida with family
1929. California with family
1930. Southern Florida with family

Here, again, the family man is in evidence. Mrs. Bent quite unconsciously summarizes much in writing, "Time was such a precious commodity to him, and although he gave much of himself to his family and friends, most of his days were spent in accomplishment in many walks of life."

On November 18, 1888, just before his twenty-second birthday, a senior at Harvard, he was elected a member of the Nuttall Ornithological Club. Under the then by-laws of the club his membership automatically ceased when he left Cambridge upon graduation. Of this brief initial membership, however, C. F. Batchelder wrote in "An Account of the Nuttall Ornithological Club, 1873 to 1919," that "even in that short time he had taken such a place that he was not to be forgotten." To the end of his life it was a bitter blow that, as one of the oldest members of the club in 1938, yet still physically active, there could be no fiftieth anniversary celebration at Mr. Batchelder's home. Actually, Bent had been re-elected, under revised by-laws, in 1896, and he had served on the Council from December 1, 1902, to December 7, 1914. Some compensation for this unfortunate situation did occur when, on October 15, 1945, he was elected to honorary membership. To the best of my knowledge such rank has otherwise been held only by Henry Wetherbee Henshaw, John Hall Sage, and Witmer Stone, all of whom were elected on the occasion of the Club's fiftieth anniversary celebration on December 7, 1923.

In 1893, Bent became a member of the Wilson Ornithological Club. Not until 1909 did he become an Associate of the American Ornithologists' Union, but by 1920 he was a Fellow. He became a vice president in 1929 and was elevated to the presidency in 1935. In 1909 he also joined the Cooper Ornithological Club. He was elected an honorary member of this organization in 1933. Other associations included the old Boston Society of Natural History, the Linnaean Society (honorary), the Philadelphia Academy of Natural Sciences, the California Academy of Sciences, and the Maine Audubon Society. He was a recipient of the William Brewster Award from the American Ornithologists' Union, and the Daniel Giraud Elliot Medal from the

National Academy of Science. At Harvard University, he was Associate in Ornithology attached to the Museum of Comparative Zoology. In Washington, he held the Asher Chair of Biology at the Smithsonian Institution and the title of Collaborator, United States National Museum. Modestly, he writes: "In considering the amount of ornithological work that I have done, allowance must be made for the fact that I was deeply engaged in various business enterprises until I was 48 years old, and only partially retired then. I did not wholly retire from business until I was over 60. Most of my ornithological exploration was done between the ages of 35 and 60. I have not travelled far from home since I was 65."

Not until 1910 did he undertake to carry on the work left unfinished by Major Charles Bendire. In that year, under the instigation and encouragement, especially, of Charles Foster Batchelder, who continued a lifelong admirer, he engaged with the Smithsonian Institution to write "six large volumes" of "Life Histories of North American Birds," as he calculated in 1914. Another forecast, "It will be my life work," proved far more accurate. Characteristically, he elected to lay out a framework uniformly applicable throughout the entire Check-list and to start anew from the very beginning. He gathered material himself. He engaged the cooperation of ornithologists throughout the Western Hemisphere—and ultimately even abroad—originally as contributors of information, later as collaborating authors. His vision stood the test of time and expanding knowledge. Minor changes or additions sufficed to maintain the standards at modern levels. The consensus of many qualified ornithologists today is that the series should be completed in its original style.

The Smithsonian Institution has published nineteen volumes of "Life Histories of North American Birds" by Arthur Cleveland Bent. These carry through the North American Wood Warblers. The twentieth volume, on the Icteridae and Thraupidae, has long been in Washington awaiting publication. Except for a few papers in process of preparation by collaborating authors, a twenty-first volume, as planned by him and extending through the Green-tailed Towhee, *Chlorura chlorura,* is in manuscript.

Rare, indeed, is the person so showered with success in whatever he touched who, though exhibiting justifiable pride and pleasure at times, could in the same moment display that modesty so distinctive in and dominative of his entire life. What better manifestation than his comments in the first of the Life History volumes—"No one is so well aware of the many shortcomings and omissions as the author. Allowance must be made for the magnitude of the undertaking."

His work commenced in 1910. The first volume was published in 1919. With the publication of the volume on Wood Warblers in 1953 the business man, impatient for action, but long accustomed by that time to protracted delays between completion of manuscript and appearance in print, took the offense as the best defense. Smarting a bit, perhaps, from criticisms of having omitted important recently published papers from his compilations (an unfair criticism), he remarks in the Introduction. "The manuscript for this Bulletin was written in 1945; only important information could be added. If the reader fails to find in these pages anything that he knows about birds, he can only blame himself for failing to send the information to—The Author."

The long delays in publication might well have caused a weaker personality to give up. Bent went doggedly on. The work necessarily made him almost a hermit during working hours—yet this was not such in fact. The vital correspondence served as a substitute, keeping his brain in active contact with other brains. The sedentary nature of his work, commenced so late in life, coupled with his enthusiasm, may well have been a major factor in his longevity.

Seldom does it fall to the lot of man to have evidenced in his old age the esteem not only of his contemporaries—those that remain—but of younger generations in addition. On his eightieth birthday, November 25, 1946, after his customary spell with his ax, he went to attend in Boston a birthday dinner given under the auspices of the Nuttall Ornithological Club. From far and wide assembled 112 men. James Lee Peters, president of the Club, presided. Also at the head table was Hoyes Lloyd, at that time president of the American Ornithologists' Union. Other Fellows present were James P. Chapin, L. Griscom, A. O. Gross, F. C. Lincoln, H. C. Oberholser, and A. Wetmore. Charles Foster Batchelder, Bent's senior by over ten years, was able to attend in spirit, only. Jim Peters, commenting on the presence of nine Fellows and seven Members, remarked he had never seen so much North American ornithological talent assembled at once outside of an "A.O.U. Meeting." Of the other persons present, five have since been elected Members.

Meeting for the first time this man in his middle eighties, one might well have been startled to see him suddenly galvanize and become the alert, tense young business executive, sparkling with power and confidence as he responded in emergency with a flashing, concluding major decision. Incredible? No! Underneath, never dormant, was that driving force and first-hand knowledge of humanity which had taken him to the top in the business world. One saw only the decision. Long in advance he had been thinking, thinking, laying plans against what his calm, analytical judgment told him *could* happen. The crisis came! He was ready!

3 Mercer Circle, Cambridge 38, Massachusetts, May 30, 1955.

LOONS—ORDER GAVIIFORMES

LOONS Family Gaviidae

COMMON LOON *Gavia immer*

Among the picturesque lakes of the wilder, wooded portions of the Northern States and Canada—where dark firs and spruces mingled with graceful white birches, cast their reflections in the still, clear waters [we hear] the weird and mournful cry of the loon. Who has ever paddled a canoe, or cast a fly, or pitched a tent in the north woods and has not stopped to listen to this wail of the wilderness? And what would the wilderness be without it?

Dr. P. L. Hatch (1892) relates the following account of an early morning performance [in Minnesota]:

It has been my privilege to witness some scenes of their matutinal jollifications, which have always occurred at the earliest dawn, and have terminated with the advent of the sun. The night is spent in proximity to each other on the water, somewhat removed from the land. And in the earliest morning, notes of the parent male soon call out a response from the other members of the family, when they all draw near, and after cavorting around each other after the manner of graceful skaters for a brief time, they fall into line, side by side, and lifting their wings simultaneously, they start off in a footrace on the water like a line of school children, running with incredible speed a full quarter of a mile without lowering their wings or pausing an instant, wheel around in a short circle (in which some of them get a little behind) and retrace their course to the place of starting. This race, after but a moment's pause, is repeated over and over again, with unabated zest, until by some undiscoverable signal it ceases as suddenly as it began. Its termination is characterized by a subsequent general congratulation manifested by the medley of loon notes. This walking, or rather running, upon the face of the quiet lake waters is a marvel of pedal performance, so swiftly do the thin, sharp, legs move in the race, the wings being continuously held at about half extent. Soon after this is over, the male parent takes to wing to seek his food in some distant part of the same or some other lake, which is soon followed by the departure of the

1

female in another direction, while the young swim away in various directions to seek their supplies nearer the place of nightly rendezvous.   1919

YELLOW-BILLED LOON   *Gavia adamsii*

This large and handsome diver is essentially a bird of the Arctic coast. Few naturalists have ever seen it.

Mr. John Murdoch (1885) says of its appearance at Point Barrow [Alaska]:

They are first to be seen about the end of May, or early in June, at the "lead" of open water and flying inland to their breeding grounds. As the sea opens along the shore and open holes are found in the lagoons they are to be looked for in such places, gradually going out to sea as the season advances. Fully fledged young were seen August 7, 1883. The breeding grounds are probably around the swamps and lakes some distance inland.

Mr. Joseph Dixon (1916) refers to the flight of this species as follows:

The flight of the yellow-billed loon in migration was one of the most impressive sights of our Arctic trip. A dim speck low over the frozen tundra or glaring ice fields suddenly develops wings which beat rapidly with the rhythm and energy of a steam engine. The huge bill and neck seem to be extended slightly upward and the bird glides swiftly forward in a straight line with none of the undulating movements of the brant and eider ducks. The rapid "swish, swish," of the huge wings dies away in the Arctic silence, and the next moment one is gazing in the distance where a rapidly diminishing dark object seems to be boring a hole in the low clouds in the east. There was no variation in speed or direction, and the birds traveled at least 40 miles an hour over a measured distance.   1919

ARCTIC LOON   *Gavia arctica*

Coues (1877) gives an interesting account of the habits of this species on the coast of southern California; he writes:

They were very plentiful about the Bay of San Pedro [November 1865]. The first thing that attracted my attention was their remarkable familiarity; they were tamer than any other waterfowl I have seen. They showed no concern at the near approach of a boat, scarcely availed themselves of the powers of diving, in which the whole family excels, and I had no trouble in shooting as many as I wanted. They even came up to the wharves, and played about as unconcerned as domestic ducks; they constantly swam around the vessels lying at anchor in the harbor, and all their motions, both on and under the clear water, could be studied to as much advantage as if the birds had been placed in artificial tanks for the purpose. Now two or three would ride lightly over the surface, with the neck gracefully curved, propelled with idle strokes of their broad paddles to this side and that, one leg after the other stretched at ease almost horizontally backward, while their flashing eyes, first directed upward with curious sidelong glance, then peering into the depths below, sought for some attractive morsel. In an instant, with the peculiar motion, impossible to describe, they would disappear beneath the surface, leaving a little foam and bubbles to mark where they went down and I could follow their course under water; see them shoot with marvelous swiftness through the limpid element, as, urged by powerful strokes of the webbed feet and beats of the half-opened wings, they flew rather than swam; see them dart out the arrow-like bill, transfix an unlucky fish, and lightly rise to the surface again. While under water, the bubbles of air carried down with them cling to the feathers, and they seem bespangled with glittering jewels, borrowed for the time from their native element, and lightly parted with as they leave it, when they arrange their feathers with a slight shiver, shaking off the last sparkling drop. The feathers look as dry as if the bird had never been under water; the fish is swallowed head first, with a curious jerking motion, and the bird again swims at ease, with the same graceful curve of the neck.

Murdoch (1885) refers to the vocal powers of this species as follows [at Point Barrow, Alaska]:

Their peculiar harsh cry, "kok, kok, kok," from which they get their name, "Kaksau," is to be heard all summer, and the birds were seen nearly every day, flying backward and forward and inland from the sea. During the breeding season these smaller loons have a habit of getting off alone in some small pond and howling like a fiend for upward of half an hour at a time. It is a most bloodcurdling, weird, and uncanny sort of a scream, and the amount of noise they make is something wonderful. They can be heard for miles.   1919

RED-THROATED LOON   *Gavia stellata*

The rugged coast of Labrador, with its chain of rocky islands, ice-bound for nine months of the year, and enveloped in fog or swept with chilling blasts from drifting icebergs during most of the other three, seems bleak and forbidding enough as we pick our way through the narrow channels back of the outer islands. But in the interior it is different. Though the summer is short, the sun is high in the heavens and the days are long; the abundant moisture in the air stimulates the growth of vegetation; the snow disappears rapidly and the verdure of spring follows quickly in the wake of retreating winter. Within a few feet of a vanishing snowbank I have seen the dwarfed willows, recently uncovered, already budded and bursting into leaf and a few yards farther away fully leaved out or even blossoming. Back from the rocky coast only a short distance the rolling hills are softly carpeted with deep mosses, covered with fresh verdure, and dotted with blooming wild flowers in great variety and profusion. Here among the thousands of small lakes and ponds in the sheltered hollows, fed with the water from melting snow, and studded with little islands, the red-throated loons find a congenial summer home and hither they come as soon as the fetters of winter are unlocked. We saw them everywhere along both the south and north coasts almost daily, flying inland to the lakes or even about the little ponds on the islands.

Throughout northern Alaska the red-throated loon is the most abundant and most widely distributed species, a characteristic feature of the Arctic tundra, where it can be seen at any time flying up or down the rivers or to and from the tundra pools. The harsh, goose-like, honking calls or the weird, shrill cries of this species may be heard at all hours of the day, or even during the short Arctic night, the most characteristic sounds of these northern solitudes.   1919

GREBES—ORDER
PODICIPEDIFORMES

GREBES   Family Podicipedidae

RED-NECKED GREBE   *Podiceps grisegena*

One beautiful moonlight night in June, as we lay at anchor near some Manitoba marshes, I had a good chance to study the love song of this interesting bird. The night was calm and the mosquitoes made sleep impossible, as we lay rolled in our blankets on the deck of our little boat, listening to the varied voices of the marsh. The real striking features of the concert, the solo parts, were the weird cries of the Holbœll's grebes,[1] heard only at infrequent intervals. The performance begins with a series of loonlike wailing cries, loud and piercing at first, and then runs off into a series of short, plaintive, vibrating wails, "*ah-ooo, ah-ooo, ah-ooo, ah-ah-ah-ah-ah;*" sometimes it ends in a more staccato, chattering trill and might be indicated thus: "*whaaa, whaaa, whaaa, whaaa, whaaa, chitter-r-r-r-r-r-r.*" There is considerable variation in the length and form of the song in different individuals. The love song of the Holbœll's grebe may be heard at any time during the day or night, but it is indulged in more freely in the early morning and toward the dusk of evening.

Mr. Alvin R. Cahn (1912), who had an excellent opportunity to study this species at close range through an opening in the ice of Cayuga Lake [New York], describes its movements under water as follows:

The water was clear, and the bird could be seen plainly, shooting and zig-zagging about, midway between the surface and the bottom. While swimming under water, the neck is extended to its utmost, and both legs and wings are used. With neck outstretched, the bird offers the least possible resistance to the water, there being a smooth and gradual transition from the tip of the slender bill to the middle of the back, the widest part

[1] As this species was then called.

5

of the body. The speed which is developed under water is marvelous, at times it being almost impossible to follow its movements, which were so rapid that the bird appeared more like a large, gray fish darting about. When coming to the surface the bill and head appeared slowly, when a glimpse of the observer caused it to dive again. In diving, even though the body was under water, the bill went down first, so that it really dove instead of sinking quietly.

The freezing of Cayuga Lake offered a rare opportunity for a study of this most interesting and apparently little known bird. Until the present time, the Holboell's grebe has been considered only a rare visitant at the southern end of the lake, one or two being recorded almost every winter. It has proved, however, to be the predominant grebe during this winter, 28 individuals having been taken. The reason of its unprecedented abundance here is undoubtedly to be found in the six weeks of extremely cold weather, and the consequent closure of waters in other regions. The sudden closing of the lake's surface in one night left these birds in an absolutely helpless condition, since open water is a necessity for taking flight in this group of birds, Holboell's grebe being no exception to the rule. As a result eleven beautiful specimens were picked up alive from the ice in perfectly good physical condition. If approached while sitting on the ice, these birds made no attempt to escape. They would strike at the outstretched hand, and would emit calls very loonlike in general quality. Once the bird alights upon the ice, it is unable to take flight, and must await starvation or other tragic end. At best, all it can do is to flap its wings and possibly scrape along over the ice a few feet. The position of the legs, together with the smooth surface of the ice, rendered these efforts at locomotion entirely futile.   1919

HORNED GREBE   *Podiceps auritus*

In its winter haunts on our coasts the horned grebe is commonly seen singly, or in small flocks, just outside the breakers along the beaches or near the rocky shores, diving for its food, playing about in the waves, or riding buoyantly over them; occasionally one is seen asleep with its bill tucked under its scapulars. Often it is more gregarious, particularly on inland lakes, where sometimes as many as one hundred and fifty to two hundred are seen in a flock. When alarmed the whole flock suddenly disappears, all diving in unison.

The flight of the horned grebe is strong, direct, and well-sustained; it looks, when on the wing, much like a miniature loon. Its neck and its legs are stretched out to their full extent, fore and aft, and its wings vibrate very rapidly. In winter it is difficult to distinguish from the eared grebe, but it can be easily distinguished from the pied-billed grebe by the absence of brown in its plumage and by its white secondaries, which are very conspicuous in flight. Its wings are small in proportion to its weight, so that it experiences some difficulty in rising from the water or from the ground; in rising it has to run along the surface for a long distance, beating the water with both wings and feet; but, when well under way, it attains very good speed. When migrating it usually travels singly or in small scattered flocks.

Dr. Charles W. Townsend (1905) has well described its diving power, as follows:

The diving of this grebe is often a beautiful piece of work. The bird springs vigorously upward and forward, the bill cleaves the water on the downward curve just as the feet leave it, while the whole body describes an arc. The wings are closely applied to the sides, and do not flop out as in the Alcidae, where they are used for flight under water. In the grebes the feet are the propelling power in the forceful initial spring and in the movements below the water. That the wings are kept close to the sides under water I have been able to observe when the grebes were borne up in the advancing rollers on Ipswich Beach [Massachusetts]. The clear water before the waves broke revealed the diving birds.   1919

EARED GREBE   *Podiceps caspicus*

The little eared grebe is widely and evenly distributed throughout western North America; from the Great Plains west to the Pacific coast and in most of the inland marshy lakes it is an abundant species.

Mr. Robert B. Rockwell (1910) gives us the following good account of the behavior of young grebes:

A baby grebe half the size of a chick can swim as fast as a man can wade through the water comfortably, and the distance they can swim under water at this tender age is surprising. They hide very effectively by diving and coming up to the surface under tiny bits of floating moss or rubbish, where they lie perfectly still with only the tips of their tiny bills exposed above the water. Their feet are abnormally large, which probably accounts for their remarkable swimming ability, and when quiet in the water the feet and head float on the surface, the rest of the body being submerged. The only note of the young grebe is very similar to the "cheep" of the domestic chick, first heard when the egg is pipt—very weak and tiny at first, but growing in strength and power as the bird becomes larger, until by the time the young are three-fourths grown the note is quite loud and clear.

The young birds have a peculiar habit of riding on the back of the parent birds. This is apparently done for the purpose of imaginary protection to the young, as we only observed it when broods of young were surprised close to the shore, and were seeking safety in the middle of the lakes. At such times the parent would swim close alongside the young bird and by raising the fore part of the body out of the water would submerge the posterior portion, upon which the youngsters would scramble with alacrity. The wings of the parent were then raised something after the fashion of a brooding hen, and often several babies would be cuddled comfortably beneath them. It was quite comical to see a well-laden parent bird attempt to take on an additional chick, as this often precipitated the entire brood into the water, and this was always the signal for a wild scramble back on "board ship," during which rather strenuous performance the doting parent was the victim of an animated mauling. This additional weight on the parent's back did not seem to affect their swimming powers, and the speed with which a mother grebe carrying a half a dozen babies could leave danger behind was surprising.

This species, as well as the western grebe, has suffered seriously from market hunting for the millinery trade, notably in the lake regions of Oregon and California, where thousands were shot every week during the breeding season; they were tame and easily killed. The breasts were stripped off, dried, and shipped to New York, where they were much in demand for ladies' hats, capes, and muffs. The hunters realized about twenty cents for each skin, which brought them in a handsome income.[1]   1919

LEAST GREBE   *Podiceps dominicus*

Mr. Vernon Bailey (1902) observes:

These tiny grebes are as common in the ponds of southern Texas as the dabchick[2] in the North. In open water they bob on the little waves, and in quiet pools where the willows overhang the banks swim and dive among the sedges and pink water lilies. When not seeking food below the surface of the water they usually keep close to some cover, and in the middle of the day if not hidden in the sedges are found sitting close under the shore grass or in the shade of a bush or low-hanging tree.

The Mexican grebe[3] has recently been found breeding in Bexar County, Texas, by Messrs. Roy W. Quillin and Ridley Holleman (1916), who say:

About ten miles south of San Antonio there is a large marshy lake which covers something like a thousand or twelve hundred acres. Being the only body of water of this size in this part of Texas, and having exceptional surroundings, it is the mecca of the water birds of this county. Practically the entire lake is surrounded by a barrier of cat-tail reeds, tules, and marsh grass, which in some portions is one hundred or more yards in width.

[1] This species has now long been protected.
[2] Pied-billed Grebe.
[3] As Bent called this species.

While seaching for nests of the American eared grebe in a secluded inlet of this like we located our first nest with eggs of the San Domingo grebe[1] (*Colymbus dominicus brachypterus*). Both cat-tails and tules were growing at this point, but not so thickly as they are generally found. In one of the small patches of open water which break the monotony of these reed jungles the nest was anchored. In general appearance the nests examined by us average somewhat smaller than nests of the American eared grebe, this being especially true of the hollow in which the eggs are deposited. The nests were composed of decayed reeds of every description, heaped into a cone-shaped mass measuring from four to six inches in height and from fourteen to twenty-four inches in diameter at the base, tapering to six or eight inches at the top, and they were liberally plastered with mud, especially the depression which held the eggs. The area of this depression, the depth of which is about one inch, is determined by the number of eggs in the clutch, as they fit snugly into it.   1919

WESTERN GREBE   *Aechmophorus occidentalis*

Where the sweet waters of Bear Creek empty into Crane Lake the bare shores of a somewhat alkaline lake are transformed into a verdant slough of tall waving bulrushes surrounding a small grassy island overgrown with scattering patches of wild rose bushes, a green oasis of luxuriant vegetation in the waste of bare rolling plains of southwestern Saskatchewan. I shall never forget the picture, as I stood in water more than waist deep, of one of these beautiful "swan grebes" sailing out from a dense wall of cat-tails, causing scarcely a ripple as it glided along, the body submerged, the long white neck sharply outlined against the green background, the glossy black crown, the fiery red eyes, and the javelin-like beak. Who could help admiring such a picture of aquatic grace, such specialized mastery of its native element? Its delicately poised head was ever alert, its keen red eyes were watching every motion and, as I moved one step nearer, the graceful neck was arched, the javelin beak plunged downward, and the slim body followed in a curve below the surface, leaving scarcely any wake behind it. The water was clear and I was near enough to follow its course as it sped away beneath the surface, a long slender pointed craft, propelled by two powerful paddles and with wings tightly closed. The western grebe is certainly a water nymph of the first class, built for speed and action, the most highly specialized of all our diving birds.

The large grebe colonies of the Klamath Lake region in southern Oregon and northern California have been described by several well-

[1] As this species was then called.

known writers. The lakes in this region contain probably the largest western grebe colonies in this country where thousands of them breed in harmony with Caspian and Forster's terns, white pelicans, and other water birds. This region has long been famous as a profitable field for plume hunters, where they have reaped a rich harvest, making $20 or $30 a day and during the height of the breeding season killing several thousand birds a week. The breasts of the western and other grebes were in great demand for the millinery trade; for the paltry sum of 20 cents apiece they were stripped off, dried, and shipped to New York. Such slaughter could not have continued much longer without disastrous results. Through the activities of the Audubon Societies, the attention of President Roosevelt was called to the need of protection, and on August 8, 1908, he set apart the Klamath Lake Reservation, and on August 18, 1908, the Lake Malheur Reservation, thus saving from destruction the largest and most interesting wild-fowl nurseries on the Pacific coast.   1919

PIED-BILLED GREBE   *Podilymbus podiceps*

This species is less often seen in flight than the other grebes, for it seems to prefer to escape by diving or skulking, but it is well capable of rapid flight, when necessary, in spite of its small wings. When rising from the water it runs along the surface for a long distance, beating the water with its broad paddles until it can rise into the air, when it flies swiftly away in a straight line, moving its wings very quickly and with its neck and feet outstretched. When migrating it often flies high in the air.

Mr. William Brewster (1906) describes a former nesting site of the pied-billed grebe in Massachusetts as follows:

On June 13, 1891, Mr. Walter Faxon found a number of pied-billed grebes breeding at Great Meadow. There can be little doubt that they had been established there for some time previous to this, for the shallow brush-grown reservoir which they inhabited had then been in existence for nearly twenty years. On the occasion just mentioned, Mr. Faxon saw or heard at least six or eight different birds, one of which was accompanied by chicks only a few days old, and on April 27, 1892, he discovered a nest containing five fresh eggs.

During the following eight years Great Meadow was frequently visited by our local ornithologists, and the manners and customs of the grebes were closely studied. One or two birds often appeared in the pond as soon as it was free from ice—this sometimes happening before the close of March—and by the middle of April the full colony was usually reestablished. It was difficult to judge as to how many members it contained, for they were given to haunting the flooded thickets, and we seldom saw more than three or four of them on any one occasion; but at times, especially in the early morning and late afternoon when the weather was clear and calm their loud cuckoo-like calls and odd whinnying outcries would come in quick succession from so many different parts of the pond that one might have thought there were scores of birds. Probably the total number of pairs did not ever exceed a dozen, while during some seasons there were apparently not more than five or six. They built their interesting floating nests in water a foot or more in depth, anchoring them to the stems of the sweet gale and button bushes, and laying from five to eight eggs, which usually were covered by the bird whenever she left them. Although a few sets of eggs were taken by collectors, the grebes reared a fair number of young every season, and without doubt they would have continued to resort to Great Meadow for an indefinite period had not the reservoir been abandoned, and its waters almost completely drained in the autumn of 1901; since then the birds have ceased, of course, to frequent the place.

1919

ALBATROSSES, SHEARWATERS, PETRELS, AND ALLIES—ORDER PROCELLARIIFORMES

ALBATROSSES   Family Diomedeidae

SHORT-TAILED ALBATROSS   *Diomedea albatrus*

The short-tailed albatross bears a superficial resemblance to the wandering albatross, but it is decidedly smaller and certain details of its color pattern are different. It is said to be less active than some of the other species. In the dark immature plumage it is likely to be confounded with the black-footed albatross, but it is larger and darker, lacks the white face, and has a pink bill.

Dr. E. W. Nelson (1887) says that he:

found them very common between the islands east of Unalaska. The birds were very conspicuous from their white plumage and great size. During calm days they were most numerous, and ten or fifteen were frequently seen at a time. Unlike the black-footed albatross, these birds do not appear to follow vessels, and, in fact, are so shy that as a rule they give a wide berth to any species of sailing craft.

Mr. H. W. Elliott (1875), in writing of the birds of the fur seal [Pribilof] islands, about 1875, says:

Twenty or thirty years ago, when whaling vessels were reaping their rich harvests in Bering and the Arctic Seas, the albatross was often seen about the islands, feeding upon the whale carrion which might drift on shore. But with the decrease of the whale fishery the birds have almost disappeared. Only a single individual was noted during my two years' residence. This was taken by Dr. Meany on the north shore of Saint George's.

The decline of the whale-fishing industry since that time has probably still further reduced the abundance of this species in those waters. [Almost exterminated by Japanese feather hunters who killed some 5,000,000 of these birds on Tori-shima Island of Izu group,

Japan, between 1889 and 1902; Tori-shima made a bird sanctuary in 1933; 1954 population of these birds, 10 pairs.]   1922

BLACK-FOOTED ALBATROSS   *Diomedea nigripes*

As we steamed out through Dixon Entrance [Alaska] we soon realized that we were actually going to sea. We began to see the long saber-like wings of the black-footed albatrosses or "goonies," as they are called, skimming low over the heaving billows of the ocean, pelagic wanderers from warmer climes, gleaning a scanty living from the watery wastes. During our four days' trip over the Pacific Ocean to Unimak Pass they were our constant companions. In stormy weather, of which we had plenty, they were more numerous and active, sometimes as many as six being seen about the ship at one time. They will always be associated in my memory with the ocean storms, with the plunging of the ship over mountainous seas, and with the whirr of racing propellers over the crests of mighty waves. Amid all the grandeur, exciteme⌐⁺ and danger of a storm at sea the albatross glides calmly on, rising easily over the crests of the highest waves, and gracefully sailing down into the valleys between them, frequently lost to sight but never troubled or confused, thoroughly at home in its native element.

It was a constant source of delight to watch the graceful evolutions of this albatross, as it followed our ship day after day, rising and falling at will and sailing straight with the wind on rigid wings. The large webbed feet were stretched out beyond the tail, and, with webs extended, served as a rudder in turning. When alighting on the water the feet were spread wide apart, the tail was spread and depressed and the wings were held upwards as it dropped gently down onto the crest of a wave; it deliberately folded its long wings without wetting them. After alighting, it often drifted far astern before rising again. This it could easily do in rough weather by slowly unfolding its wings and launching into the air off the crest of a wave, but in calm weather it was necessary for it to run along the surface to gain a little headway. If the wind was blowing strongly it could easily catch up with the ship without flapping its wings. It sits very high on the water and swims slowly.

Doctor Fisher (1906) has described the flight of this species so well that I can not do better than quote his remarks as follows:

As is well known, albatrosses are past masters at soaring or sailing. If the wind is favorable they are able to skim over the water for a long time without once flapping their wings. *D. nigripes* is certainly no exception to the general rule, and we had ample opportunity to witness their powers. The long slender wings, with long humeral bones, are eminently fitted for this sort of existence, and their construction renders flapping laborious, for in proportion to its size the albatross is not a very muscular creature and could not fly a great distance if obliged to do so by wing beats. When a stiff breeze is blowing albatrosses can sail only against the wind or with it, and are able to quarter a breeze, or go directly across it only for a short distance and when under great momentum. When we were steaming directly against the wind the albatrosses had no trouble in following us, and they would fly all around the ship without flapping their wings except when the breeze was strong, and then they were obliged to give a few vigorous beats when turning up into the wind. When, however, our course lay at an angle to the wind, they followed us by sailing in a series of ellipses. They would, in this case, sail directly against the wind, approaching us on the starboard quarter, go over the stern a short distance to port, then wheel and scud before the breeze perhaps 100 yards off the starboard quarter, when they turned and approached us as before. Their speed was so superior to ours that they were able to keep up without any trouble, and their frequent trips astern and rapid overhauling again made our cumbersome gait all the more apparent. Of course as they neared the turning point each time they had to quarter the breeze a little and for a moment sail directly across it.   1922

LAYSAN ALBATROSS   *Diomedea immutabilis*

On their arrival[1] and all through their breeding season these birds indulge in a very peculiar and interesting dance, which the sailors refer to as a "cake walk." Doctor Fisher (1904) has fully described the performance, as follows:

This game or whatever one may wish to call it, very likely originated in past time during the courting season, but it certainly has long since lost any such significance. At first two birds approach one another, bowing profoundly and stepping heavily. They swagger about each other, nodding and curtseying solemnly, then suddenly begin to fence a little, crossing bills and whetting them together, sometimes with a whistling sound, meanwhile pecking and dropping stiff little bows. All at once one lifts its closed wing and nibbles at the feathers beneath, or rarely, if in a hurry, quickly turns its head. The partner during this short performance, assumes a statuesque pose, and either looks mechanically from side to side, or snaps its bill loudly a few times. Then the first bird bows once, and pointing its head and beak straight upward, rises on its toes, puffs out its breast, and utters a prolonged, nasal, *Ah-h-h-h,* with a rapidly rising inflection, and

---

[1] At Laysan Island, now part of the Hawaiian Islands National Wildlife Refuge.

with a distinctly "anserine" and "bovine" quality, quite difficult to describe. While this "song" is being uttered the companion loudly and rapidly snaps its bill. Often both birds raise their heads in air and either one or both favor the appreciative audience with that ridiculous and indescribable bovine groan. When they have finished they begin bowing to each other again, rapidly and alternately, and presently repeat the performance, the birds reversing their role in the game or not. In the most successful dances the movements are executed in perfect unison, and this fact much enhances the extraordinary effect.

In 1902, the glories of Laysan Island were in their prime and the number of breeding sea birds was at its maximum. Doctor Fisher agreed with Prof. C. C. Nutting that there were, at least, a million albatrosses breeding on the island, in addition to all the hosts of other species. The nests were so close together that the birds were almost touching each other and it was difficult to walk without treading on eggs. But a great change took place during the next ten years, for a party of Japanese feather hunters visited the island and materially reduced its wonderful bird population. In comparing the conditions, noted by him in 1903 and in 1911, Mr. William Alanson Bryan (1912) says:

The slaughter wrought by the plume hunters is everywhere apparent. One of the work buildings formerly used by the guano company and later as a storehouse by the poachers is still standing. With a side torn out and left open to the weather by the men of the *Thetis*, it is still filled with thousands of pairs of albatross wings. Though weatherbeaten and useless, they show how they were cut from the birds whose half-bleached skeletons lie in thousands of heaps scattered all over the island.

This wholesale killing has had an appalling effect on the colony. No one can estimate the thousands, perhaps hundreds of thousands, of birds that have been wilfully sacrificed on Laysan to the whim of fashion and the lust of gain. It is conservative to say that fully one-half the number of birds of both species of albatross that were so abundant everywhere in 1903 have been killed. The colonies that remain are in a sadly decimated condition. Often a colony of a dozen or more birds will not have a single young. Over a large part of the island, in some sections a hundred acres in a place, that ten years ago was thickly inhabited by albatrosses, not a single bird remains, while heaps of the slain lie as mute testimony of the awful slaughter of these beautiful, harmless, and without doubt beneficial inhabitants of the high seas.   **1922**

SHEARWATERS AND FULMARS
Family Procellariidae

FULMAR   *Fulmarus glacialis*

The fulmar is a distinctly pelagic species of arctic seas, where it is ever associated with drifting icebergs and floating pack ice. Like the albatross it spends much of its time on the wing and is particularly active in rough and stormy weather. It is well known to the explorers who risk their lives in dangerous northern seas, where it follows the ships to gorge itself on what scraps it can pick up, rests to digest its unsavory food on some rugged block of ice, and retires to some lonely crag to rear its young. There is little that is attractive in its surroundings at any time, in the forbidding climate of the rugged, frozen north, but there it seems to live and flourish, rising successful and triumphant over adverse conditions.

Much has been written about the feeding habits of the fulmar, which are interesting though not attractive. The following quotations will show that it is a greedy and voracious feeder on a varied diet. The best account seems to have been given by Macgillivray (1852) as follows:

From the various statements made by observers, it appears that the fulmar feeds on fishes, cephalopodous mollusca, cirripedia, most other kinds of animal substance, especially such as are oily or fatty. The Rev. Mr. Scoresby, in his "Arctic Regions," states that it is the constant companion of the whalefisher, joining his ship immediately on passing the Shetland Islands, and accompanying him to the highest accessible latitudes, keeping an eager watch for anything thrown overboard. Fulmars are extremely greedy of the fat of the whale. Though few should be seen when a whale is about being captured, yet, as soon as the fleshing process commences, they rush in from all quarters and frequently accumulate to many thousands in number. They then occupy the greasy track of the ship; and, being audaciously greedy, fearlessly advance within a few yards of the men employed in cutting up the whale. If, indeed, the fragments of fat do not float sufficiently away, they approach so near the scene of operations that they are knocked down with boat hooks in great numbers, and sometimes taken up by the hand. The sea immediately about the ship's stern is sometimes so completely covered with them that a stone can scarcely be thrown overboard without striking one of them. When anything is thus cast among them those nearest the spot where it falls take the alarm, and these exciting some fear in others more remote sometimes put a thousand of them in motion; but, as in rising into the air, they assist their wings for the first few yards by striking the water with their feet, there is produced by such a number of them a loud and most singular splashing. It is highly amusing to observe the voracity with which they seize the pieces of fat that fall in their way; the size and quantity of the pieces they take at a meal; the curious chuckling noise which, in their anxiety for dispatch, they always make; and the jealousy with which they view and the boldness with which they attack any of their species that are engaged in devouring the finest morsels. They frequently glut themselves so completely that they are unable to fly; in which case, when they are not relieved by a quantity being disgorged, they endeavor to get on the nearest piece of ice, where they rest until the advancement of digestion restores their wonted powers.   1922

CORY'S SHEARWATER   *Puffinus diomedea*

. The Chatham bars, dangerous, shifting sand shoals, guard the entrance to a broad and placid bay at the elbow of Cape Cod which is separated from the ocean by a narrow strip of beach many miles long, known as Nauset Beach and made famous by Thoreau. Exposed to the unbroken swell of the Atlantic Ocean these bars are nearly always white with combing breakers and during easterly storms are seething masses of foam and flying spray, beautiful to look upon, but much dreaded by sailors, as they have proved to be the graveyard of many a good ship. Only during the smoothest weather do the fishermen dare to venture out across the bars to their fishing grounds offshore. Many a time have I joined them on their trips in their staunch catboats, picking our way safely among the bars, leaving the gulls and terns behind us as the land faded in the distance. When safely over the bars we could feel the gentle ground swell of the ocean and begin to look for the gliding forms of the shearwaters, the slender winged ocean wanderers. We were seldom disappointed, for this is a famous summer resort for *Tubinares* [Procellariiformes] and the birthplace of the so-called species *Puffinus borealis*.[1] Here on October 11, 1880, Mr. Charles B. Cory (1881) obtained the type specimen from which he described the species.

Mr. Ogilvie-Grant (1896) writes of the habits of this species on the Salvages [near Madeira]:

Our arrival on Great Salvage apparently caused great excitement among the bird inhabitants, our tent being a special object of wonder, the pardelas, or Mediterranean shearwaters,[2] being especially bold and noisy in their

[1] As it was named by Cory.
[2] *P.d. diomedea;* our western Atlantic form is *P.d. borealis.*

greeting. The high volcanic rocks surrounding the south bay are full of miniature caves, in most of which a pair of the pardelas had their home, and toward sunset the whole population turned out, wheeling and screaming around our encampment and offering the most tempting rocketing shots as they swept over the high rocks above us.

The male, in a harsh guttural voice, cried "*ia-gow-a-gow-a-gow*," and the female chimes in "*ia-ia-ia*," and it may be imagined that with thousands of these miscreants circling close round our tent during the entire night, tired as we were, sleep was almost impossible on the first evening of our stay. During the whole of our visit we used every night to be mobbed by these noisy birds. The "march past," as we called it, generally commenced about six and continued with unabated zest till we turned in about 10:30 and heard no more. In spite of the tempting shots they offered, we killed very few of these birds, only such as we required for specimens; but our men were not so sparing, for they used every day to catch numbers for food (they skinned and boiled them!) and took back sackfuls to Las Palmas, where, when salted, they are much esteemed by the Spanish fishermen.

1922

PINK-FOOTED SHEARWATER   *Puffinus creatopus*

Nothing was known about the nesting habits of this species until Mr. Rollo H. Beck, of the Brewster-Sanford expedition to South America, found them breeding on islands in the Juan Fernandez group, off the coast of Chile. He has kindly sent me the following notes:

On December 12, 1913, I started out from the settlement on Masatierra Island, on the Juan Fernandez group (which lies about 400 miles to the westward of Valparaiso, Chile), to find the nests of the pink-footed shearwater. About four miles from the village many holes were found, but nearly all were too deep and long to be opened without pick or shovel. One hole 6 feet long was opened and a pair of birds was found at the end. Burrows were found from near shore up into the ferns at 1500 feet elevation. On the 15th I went again to the colony with a man to dig for me. One burrow was followed for 10 feet. It then branched for the third time and went too deep to follow. Nearly all the burrows were 6 feet or more in length; sometimes a little grass was found in the nest, but usually only bare earth in the enlarged end of the burrow. Three eggs only were taken, although a number of holes were opened. On the 31st of January we tried the colony again and found a few birds on eggs nearly ready to hatch.

On the 19th of January 1914, I visited Santa Clara Island 10 miles off Masatierra and found colonies of birds nesting in the soft ground on top of the island. Some of the burrows here were just below the grass roots and easily opened while others ran deep down. Nearly all the nests were nicely lined with foxtail straws and an occasional burrow also had a lining. Most of the eggs were well advanced in incubation and in one nest I found a bird setting on two eggs. One of these proved however to be rotten and was probably a last year's egg. The pink-footed shearwater when disturbed on its egg becomes decidedly pugnacious picking wildly at any object and frequently at a single blow will break its egg before it can be removed from the nest. The birds about the island in the daytime spend most of their time sitting on the water in flocks differing in this respect from their neighbors, the neglected petrels which nest along the cliffs, and spend their daylight hours in swinging singly about over the ocean.   1922

PALE-FOOTED SHEARWATER   *Puffinus carneipes*

This large dusky shearwater resembles the sooty shearwater and might easily be mistaken for it in life, but it is distinguished from it by having a light-colored bill and flesh-colored feet and by the absence of any whitish or ashy gray on the under wing coverts.

The following quotation from Prof. Leverett M. Loomis (1918) tells us about all we know[1] of the pale-footed shearwater as a North American bird:

So far as I am aware, this Southern Hemisphere shearwater has been reported for the eastern side of the Pacific only from the vicinity of Point Pinos, California, where Mr. R. H. Beck has secured during his various expeditions ten specimens for the Academy and four for the University of California. Mr. Beck's notes concerning them are as follows:

During my eleven months' stay in 1907 I saw nine flesh-footed shearwaters.[2] They were then perhaps more plentiful than in other seasons, though the close watch I kept on shearwaters that year and the abundance of sooty shearwaters partly account for so many being seen. On February 27, while I was out six miles northwest of the buoy amongst a large flock of fishing birds, I noticed a flesh-footed shearwater flying past. A long shot caused him to circle off and drop, but in the choppy sea I would have lost him had not a Cooper's [Pink-footed] shearwater circled about and showed me the dead bird's position. On April 29, about six miles northwest of the buoy, I scared up a small bunch of sooty shearwaters, and a flesh-footed swung up and was shot. June 25 was foggy, with shearwaters abundant from Moss Beach to Seal Rocks. A mile or so off Seal Rocks a flesh-footed shearwater, two hundred yards away, was seen flying along toward Point Pinos. A dead sooty shearwater thrown into the air called him over and he was secured. He flew with slower wing beats and was more deliberate in flight than the sooty shearwater.   1922

[1] Or did as of 1922.
[2] As Beck called this species.

GREATER SHEARWATER   *Puffinus gravis*

(Townsend)

To the bird student who rarely ventures from the beaches or sheltered bays out onto the unprotected ocean a glimpse of a shearwater—the hag, hagdon, or hagdown of sailors—is most unusual. In easterly storms, however, these birds may sometimes be seen close to our Atlantic shore and I have seen them fly within a stone's throw of Ipswich [Massachusetts] beach. Under ordinary conditions, however, they are not often found less than five miles from land. Graceful birds they are and well do they deserve their name, for on nimble wing they are ever on the alert to cut or *shear* the water in their search for food.

The largest number I ever saw was on a July day on the Labrador coast between Battle and Spear Harbors. The wind was strong on shore, bringing in wisps and clouds of fog from the numerous icebergs which beset the coast. At first our steamer disturbed from the water groups of fifty to a hundred shearwaters, but, as we pushed north, larger and larger flocks arose and flew outside until we had seen at least ten thousand of these splendid birds. The great flock extended for several miles along the rugged coast and with the exception of three sooty shearwaters all were the greater species.

The following graphic account of the greater shearwaters on the fishing banks is contributed by Mr. Walter H. Rich:

The discovery of a morsel of food adrift means that every hag within reach will come charging down at full speed and plump headforemost into the midst of a plunging, striking mass of birds upon the water. Presently one will get a good hold upon the prize and strive to bear it away. Instantly he is mobbed, and a mix-up as desperate as any college football game can show is in progress at once. Here and there a bird slips quietly out of the mass and hurriedly gulps down the bit he has managed to secure, gasps a couple of times, sounds his squealing war cry, and runs upon the water with rapidly moving feet, his half-opened wings fanning the surface, his body held almost erect upon his tail, and plunges again head long into the mêlée. Here and there the curving fin or the waving fluke of the big blue shark shows above the water where he sculls lazily through the seas, rolling clumsily to snap at floating fish or waste and missing as often as he wins, for the hags take desperate chances with him, scuttling clear only at the last instant. Perhaps they are not always fortunate, for birds minus a foot or otherwise maimed are not lacking in the flocks. I saw one whose upper mandible was missing from the nostrils out. The bird seemed in pretty good condition, too, for food was plentiful and easily secured.

The meal finished they rest upon the water, if the weather is fine, bathing and dipping like sparrows in a puddle, with much shaking of wings, wagging of tails, and dipping of heads and beaks, rising on their tails to splash, dive, and splutter. This over, they settle down upon the sea to drift at ease, only rising to fly lazily to a position slightly in advance of the steamer, thus paralleling her course and making sure that they are properly placed at the next signal for hauling the net.   1922

NEW ZEALAND SHEARWATER   *Puffinus bulleri*

To Mr. Leverett M. Loomis (1900) belongs the honor of definitely adding this species to the North American list by actually taking a specimen; he describes the event as follows:

On the 6th of November, about six miles west of Point Pinos [California], two white-breasted shearwaters dashed up to the boat—one a pink-footed, the other a slender bird without conspicuous mottling on the sides of the head. The first glance revealed that the bird was a stranger. It was only a few yards away and I had to wait a moment for it to pass astern and get within proper range. A successful shot brought it down in perfect condition for a specimen. Dissection proved that it was a female, perhaps a young one, for the ova were indistinct as in a bird that had never bred.

Since the above statements were made Mr. Rollo H. Beck has taken fifteen specimens of this rare bird off Point Pinos. Mr. Loomis (1918) quotes from his notes, as follows:

1907. On November 4 I went out seven or eight miles north of Point Pinos and finally reached the gathering of shearwaters I was looking for. There were about twenty thousand sooty, two hundred or more black-vented, and about thirty Cooper's [pink-footed] shearwaters. They were scattered about over considerable water, and as I approached one of the larger bunches I saw two Buller's[1] shearwaters fly around it and enter the bay. Farther on I discovered one on the water apart from a flock of sooty shearwaters, and I secured it. Another was seen sitting in the midst of a flock of sooty shearwaters. Another still was sitting close to two of these shearwaters.   1922

SOOTY SHEARWATER   *Puffinus griseus*

The ocean wanderers from Antarctic seas that spend their winters during our summer months off our coasts are better known to fishermen than to ornithologists.

The sooty shearwater is known to the fishermen as the "black hagdon," "hag," or "haglet." On the fishing grounds about the Grand

[1] As this species was then called.

Bank off Newfoundland the shearwaters are very abundant and were formerly caught, with hook and line, in enormous numbers to use for bait.

Capt. J. W. Collins (1884) says in regard to their food:

From my observations I am of the opinion that the hag subsists chiefly on squid, which, of course, it catches at or near the surface of the water. I have opened many hundreds of them and have never, to my recollection, failed to find in their stomachs either portions of the squid, or, at least, squid's bills. It may be interesting also to mention the fact that in the fall of 1875, when the giant *Cephalopods,* or "big squid," were found on the eastern part of the Grand Bank between the parallels 44° and 45° north latitude, and the meridians of 49° 30′ and 50° 30′ west longitude, flocks of hagdons were invariably found feeding on the dead "devil fish" which were floating on the water. In nearly all cases these "big squid" were found in a mutilated condition, usually with their tentacles eaten off almost to their heads, and the fishermen soon learned to detect their presence by the large flocks of birds collected about them.

Mr. F. Ducane Godman (1907) gives the following account of the nesting habits of this species:

It breeds in great numbers on some of the small islands off the coast of New Zealand, the nesting places being much harried by the natives, who esteem these shearwaters as an article of food. The burrows on the Chatham Islands are usually formed in peaty soil, running horizontally for three or four feet and then turning. The nest, a rude structure composed of sticks and dead leaves, is placed at the end of the hole. A single egg is laid, both sexes assisting in the work of incubation, and when the parents return to roost on shore in countless thousands, the noise they make is deafening. If removed from their burrows they flutter about on the ground for some time in a confused way, but eventually make for the sea.   1922

SLENDER-BILLED SHEARWATER   *Puffinus*
tenuirostris

Among the vast flocks of dark colored shearwaters which we saw as we passed through Unimak Pass and entered Bering Sea, on June 4, 1911, we were confident that this species was represented. Unfortunately, we were unable to collect any specimens for identification and we shall therefore never know whether these immense gatherings of sea birds were made up of sooty or slender-billed shearwaters or both.

Whatever the species may have been, its numbers were beyond estimate, the smooth surface of the sea was covered with them for miles and miles, a vast multitude, far greater than I had ever seen, or ever conceived, and as we passed through this great sea of birds they merely parted under our bow sufficiently to let us pass. After seeing such a spectacle, I can more easily believe the accounts I have read of the astonishing abundance of the "mutton bird," as this shearwater is called, on its breeding grounds about New Zealand, Australia, and Tasmania.

The following remarkable statement by Flinders, quoted by A. J. Campbell (1901), seems almost incredible [December 9, 1798]:

A large flock of gannets was observed at daylight, and they were followed by such a number of sooty petrels[1] as we had never seen equaled. There was a stream of from 50 to 80 yards in depth and 300 yards or more in breadth. The birds were not scattered, but were flying as compactly as a free movement of their wings seemed to allow, and during a full hour and a half this stream of petrels continued to pass without interruption, at a rate little inferior to the swiftness of the pigeon. On the lowest computation, I think the number could not have been less than a hundred millions. Taking the stream to have been fifty yards deep by three hundred in width, and that it moved at the rate of thirty miles an hour, and allowing nine cubic yards of space to each bird, the numbers would amount to 151,500,000; the burrows required to lodge this quantity would be 75,-750,000; and allowing a square yard to each burrow, they would cover something more than 18½ geographical square miles of ground.

Of the several accounts that have been published I have selected the following, by the Rt. Rev. H. H. Montgomery, D. D., bishop of Tasmania (1898), which describes most fully and graphically the nesting habits of the slender-billed shearwater in the neighborhood of Bass Strait, Australia:

For many years, as episcopal duties have called me to the Furneaux Islands in Bass Strait, I have given attention to the habits of what is locally called the "mutton-bird." This petrel is now adequately protected by an act of the Tasmanian Parliament; and although some 400,000 young birds are salted down for consumption in a good year, chiefly by half-castes, yet there is no chance of the extinction of this species under present conditions.

Let us now imagine ourselves standing on a rookery in the evening awaiting the arrival of the old birds as the sun approaches the horizon. The islands where the petrels breed are as a rule devoid of trees. They are sandy knolls covered with long grass, and seem useless, except to feed a few sheep. Chappell Island has an area of 1200 acres, Little Dog Island about 120 acres. These are fair specimens of the rookeries, and I have calculated that 40,000 holes per acre is not an exaggerated estimate. All day long the young birds are absolutely silent. The uninitiated might imagine that nothing edible existed underfoot, and that they stood upon a deserted rabbit-warren. Gazing out to sea on all sides, the watcher will not yet

[1] As these birds were then called in that area of Bass Strait, Australia.

detect a single petrel; not till the sun has set and the darkness is increasing is there any sign of the wonderful rush of birds, which, to a naturalist, is so fascinating a sight. The following figures, noted in the month of February, may be of interest: 6:36 p.m., not a petrel in sight; 6:40, the first bird visible out at sea; 6:43, the sun disappeared; 6:48, sunset from the top of the lighthouse (Goose Island) and the light flashed out; 6:53, the first petrel flew rapidly over the island without settling; 6:56, the numbers so great that I ceased counting; 6:58, the numbers become bewildering; 7:06, the numbers at their maximum—tens of thousands whirling, wheeling, flashing up from all sides, are whistling like bullets past one's head, till it seemed almost dangerous to stand up; 7:30, nearly all the birds had arrived. Then, and not till then, do the noises commence. The flight inward of the parent birds is conducted in absolute silence. Nothing, indeed, can be more weird than this rush of dumb creatures, so perfect in flight, but uttering no sound. As soon as the majority have arrived the ground emits the most extraordinary sounds—gurglings, groaning, and hoarse laughter. It must be confessed that there is no music in the note. On Chappell Island some 300,000 young birds would at this moment be receiving oil into their throats, poured into them by the parents, who thus give them the one meal the fledglings receive in the 24 hours.   1922

MANX SHEARWATER   *Puffinus puffinus* (Townsend)

P.p. puffinus (Manx Shearwater)

The Manx shearwater, so called because it formerly bred in great numbers on the Isle of Man, is mainly a bird of the British Islands. [It is casual on our Atlantic coast.]

[It] breeds in colonies on high cliffs, turfy slopes, and rocky islands. A single smooth white egg of fine texture is laid at the end of a burrow or in a crevice or under a fragment of rock, either on the bare rock or soil, or in a nest loosely constructed of dry grass or leaves. Turle (1891) says of its nesting habits on the Skellig Rocks:

There are plenty of shearwaters on the Little Skellig, but their great breeding grounds are on Puffin Island, between the Little Skellig and the mainland. This island ought to be called Shearwater Island rather than Puffin Island. I was astonished at the enormous number we found nesting; they seem completely to have taken possession of the island, and far predominate over the puffins; indeed, the whole of both sides of the island was inhabited by them. They lay only one egg, some considerable distance down their burrows; several which I dug out were four feet from the entrance. They make no nest, but lay their egg on the bare ground. In every case where I took an egg the old bird allowed itself to be lifted off the egg upon which it was sitting. These birds are never seen at their breeding grounds in the day time.

Bewick (1847) quotes Willughby to the effect that at the Isle of Man the young of this species "become extremely fat, and are taken and salted down for keeping, and that the Romish Church permitted them to be eaten in Lent. . . . They usually sell them for about nine-pence the dozen, a very cheap rate." It hardly seems necessary to invoke the agency of rats as a cause of the extermination of this bird in the Isle of Man.

P.p. opisthomelas (Black-vented Shearwater)

Mr. Anthony (1896*b*) writes:

They are often seen in flocks of several thousands where fish are plenty. On one occasion I met with a flock on the coast of Lower California that I estimated contained not less than 50,000 shearwaters. Many were so gorged with herring that they could not rise from the water, but flapped along the surface in advance of the steamer until nearly overtaken, when they would dive. They would usually come up near enough to the vessel to be, if anything, more frightened than before, but could not take wing until they had disgorged a quantity of half-digested fish, after which they flew off with apparent ease.

It is only during very calm weather that this species is seen resting on the water. At such times they collect in very compact flocks, covering the water till there is but little room left within the circle that they almost invariably form. The first gentle breeze will start them on their journey again, and I have learned to have confidence in a breeze that starts them flying, for as far as my observations go, they only rise if the wind is to be continuous, and will pay no attention to a gentle puff that will die out in a few minutes.

None of our Pacific coast sea birds adhere so closely to established fly lines as do the three species of *Puffinus;* even when flying fifty miles or more from land the first flock that passes will, with almost absolute certainty, mark the line which the next will follow, even though they be an hour behind. And I have long since discovered that in order to secure specimens of these shy species the boat must be placed in their fly lines. A flock will, on encountering a skiff directly in their path, either divide and pass on either side or all swerve slightly to one side, immediately resuming their line of travel in either case. At times, however, they are easily turned from their course.   1922

AUDUBON'S SHEARWATER   *Puffinus lherminieri*
(Townsend)

Audubon in *The Birds of America* begins his account of this species by the following sentence:

On the 26th of June 1826, while becalmed on the Gulf of Mexico, off the western shores of Florida, I observed that the birds of this species, of which some had been seen daily since we left the mouth of the Mississippi, had become very numerous. The mate of the vessel killed four at one shot, and, at my request, brought them on board. From one of them I drew the figure which has been engraved. The notes made at the time are now before me and afford me the means of presenting you with a short account of the habits of this bird.

About the breeding ground, the birds are seen and heard only at night, when they appear to be very active. The daytime is spent by those who are not on the eggs at a distance on the sea generally out of sight of land, where they rest on the water in large flocks. At times they are very shy, but in the Martinique Channel the birds are said to be so bold as to attempt to rob the fishermen of their fish in the canoes. Audubon (1840) says they skim low over the water near bunches of gulf weeds. [They]

flap their wings six or seven times in succession and then sail for three or four seconds with great ease, having their tail much spread and their long wings extended at right angles with the body. On approaching a mass of weeds, they raise their wings obliquely, drop their legs and feet, run as it were on the water, and at length alight in the sea, where they swim with as much ease as ducks, and dive freely, at times passing several feet under the surface in pursuit of fishes, which, on perceiving their enemy, swim off but are frequently seized with great agility. Four or five, sometimes fifteen or twenty, of these birds will thus alight, and, during their stay about the weeds, dive, flutter, and swim with all the gaiety of a flock of ducks, newly alighted in a pond. . . . At times, as if by way of resting themselves, they alighted, swam lightly, and dipped their bills frequently in the water, in the manner of mergansers.   1922

BERMUDA PETREL   *Pterodroma cahow*

The earlier writers on Bermuda birds had much to say about a mysterious bird, now supposed to be extinct[1] which was very abundant at one time, and very well known by the earliest inhabitants as the "cahow," "cowhow," or "cowkoe."

Prof. Addison E. Verrill (1902) has given us the following interesting account of the early history of the cahow:

The most interesting as well as most important native bird, when the islands were first settled, was called the cahow, from its note. It bred in almost incredible numbers on some of the smaller islands near St. Georges and Castle Harbor, especially on Coopers Island. It was nocturnal in its habits and was readily called by making loud vocal sounds, and then easily captured by hand, at night. Its flesh was described as of good flavor

[1] A small nesting colony was rediscovered in the Castle Roads group of islands, Bermuda, in 1951, by Robert Cushman Murphy and Louis C. Mowbray.

and its eggs were highly prized as food. As it came to land and bred in the early part of the winter, when no other birds or eggs were available, it was quickly exterminated for food by the reckless colonists.

The following graphic account of the bird and its habits was written by Mr. W. Strachy, one of the party wrecked with Sir George Somers in the *Sea Venture*, July 1609:

"A kind of webbe-footed Fowle there is, of the bigness of an English greene Plover, or Sea-Meawe, which all the Summer we saw not, and in the darkest nights of November and December (for in the night they onely feed) they would come forth, but not flye farre from home, and hovering in the ayre, and over the Sea, made a strange hollow and harsh howling. They call it of the cry which it maketh, a cohow. Their colour is inclining to russet, with white bellies, as are likewise the long feathers of their wings, russet and white, these gather themselves together and breed in those lands which are high, and so farre alone into the Sea that the Wilde Hogges cannot swimme over them, and there in the ground they have their Burrowes, like Conyes in a Warren, and so brought in the loose Mould, though not so deepe; which Birds with a light bough in a darke night (as in our Lowbelling) wee caught, I have beene at the taking of three hundred in an houre, and wee might have laden our Boates. Our men found a prettie way to take them, which was by standing on the Rockes or Sands by the Sea-side, and hollowing, laughing, and making the strangest outcry that possibly they could; with the noyse whereof the Birds would come flocking to that place, and settle upon the very armes and head of him that so cried, and still creepe neerer and neerer, answering the noyse themselves; by which our men would weigh them with their hand, and which weighed heaviest they took for the best and let the others alone, and so our men would take twentie dozen in two hours of the chiefest of them; and they were a good and well relished Fowle, fat and full as a partridge. In January wee had great store of their Egges, which are as great as an Hennes Egge, and so fashioned and white shelled and have no difference in yolke nor white from an Hennes Egge. There are thousands of these Birds, and two or three Islands full of their Burrows, whether at any time (in two houres warning) we could send our Cockboat and bring home as many as would serve the whole Company: which Birds for their Blindnesse (for they see weakly in the day) and for their cry and whooting, wee called the Sea Owle; they will bite cruelly with their crooked Bills."   1922

SCALED PETREL   *Pterodroma inexpectata*

Although the Peale[1] petrel seems to be a fairly common species in the North Pacific Ocean in summer, very little seems to be known about its ranges and nesting habits. Mr. S. Percy Seymour found a breeding colony of these petrels on Preservation Inlet, New Zealand, which he evidently visited several times for he collected a series of the

[1] As this species was then called.

birds, as well as their eggs and young, which have found their way
into American collections through the late Manly Hardy and his
family. I have recently examined eighteen of these birds, now in
the Thayer [collection at Harvard University].

There are also in the Thayer collection three eggs, collected by
Mr. Seymour, on Preservation Inlet, on December 12, 1899, and January 7, 1900. The parent birds were collected with the single eggs in
each case. The nests are described as made of "small sticks, ferns, etc.,
in a burrow." The eggs are oval or elliptical oval in shape; the surface
of the shell is smooth but lustreless and the color is dirty white.

Little is known about the habits of *inexpectata*, but Godman (1907)
gives us the following scanty facts in regard to it:

> Peale says this fulmar was found among icebergs buffeting the storms
> and fogs of the Antarctic regions. He saw but few examples, and only
> obtained a single specimen, on March 21st, while the ship *Peacock* was
> enveloped in a fog, in lat. 68° S., long. 95° W. It occurs in the New Zealand
> seas, and Buller mentions many places whence he had received specimens;
> among these are the Spencer Mountains in the Province of Canterbury
> [and] the Aukland Islands.   1922

STORM PETRELS   Family Hydrobatidae

FORK-TAILED PETREL   *Oceanodroma furcata*

Among the *Tubinares* [*Procellariiformes*] of the north Pacific Ocean
this beautiful little petrel is one of the most widely distributed and
most universally common species. On our cruise from Dixon Entrance
[Alaska] to Unimak Pass some of these graceful little birds were almost constantly in sight, circling about the ship and flitting lightly
over the waves in search of some tiny morsels of food. We also saw
them frequently about the Aleutian Islands, as far west as Attu Island.

Doctor Grinnell (1897) who was forced to spend a night on St.
Lazaria Island[1] had an unusually good opportunity to study the
midnight flight of the forked-tailed petrel on its breeding grounds,
which he graphically describes as follows:

> After the sun set and the long summer twilight began to make the woods
> a little gloomy, the petrels became more active. Their curious calls came
> from every direction in the ground, though as yet not a bird was to be seen.
> Presently a little stir in the grass called attention to a petrel which clumsily
> scrambled from his hole, and after the usual fumbling put himself in
> flight and betook himself speedily out to sea. Soon others appeared and
> others and others. The crows, their enemies, had by this time gone to roost,

[1] Alaska; now a National Wildlife Refuge.

and as the gloom grew deeper the petrels became more numerous. Those which had been out to sea all day began to arrive among the trees, and were even more awkward than those leaving. They flew against branches and bushes and into my face, but all ultimately seemed to know where their respective homes were. The chorus of their cries was curious and depressing to one's spirits, and the chilly air was constantly being fanned into my face by their noiseless wings. The light-colored ghostly forms of the forktails were much more readily discernible than the dark Leach's.

The ground was alive with struggling petrels, and I picked up as many as I chose. As the twilight of evening slowly merged into dawn the height of their activity was reached. I walked from end to end of the wooded part of the island, and everywhere the petrels were equally numerous.

As I began to feel cold and likewise hungry, the novelty of these strange experiences naturally wore off. After considerable searching for dry fuel I started a smoldering little blaze, which lighted up the dusky surroundings, together with the flitting forms of the birds, thus disclosing a very impressive scene. But presently several of the petrels were attracted by the light and flew pell-mell into the fire, extinguishing the feeble flames in short order. After several similarly frustrated attempts, though partly on account of the damp wood, I gave it up.

As soon as the dawn became perceptibly brighter the petrels became quieter and fewer. Part went out to sea; others returned to their nests. By sunrise, at 2:30 a. m., not a petrel was to be seen nor a note heard where two hours before had been such a tumult of nocturnal forms and voices.

1922

LEACH'S PETREL *Oceanodroma leucorhoa*

O.l. leucorhoa (Leach's Petrel)

The most widely distributed and the best-known species of the genus *Oceanodroma* on American coasts is the Leach petrel.

Mr. Walter H. Rich, who has studied these birds on the fishing banks, found them

Instantly recognizable from the marked differences of wing action; the Wilson, with its apparently shorter, wider, and rather leaf-shaped wing and rapid fluttery, constant, mothlike flight, is unmistakable when contrasted with the slower, more irregular stroke of Leach petrel. The smaller species at once suggested to me the chimney-swift, while the fork-tailed species, with its apparently much longer wing, modeled after the pattern of that of the shorebirds and plied in much the same manner, recalled in its erratic flight and somewhat spasmodic wing action, a nighthawk gleaning its evening meal above the tree-tops. Another flight difference noted was the carriage of the wings when "scaling." The small petrel's wings were held flat and a trifle above horizontal, the tips slightly bent upward; while the fork-tailed species carried the wings down-bent, after the fashion of a shorebird when "sliding up" to the decoys.

The Leach petrel skims the surface of the ocean to pick up its floating food. It is particularly fond of animal oils or oily food and will follow in the track of a wounded seal or whale to feed on the traces of oil which have flowed from its wounds. It also follows living whales to pick up the bits of food which the feeding whale has left floating on the surface. It may also be seen flitting over the sea in wide circles in the wake of a ship to pick up what chance morsels of greasy food may have been thrown overboard. Fishermen cleaning fish at sea are soon surrounded by petrels which appear as if by magic as soon as the offal is thrown upon the waters; they are especially fond of the oily cod livers and can be easily tolled up to the boat by scattering such dainty morsels on the surface. When feeding thus they seldom settle on the water, as the albatrosses and shearwaters do, but hover close to the surface, rising over the waves, pattering occasionally on the water with their feet and pick up the smaller pieces in their bills or peck at the larger fragments. Their natural food includes shrimps and other small crustaceans, floating mollusks, perhaps small fishes occasionally, and probably many other forms of minute marine animals which are found swimming on the surface or in floating masses of seaweed.

The gentle petrels have many enemies that attack them on their breeding grounds, where they are easily dug out of their burrows in the soft ground and are too stupid to escape. Dogs and cats, introduced as domestic pets, are the chief offenders. Between my two visits to Spoon Island fishermen camping on the island with a dog seriously reduced the numbers of the petrels nesting there. On Seal Island [Nova Scotia] a Newfoundland dog, owned by the lighthouse keeper, spent much of his time hunting for and digging out petrel burrows. Apparently he did this purely for the sport of it, for we found the bodies of the petrels lying where he had killed them; perhaps the strong-smelling oily fluid which the birds ejected prevented his eating them, but did not discourage his digging out and killing them. After a few years of this persistent hunting I learned that this large and populous colony had been practically exterminated. Similar destruction was going on at Machias Seal Island [Maine] until, through the efforts of the Audubon Societies, the dog was removed. On my recent visit to Bird Rock [Gulf of St. Lawrence], in 1915, I found that the petrels had been exterminated by a cat. Mr. B. S. Bowish (1909) calls attention to "the terrible slaughter of petrels by minks upon Western Egg Rock," on the coast of Maine.

O.l. beali (Beal's Petrel)

The main breeding grounds of the Beal petrel seem to be on the islands included in the reservations off the coast of Washington, with a decided center of abundance in the Quillayute Needles. On one island in this group Mr. William L. Dawson (1908) estimated that there were about forty thousand of these petrels breeding; he estimated that there were somewhere between fifty-five and one hundred thousand of them breeding in the whole reservation.   1922

ASHY PETREL   *Oceanodroma homochroa*

This is the smallest of the brown-rumped species of the genus *Oceanodroma*, and it is not strikingly different from the other small species. Its known range seems to be limited to the coast of California, and it is known to breed only on the Farallon Islands and on some of the Santa Barbara Islands.

Prof. Leverett M. Loomis (1896) writes of this species on the Farallones:

Although these petrels were breeding abundantly in all parts of the island, every portion of it might have been passed over in daylight without a single individual being discovered, for apparently only brooding birds occurred, concealed in loose piles of stones, in stone walls, and under driftwood. After nightfall the petrels became active. They were especially conspicuous during the early morning hours of the 14th [of June] when the auklets held their concert. As I stood in the dooryard of a keeper's house every few moments one or more would pass silently by, disappearing in the darkness. Their flight recalled that of a Goatsucker.

The strong musky odor of the petrels renders their discovery in the rock piles easy. It is only necessary to insert the nose into likely crevices to find them. With little practice one may become very expert in this kind of hunting, readily determining whether it is an auklet or a petrel that has its residence in any particular cranny. Sometimes the petrels are within reach, but usually the rocks have to be removed to get at them. When uncovered they generally shrink away as far as they can, but occasionally one will remain on its egg. When tossed into the air they fly without difficulty.

It seemed strange to find these birds of the ocean rearing their young near the dwellings and within several rods of the siren. None of the feathered inhabitants of the island appeared to be alarmed at the blasts of this signal, repeated every forty-five seconds when the fog settled down.

It is evident that these petrels have a lengthy season of courtship during which they spend their nights ashore, chiefly in their burrows, and return to the sea daytimes. This is followed by a "honeymoon" period of some duration, presumably a week or more, in which both birds remain ashore all the time. As soon as the egg is laid incubation begins, and the other bird retires to sea to forage. Precisely what the division of labor is from this point on as between male and female remains to be determined, but it is certain that the male is often found alone upon the egg.   1922

BLACK PETREL   *Loomelania melania*

Mr. A. W. Anthony (1896a) found this species nesting on the San Benito Islands about seventy-five miles off the coast of Lower California and some twenty miles west of Cerros Island, between latitude twenty-eight and thirty degrees. He writes:

The San Benito Islands are small, rocky reefs only, with little vegetation, and being so far offshore are but little resorted to by gulls, cormorants, and similar species. Cassin's auklets had bred in considerable numbers, as their burrows testified, but at the time of our visit they had all left. Their burrows, however, had been appropriated by later arrivals, and during the four and a half days that we spent at the island Mr. Horace A. Gaylord and myself devoted most of our time to digging for petrels. Both black and Socorro petrels were taken from the burrows formerly occupied by the auklets, the former species outnumbering the Socorro about five to one. There was no attempt apparently on the part of the species to colonize by themselves, both being found in adjoining burrows. The Socorro petrel had evidently begun nesting somewhat earlier than its neighbor, the black, for while fresh eggs of the latter were the rule, very few fresh or even moderately incubated eggs of the Socorro were found, and several downy young were taken.

There was little, if any, attempt at nest building by either species, though in several burrows a small nest-like platform of little twigs was found upon which the egg was laid. But in most cases it rested upon the bare earth at the end of a more or less winding burrow, about three feet in length.

Mr. Anthony (1900a) writes, of the night flight of these petrels about their breeding grounds, as follows [on westernmost of San Benito Islands off coast of Lower California]:

Hauling the boat out on the shingle, a few steps places us in the city of birds, a fact we discovered by breaking through into the burrows at almost every step, but the birds themselves are very much in evidence. Hundreds of inky black objects are dashing about with bat-like flight, now here, now there, with no apparent object in their wanderings. Like butterflies they come and go, flitting so near at times that one attempts to catch them as they pass. Others are constantly coming from the burrows to join in the revel. Each, as it reaches the outer air, utters its characteristic call, flops along the ground a few feet, somewhat like an old felt hat before the wind, and is away, as gracefully and airy as the rest. Those in the air are constantly calling and from the ground under our feet come answering cries. The noise and confusion suggests a busy street in a city.   1922

LEAST PETREL   *Halocyptena microsoma*

The life history of the least petrel, the smallest of the family, long remained unknown. The type specimen, taken by Mr. Xantus, in May 1861, near San José del Cabo, Lower California, remained unique until March 1888, when Mr. Charles H. Townsend (1890) captured a second specimen, which "flew on board the *Albatross* in Panama Bay."

For all that we know regarding its habits we are indebted to Mr. A. W. Anthony (1898*b*) who discovered the breeding grounds of this rare species. He writes:

In early June I have found the least petrel migrating along the coast of Lower California in company with the Socorro and black petrels, and in late July have found them nesting on the small rocky San Benito Island, fifty miles off the coast of the peninsula. So far I have never found the least petrel nesting in burrows. They have always been taken from the crevices in rocky ledges or among the loose stones. The pearly white egg is laid on the bare rock. Usually several are found within a few feet if desirable crevices are numerous.

The San Benito Islands are small, rocky reefs only, with little vegetation, and being so far off shore are but little resorted to by gulls, cormorants, and similar species. The second day on the island Mr. James M. Gaylord, the botanist of our party, reported finding a "half-grown petrel incubating an egg" on another part of the island. Scarcely daring to hope, but suspecting that it might be the almost mythical least petrel, he was instructed to bring it back with him when he returned from that quarter next day. As we had surmised, the specimen proved to be *Halocyptena microsoma*, which we subsequently found breeding in several parts of the island.

The same writer (1900*a*) gives an interesting account of the peculiar notes of the least petrel, which I quote in full, as follows:

As soon as the rocky ground at the base of the hills is reached, a strange note is heard, which seems to come from the loose rocks fallen from a small ledge above, and resembles the "whirring" of a rapidly revolving cog wheel. For about ten seconds the whizzing continues, when suddenly a note is dropped—there is a quick gasp, as for breath—and instantly the wheels begin to revolve again, having given one the impression that there is a broken cog in the buried machine. I have no idea how long the strange note might be continued. I have waited until my patience was exhausted, and always the same "cog" was slipped, at exactly the same interval, and the bird was as fresh as ever when I left it with its unfinished song. Another note of this species which is occasionally heard from the same rock pile and which gives one a clew to the author, is exactly like the cry of the two petrels[1] above mentioned, but is higher pitched and

[1] Black Petrel and Leach's Petrel (*O.l. socorroensis*).

more hastily uttered, giving one the idea of a smaller bird, as indeed it is, the least petrel (*Halocyptena microsoma*).   1922

WILSON'S PETREL   *Oceanites oceanicus* (Townsend)

Few who have voyaged along the Atlantic coast or who have crossed to Europe have failed to see petrels or Mother Cary's chickens, as they are called. On untiring wing they skim the water, now on one side, now on the other of the vessel, all ready to gather in little bands in the wake and drop astern whenever delectable morsels are thrown from the cook's galley, and then it is that, like Peter of old, they walk upon the water.

Like most of the petrels this species prefers to nest in colonies. There is considerable variation in the nesting site and nest, dependent undoubtedly on the character of the country and the material at hand. Thus Wm. Eagle Clarke (1906) speaking of the South Orkneys [South Atlantic Ocean] says:

> There was no attempt at nest making, the egg was simply laid in a hollow in the earth in narrow clefts and fissures in the face of the cliffs, under boulders, and sometimes under stones on the screes sloping from the foot of the precipice.

The birds resort in thousands to the cliffs of Laurie Island, one of the South Orkney Islands, and nest all the way from twenty to three hundred feet above the sea. Robert Hall (1900) thus describes the nesting of this species at Kerguelen Island [South Indian Ocean]:

> The yellow-webbed Wilson petrel is a delicate creature that goes straight to sea in the early morning, and comes back to the rocks in the gloaming. Most of my time was spent among the stones below 1,000 feet, where this petrel is to be found in great numbers by diligent search. At 1,500 feet (Thumb Peak) one flew from the boulders in the daytime, which showed that a nest was there. Having returned from the sea into the harbours at dusk (8 p. m.) Wilson's petrel is then to be seen, flying to and fro before a ridge of rough-looking rocks. At 6 p. m. I observed (February 2) a gathering of from 50 to 60 birds off the South Head of Greenland Harbour. Generally they are unassociated until they come in toward night.
>
> At about 8 p. m. the croaking begins, for now the "night shift" has come in from the sea to go on duty. Many congratulations seem to be exchanged. Go straight to a wild-looking piece of the coast if you want nests. Look under large or small slabs of stone or within the crevices in the cliff-sides. Most of the nests are saucerlike and neatly put together with loose twigs. Your shovel will act as a lever to lift the slabs and expose them, when the sitting bird will move away to the farthest corner to escape the light, never offering to bite, although the act would be harmless. 1922

TROPIC-BIRDS, PELICANS, FRIGATE-BIRDS, AND ALLIES— ORDER PELECANIFORMES

TROPIC-BIRDS Family Phaethontidae

RED-BILLED TROPIC-BIRD *Phaethon aethereus*

The tropic-birds are well named, for they are always associated with those favored regions, where on the hot, sunny islands they find genial nesting sites and in the warm tropical waters fruitful feeding grounds. The red-billed species inhabits both oceans and is found as far north as the Lesser Antilles on the Atlantic side and as far as the Gulf of California on the Pacific coast.

The flight of the tropic-birds is said to be not unlike that of the terns, with rapid wing strokes; they must be graceful birds on the wing with their long tail feathers streaming in the wind. They are said to soar very high in the air at times, far above the boobies and frigate birds. Mr. Beck (1904) thought that "their flight and call as they wheeled and darted about the high cliffs closely resembled that of the white-throated swifts in California." He also says:

In this section of the world the tropic-bird wanders as far away from land as the frigate bird. We found both this species and the red-tailed tropic-bird more than 600 miles from any island."

Dr. E. W. Nelson (1899) gives the following account of the nesting habits of the red-billed tropic-bird on the west coast of Mexico [Tres Marias Islands]:

Soon after landing on Isabel, a tropic-bird was found sitting on its solitary egg at the end of a little hole in the rock close to the beach. The hole was only about 15 or 18 inches across and about 3 feet deep, so that there was no difficulty in taking the bird by hand after a little maneuvering to avoid its sharp beak. During a stay of about 24 hours on this island at least 20 nests containing eggs or young were examined. A single egg is laid directly on the rough rock or loose dirt forming the floor of the nesting site, which is always located under the shelter of overarching rock, but varies greatly in situation. The inner ends of holes in cliffs facing the sea were favorite places, but as the number of such situations was limited, the birds were forced to utilize small caves and even rock shelters. In one locality five or six nests were placed on loose earth at the bottom of rock shelters so situated that I could walk directly up to them and pick up the birds. Whenever a nest was approached the parent screamed and fought viciously, ruffled its feathers and looked very fierce, but made no attempt to escape.   1922

WHITE-TAILED TROPIC-BIRD   *Phaethon lepturus*

The warm waters of the Gulf Stream, sweeping northeastward across the Atlantic, produce in the little Bermuda group semitropical conditions and bring thither this beautiful species of tropical origin, which finds here ideal conditions for rearing its young in the numerous recesses and cavities of the honey-combed limestone cliffs, so characteristic of these islands. Mr. A. Hyatt Verrill (1901) writes:

The most striking bird of the Bermudas is the yellow-billed tropic-bird or "Long Tail" of the natives. These beautiful creatures arrive about March 25th, and within a few days become exceedingly abundant. As many as 300 can frequently be seen at one time, flying about the cliffs or skimming the surface of the wonderfully colored water, the reflection from which causes their breasts to appear the most lovely and delicate sea-green. They are very tame and unsuspicious, flying close to moving boats and breeding everywhere, often within a few yards of houses or settlements.

The value of properly enforced bird protection is nowhere better exemplified than in the case of this bird. A few years ago the tropic birds were threatened with extinction from the Bermudas, whereas, since the passing of strict laws, prohibiting killing of birds or taking the eggs, they have rapidly increased, until at present the number breeding yearly on the islands is calculated at fully 5000.

Dr. Alfred O. Gross (1912) has made a most valuable contribution to the life history of this species, based on an exhaustive study of its breeding habits during two seasons at the Bermudas. He says of the migration:

The tropic birds migrate from the West Indies and, except for occasional stragglers, none are to be found in the Bermudas during the winter months. This annual migration flight is remarkable when it is considered that the birds must necessarily fly over open water for a distance of more than 600 miles without any landmark to guide them.

Mr. Plath (1913) writes:

They spend much time in the air, and may be seen flying in graceful curves, sometimes swooping in a spiral, with half-closed wings, to the surface of the water, and often alighting there after a skim over the waves. In the water they sit very high, with their tails held well above it. They frequently utter their peculiar cry, which varies—sometimes a rasping *t-chik-tik-tik* or *clik-et-clik-et;* again, the noise produced by several birds in the air reminds me of the noise of a greaseless axle on a wagon wheel.

Their manner of flight differs from most sea birds; the wings move much more rapidly, and at a distance one might easily mistake them for pigeons, as their long tails are not then conspicuous. Against the blue of the sky their plumage is dazzling; but see them against the dark background of a cliff, and they appear of a beautiful pale green, due to their glossy plumage reflecting the bright emerald of the water below.   1922

PELICANS   Family Pelecanidae

WHITE PELICAN   *Pelecanus erythrorhynchos*

The day we reached Big Stick Lake, after a thirty-mile drive over the rolling plains of Saskatchewan, was cold and blustering; the lake looked forbidding enough, for its muddy waters were covered with white caps and heavy breakers were rolling in on the pebbly beach before a strong northerly gale; but we could not resist the temptation to visit a small island, which lay less than two hundred yards offshore, and over which a cloud of white gulls were hovering. The chief attraction was a great white mass of birds standing on one end of the island, conspicuous as a snow bank in spring, but recognized at once as a flock of pelicans.

But the pelicans stood silent and dignified until they decided to leave and then, as if by one common impulse, they all rose at once with a great flapping of long black-tipped wings; they seemed heavy, awkward, and ungainly at first, but they soon gained headway and showed their marvelous mastery of the air, as they swung into line forming one large V-shaped flock; they circled around the island two or three times, with slow and dignified wing beats in military precision, or all scaled in unison like well-drilled soldiers; and finally, when satisfied that they must leave and when fully arranged in proper marching order, they all followed their leader and departed northward over the lake; the last we saw of them they were flying in a long straight line, just above the horizon, their black-tipped wings keeping perfect step and their snowy plumage showing clearly cut against the cold gray sky even when miles away. It was a fascinating spectacle to stand and gaze at that departing flock of magnificent birds and to dream of nature's wonders, the marvels of creation, which only those may see who seek the solitudes of remote wilderness lakes.

Rev. S. H. Goodwin (1904) has published the following interesting account of the behavior of young white pelicans [on Rock Island, Utah Lake, Utah]:

Young pelicans must certainly be given a prominent place in the front rank of the ridiculous and grotesque in bird life. Their excessively fat, squabby bodies, the under parts of which are bare, while the upper parts are covered with a wool-like coating, hardly distinguishable from that on the back of a four weeks' old lamb; these bodies set on a pair of legs, of the use of which the youngsters seem to have no clear notion, so that when they undertake to move about they wobble and teeter and balance themselves with their short, unfledged wings, often tumbling over; many of them (on this occasion) with their mandibles parted, and panting like a dog after a long run on a hot day, the pouch hanging limp and flabby, like an empty sack, shaken by every breath—form, appearance, movement, all combined to make these birds absurdly ridiculous.

When we approached these birds, those nearest the water would not move an inch, while those nearest us in their frantic endeavor to get away would try to climb up and over the struggling, squirming mass in front of them, sometimes succeeding, but oftener rolling back to the ground where, not infrequently they alighted upon their backs, and lay helplessly beating their wings and kicking their feet in the air—after the fashion of some huge beetle—till they were helped to right themselves. When left to themselves, not a few of these birds would "sit down," just as a dog sits on his haunches, the wings sometimes hanging limp at the sides, at others folded back. The larger part of them, however, simply squatted in the usual manner. They made no sound, save when we attempted to drive them, when an occasional puppy-like grunt would be heard, as if some hapless youngster had fallen or been trodden upon.

Mr. Finley (1907) describes their daily performance [on Lower Klamath Lake, Oregon, in 1895] as follows:

After returning from the fishing grounds and lounging about the nests for a while the pelicans began to circle over the colony in a large company, rising higher and higher till they were almost lost in blue. By watching we could occasionally see the faint flashes of white as the snowy breasts reflected a gleam of the sun. For hours the sky would glitter with these great birds as they soared about. Then it was thrilling to see some of them descend with rigid, half-closed wings. They used the sky as a big toboggan slide and dropped like meteors, leaving a trail of thunder. Several times when we first heard the sound we were deceived into thinking it was the advance messenger of a heavy storm and jumped up expecting to see black clouds rising from behind the mountains.   1922

BROWN PELICAN   *Pelecanus occidentalis*

My first morning in Florida dawned clear, calm, and hot, a typical April morning. The rich, varied whistle of the cardinal and the striking song of the Florida wren[1] attracted me outdoors to explore my surroundings and make new acquaintances. An attractive path led through a dense hammock of large, grotesque live oaks, festooned with hanging mosses and a forest of heavily booted palmettos toward the shore. I had hoped to enjoy the cool of the early morning hours, but I had not then learned that the morning is the hottest part of the day on the east coast, before the cool sea breeze of midday brings relief. The heat was intense as I crossed a broad tract of saw palmettos back of the beach, and I was glad to seek shelter under an old bathhouse. The sea was smooth as glass and the horizon hardly visible, but the ocean swell rose and fell on the white sand in a long line of rolling breakers. Way off to the southward, in the shimmering heat which obstructed the shore line, I made out a long waving line of black specks, a flock of large birds coming toward me; they were flying close to the water and just off the beach over the breakers; with slowly measured wing beats they came on in regular formation. They were pelicans, of course, for at regular intervals they all set their wings and scaled along, barely skimming the tops of the waves or sailing along the valleys between them. With grotesque and quiet dignity they passed, and with the military precision of well-drilled soldiers they alternately scaled or flapped their wings in perfect unison, as if controlled by a common impulse. Before they had disappeared to the northward another flock was in sight, and so they came and passed on as long as I cared to watch them, with one or more flocks constantly in sight.

Mr. Stanley Clisby Arthur has sent me the following notes on the courtship, which I have never seen:

The courtship of the pelican is quite what one would expect from a bird of its other undemonstrative habits. I witnessed it once on *Isle Grandgosier* and it marks the only time I have seen a pair of brown pelicans together when I could unhesitatingly identify the male from its mate. The female

[1] A subspecies, *Thryothorus ludovicianus miamensis*, of the Carolina wren.

squatted close to the bare ground while the male slowly circled her with ponderous, elephantine tread. While he circumnavigated the course he lifted his wings slightly and tilted his neck far back, but there was none of the pronounced strutting usually indulged in by other birds, particularly those of the gallinaceous order. Both wore most lugubrious expressions during the whole of the courtship and the occasion was more befitting the solemnity of a funeral than the joyous display attending most nuptials. Neither uttered an audible sound while the male pursued his dignified circuitous meandering. Suddenly she rose from her squatting position with a *gruff-gruff* of wing strokes and flew to the ocean, but a short distance from the shore, and after stolidly watching her going, he followed, still wearing his mask-like expression of weighty solemnity, to the consummation of the courtship on the surface of the quiet swelling waters of the gulf.

1922

BOOBIES AND GANNETS   Family Sulidae

BLUE-FACED BOOBY   *Sula dactylatra*

The blue-faced booby is an inhabitant of the tropical oceans, breeding as far north as the West Indies, in the Atlantic, and as far as San Benedicto Island, off the coast of Mexico, in the Pacific Ocean.

Mr. A. W. Anthony (1898e) writes of their nesting habits in the Revillagigedo Islands[1] as follows:

On May 19 we found some colonies of blue-faced boobys on Clarion Island, in which there were fresh eggs and young birds, and even a few well-grown young were seen. The nests were mere hollows in the coral sand, anywhere from just above high tide to the top of the island, at 500 feet altitude. The nests were all vigorously defended by the birds, who greeted our approach with deafening shrieks and threatening bills. Indeed, their bill is not to be despised. It is as sharp as a bayonet and is wielded with no little force, as my shins could testify after an hour's collecting among the nests. If the Webster booby[2] required a kick to drive them from their nests, the blue-faced required a charge of dynamite. I have repeatedly put my foot under a sitting bird—gently to save the eggs—and thrown her as far as I could—with vigor to save my shins—but before I could grab the eggs, was driven back by a shrieking demon in snowy white that charged at me with agility surprising in so large a bird. On one occasion a bird came in from out at sea and with a scream threw itself between me and a sitting bird I was approaching, constantly moving about so as to interpose its body between its nest and the threatening danger. The

---

[1] Off the west coast of Mexico.

[2] Presumably Brewster's booby, now *Sula leucogaster brewsteri,* a subspecies of the Brown Booby.

defense being so spirited and gallant I concluded that the eggs were far
advanced in incubation.   1922

BROWN BOOBY   *Sula leucogaster*

The common brown booby, or white-bellied booby, often called
the brown gannet, is a widely distributed species among the islands
of the tropical seas of both hemispheres.

Dr. Alexander Wetmore has contributed the following notes:

Off the west coast of Porto Rico, seven leagues from the port of Aguadilla,
lies the small island of Desecheo, hot and dry for a large part of the year,
but swept occasionally by tempestuous downpours of rain. The island is
little more than an isolated rock rising from the restless waters of Mona
passage with its treacherous changing currents, profound depths all about
cutting it off from other land connection. In shape it is roughly an ellipse a
mile and a half long and three-fourths of a mile wide with abrupt rocky
shores and steep slopes rising into two pointed hills, the highest about
three hundred feet above the sea. Three or four small indentations boast a
rough gravelly beach where with care a landing can be made in the surf
and behind these are small semicircles backed by water-worn cliffs on the
landward side and floored with sand and huge rocks fallen from the overhang above. The thin soil of the island supports a considerable growth
of vegetation, bound with thorny creepers into an impassable jungle, with
only small grass-grown openings offering a pathway. The West Indian
birch (*Bursera simaruba*), with its trunk and limbs curiously shortened,
thickened and gnarled in the struggle for life, is the common tree, while
growths of three species of cactuses are common.

On this interesting island, boasting of but eleven resident avine forms,
the booby (*Sula leucogastra*) has chosen its home and here in June 1912,
I spent a few days in studying the habits of these ungainly birds. Between
eight and ten thousand of them at a conservative estimate occupied the
rookeries, spread over the entire island, but they were so distributed on
the steep brush-covered slopes that a more accurate census was impractica-
ble. Though they were seen at the top of the higher of the two hills, the
greater number were found within four hundred feet of the beach,
gathered usually in groups.

The young birds were averse to flying when they could avoid it, but
preferred to scramble away under the bushes awkwardly, falling over sticks
and stones in their haste. Even the adults could not take flight from a level
surface, but had to launch themselves from the cliffs and sail down for a
distance before being able to rise with strong wing beats.

On the rough limestone blocks above the sea they sat in rows in the
blazing sun, rather upright, occasionally waddling along a foot or two, but
usually motionless. Birds came and went during the day, flying out to sea

to feed, sometimes at considerable distances off shore, but they were most active in the morning and evening. The common call note was a loud *quack quack quack,* and at night, whenever I awoke, there was always much commotion among them.   1922

GANNET   *Morus bassanus*

Day after day we had gazed, from the hilltops of the northern Magdalens, across the waters of the stormy Gulf of St. Lawrence toward the distant Labrador coast, where we could see looming up on the horizon a lofty reddish mass of rock, the goal of our ambitions and the mecca of many an American ornithologist, Bird Rock.

When Audubon (1897) visited Bird Rock in 1833 it was a most wonderful sight, as the following graphic description, taken from his journal for June 14, 1833, well illustrates:

About ten a speck rose on the horizon which I was told was the rock. We sailed well, the breeze increased fast, and we neared this object apace. At eleven I could distinguish its top plainly from the deck, and thought it covered with snow to the depth of several feet; this appearance existed on every portion of the flat, projecting shelves. Godwin said, with the coolness of a man who had visited this rock for ten successive seasons, that what we saw was not snow, but gannets. I rubbed my eyes, took my spyglass, and in an instant the strangest picture stood before me. They were birds we saw—a mass of birds of such a size as I never before cast my eyes on. The whole of my party stood astounded and amazed, and all came to the conclusion that such a sight was of itself sufficient to invite anyone to come across the gulf to view it at this season. The nearer we approached the greater our surprise at the enormous number of these birds, all calmly seated on their eggs or newly hatched brood, their heads all turned to windward and toward us. The air above for a hundred yards, and for some distance around the whole rock, was filled with gannets on the wing, which, from our position, made it appear as if a heavy fall of snow was directly above us.

At that time the whole top of the rock was covered with their nests and it was regularly visited by the fishermen of that vicinity, who killed the gannets in large quantities for codfish bait. The stupid birds were beaten down with clubs as they tumbled over each other in their attempts to escape. Sometimes as many as 540 of them have been killed by half a dozen men in an hour, and as many as forty fishing boats were supplied regularly with bait each season in this way, the birds being roughly skinned and the flesh cut off in chunks.

When Dr. Henry Bryant visited Bird Rock on June 23, 1860, the colonies were very much reduced in numbers, although the lighthouse had not been built at that time and the gannets were nesting over all of the northern half of the flat top of the rock. He estimated that there were at least one hundred thousand birds in this colony and about fifty thousand that were nesting on the side of the rock. Mr. C. J. Maynard visited the rock in 1872, three years after the lighthouse was built, and found the colony on the summit reduced to five thousand birds. In 1881 Mr. William Brewster reported only fifty pairs still nesting on the flat top of the rock, and since that time they have abandoned it entirely, resorting only to the safer locations on the ledges. In 1887 the total number of gannets nesting on Bird Rock was estimated at ten thousand, and at the time of our visit in 1904 we estimated that their numbers had been reduced to less than three thousand birds. [Bird Rock was made a Federal Bird Sanctuary in 1919; J. F. Fisher in 1939 estimated 1000-1500 nests.]

The flight of the gannet is a magnificent performance as it soars aloft on its long, pointed, black-tipped wings, its spearlike head and beak, and its slender tapering tail offering little resistance to the air, as it sweeps in great circles far above the sea until almost lost to sight in the blue sky. When traveling it flies close to the water, flapping its wings and sailing at intervals with wings fully outstretched, after the manner of the pelicans. It is well built for speed and its flight is powerful and long sustained. Its peculiar shape, forming an almost perfect cross while soaring, serves to identify it, as far as it can be seen.

The vigorous plunge of the gannet from a great height, often over a hundred feet, together with the momentum of its heavy body, gives it a decided advantage over other diving birds in reaching great depths. There have been some remarkable stories told of the depths to which gannets dive, based on their having been caught in fishermen's nets set at known depths. Mr. Gurney (1913) mentions a number of such cases from which I infer that gannets frequently dive to a depth of sixty or seventy feet and occasionally over one hundred. It is hardly conceivable that the gannet can penetrate to any such great depths as these by the impetus of its plunge; it must, therefore, swim downward, probably using both wings and feet for propulsion. The gannet is not only an expert diver, displaying great agility below the surface, but it is also a strong swimmer above, where it propels itself rapidly with alternate strokes of its great paddles. A wounded gannet is not an easy bird to catch.   1922

CORMORANTS   Family Phalacrocoracidae

GREAT CORMORANT   *Phalacrocorax carbo*
(Townsend)

[The great cormorant] has an almost world-wide distribution, and breeds in the northern part of the Northern Hemisphere from Nova Scotia to the British Isles and Kamchatka, and winters as far south as Long Island, southern Africa, and New Zealand. The bird is said to be very intelligent, easily domesticated, and to become attached to its masters. In the time of Charles the First, fishing with trained cormorants was a regular sport in England, and this species was employed. Rings around the neck, as in China at the present day, were used to prevent swallowing the prey, although in well-trained birds this was unnecessary.

The flight of the cormorant is heavy and heron-like, with slow flapping of its broad wings. It often flies close to the water, and I have seen it touch the surface with its wing tips at each stroke. From a flat station like a beach, or the water on calm days, it has considerable difficulty in rising, and strikes with its feet together in great hops several times before it can get away. From a cliff or buoy it launches itself into the air and descends in a great downward curve nearly to the water, sometimes even splashing the surface before it gets impetus enough to rise again and fly away. The stronger the wind to which it opposes its aeroplanes, the less is the depth of the curve. The reverse process of alighting on a cliff, and particularly on a small perch like a buoy, also calls for much skill on the part of the bird, and is interesting to watch. The cormorant flies with considerable velocity upwind toward its buoy, sets its wings, and with neck outstretched and feet dropped, it sails upwards toward its perch. If it has not calculated exactly right it may fail to accomplish the feat; whereupon it swings around to leeward and tries again. I watched a cormorant try four times one calm March day off Rockport [Massachusetts] on Cape Ann before it succeeded in alighting on the spindle on the salvages. Cormorants, in migration or when flying to and from their feeding grounds, maintain no regularity of flock arrangement. An irregular flock is common, as is also a perfect V-shaped formation, a long file, or a rank. In the latter case each successive bird in the rank is generally slightly behind his neighbor on one side. Although the flight is usually heavy, with slow wing beats, the birds are swift flyers in strong winds and, at times, soar like gulls or hawks to a great height.

On the water they are rapid swimmers, and they often swim with their body depressed so that the back is level with the surface. When alarmed they sink still lower so that only the head and neck are exposed. They not infrequently swim with the head and neck extended forward under water for the purpose of looking for fish. Under the surface they are especially at home, and progress with great swiftness. As the cormorant dives for fish he springs upward and forward and enters the water in a graceful curve with wings pressed close to the sides. Headly (1907) says:

The cormorant uses his feet alone to propel him (in diving) striking with both simultaneously, and holding the wings motionless, though slightly lifted from the body. The position of the wings must have given rise to the idea, common among fishermen, that the cormorant flies under water . . . but when you see him in a tank you can have no doubt that the legs are the propellers.   1922

DOUBLE-CRESTED CORMORANT
Phalacrocorax auritus

P.a. auritus   (Double-crested Cormorant)

On the flat top of Percé Rock, which stands only a few rods from the shore of Percé, Quebec, is a large breeding colony of double-crested cormorants and herring gulls, and the top of the rock is about level with the heights of Cape Cannon, the nearest point. On June 19, 1920, while watching this colony from that point through a powerful telescope, I had a good opportunity to study the courtship or nuptial greeting of this species. Many birds were standing by their mates on the nests; others were constantly coming or going. The incoming bird, presumably the male, bows to his mate and walks around her with his neck upstretched and swollen, opening and closing his bill. Then approaching his mate he begins caressing her with his bill; she steps off the nest; then both begin a series of snake-like movements of heads and necks, almost intertwining them. Finally he passes his head over, under, and around his mate, apparently caressing her from head to tail, and he or she settles down on the nest.

P.a. floridanus   (Florida Cormorant)

About the mangrove keys of southern Florida, principally in that broad expanse of shallow water known as the Bay of Florida, be-

tween Cape Sable and the Keys, this smaller form is exceedingly
abundant and one of the characteristic birds of the region. It is
decidedly gregarious in its habits, flying about in large flocks and
roosting in immense numbers on certain keys, to which it regularly
resorts, the mangroves becoming thoroughly whitewashed with the
accumulated droppings of hundreds of cormorants. These roosts
are occupied by day as well as by night and it is an interesting experience to row around one of them in a small boat and see the great
black birds pour off the trees down to the surface of the water and
go flying off in large flocks.

P.a. albociliatus   (Farallon Cormorant)

A vast breeding colony of this cormorant was found on San Martin Island, Lower California, by Mr. Howard W. Wright (1913);
he made a careful estimate of the area covered by this colony and
figured that it occupied about one and one-half square miles; then
allowing one nest for each one hundred square feet, based on a count
in an average measured area, he concluded that the colony contained
the astonishing number of 348,480 nests. This is certainly the largest
colony of cormorants of which we have any record. He says:

We became very much interested in estimating the amount of fish these
birds consumed per day. We noted the amount each young cormorant
threw up when molested, and found on several occasions a bunch of fish
as big as a man's two fists. This mass was generally composed of surf
fish, smelt, and sardines. I have heard of other estimates of from three
to six sardines a day for a cormorant, so I consider a half pound of fish a
day very conservative.

Allowing half a pound of fish a day for each of the 1,800,000 birds, the
entire population would consume four hundred tons a day or about ten
thousand tons a month. The fishing was done in San Quentin bay, exclusively, but in that bay and in Hassler's Cove, on the island, fish were found
very plentiful, and always hungry, showing that the birds do not seriously
lessen the number of fish.   1922

OLIVACEOUS CORMORANT   *Phalacrocorax olivaceus*

This small, but handsome, cormorant is a tropical species which
extends its range northward over the Mexican border and into the
southern part of the Mississippi valley.

It seems to be rare north of Texas and Louisiana, but on the coasts
of southern Texas and Mexico it is a common bird of the salt water
lagoons, rivers, and inland lakes, much resembling in appearance and

behavior the well-known Florida cormorant [subspecies *floridanus* of the double-crested cormorant].

Doctor Nelson (1903) writes of the behavior of Mexican cormorants[1] as follows:

In the summer of 1897 we found them in abundance about the lagoons and rapids of the coast country in southern Sinaloa [Mexico] and especially at some shallow rapids in the Rosario River a few miles above the town of Rosario. During the early part of the rainy season the river was low and at the place mentioned a short descent in the boulder-strewn bed of the stream made a stretch, forty or fifty yards long, of brawling rapids. Every morning dozens of cormorants flew up stream to the rapids from the mangrove-bordered lagoons near the coast. They flew low along the water, sometimes singly and sometimes in small parties, usually keeping side by side in a well-formed line when two or more were together. For a time most of them perched about on the numerous projecting stones in the river, preening their plumage and sunning themselves; others swam idly in the slow current about the rapids. At such times the brilliantly green masses of foliage bordering and often overhanging the water, the swift dark stream broken by jutting rocks on which were the numerous, black, sharply outlined forms of the cormorants, and overhead the crystalline depths of the morning sky of the rainy season made a wonderfully beautiful picture.

When a considerable number of cormorants had congregated they seemed to become suddenly animated by a common purpose and followed one another in swift flight to the foot of the rapids. There most of the assembled birds alighted and formed a line across a considerable section of the river. Then with flapping wings, beating the surface of the water into foam, the black line moved up stream, the birds showing much excitement, but keeping their places very well. The surface of the water was churned to spray by the strokes of so many powerful wings and feet, yet in the midst of the apparent confusion the birds could be seen darting to one side or the other, or spurting a few feet ahead on the line, and sometimes disappearing for a moment below the surface, but nearly always securing a fish. When they reached the head of the rapids the birds flew heavily to their perching stones, or swam slowly up the quiet surface of the river. After a short rest the line would reform and again beat up the rapids and this was repeated until the birds had satisfied their hunger. 1922

BRANDT'S CORMORANT   *Phalacrocorax penicillatus*

This large, heavy, well-marked species is perhaps the best known, the most abundant, and the most characteristic cormorant of our Pacific coast.

[1] As this species was then called.

Two interesting colonies of Brandt cormorants near Monterey, California, are described by Prof. Leverett M. Loomis (1895) from whom I quote in part as follows:

Two rookeries were discovered; one at Point Carmel and the other at Seal Rocks. June 25th I visited the former, which is situated on a rock or little islet in the ocean at the extremity of Point Carmel, about fifteen yards from the mainland. This rock rises perpendicularly some forty or more feet above the water. At first sight it does not seem that it can be scaled, but closer inspection reveals that a foothold may be had in the seams and protuberances on its water-worn sides. Only on days when the sea is very calm can the rock be landed upon, and then only from the sheltered channel separating it from the mainland. Fortunately, it happened that the sea was quiet the day of my visit. The following day a party of Stanford University students were unable to land on account of the heavy surf.

We first took a view of the rookery from the mainland. The cormorants were very tame, remaining on their nests while we clambered down the sloping rocks and while we stood watching them on the same level only a few yards away. They were safe, however, from its precipitous walls of rock, effectually cutting off further advance. They were equally tame when the boat drew near as we approached from the water.

The clefts in the sides of the rock were occupied by Baird[1] cormorants and the top by Brandt's. There were comparatively few of the former, but of the Brandt cormorants there were upwards of two hundred pairs. Their nests covered the top of the rock, every available situation being occupied. The surface was so uneven that all the nests could not be seen from one spot. Standing in one place I counted one hundred and eighteen.

All the nests of the Brandt cormorants on the rock contained eggs (apparently in an advanced state of incubation), with the exception of eleven, which had young birds in them. In ten, the young were just out of the shell. In the remaining one they were as large as "spring chickens." The eggs in seventy-seven nests were counted by a companion. Twenty-one contained four eggs each; thirty-six, three eggs; fourteen, two eggs; three, five eggs; three, one egg. The most frequent numbers were therefore three and four, probably the ordinary clutches.

Sardines were lying in little bunches near the nests, apparently placed there as food for the birds that were setting.

The smell from the accumulated excrement was sickening. The sides of the rock were so daubed that it appeared to be white toward the top. Flies swarmed about the rookery.

It was not until I fired my gun that the brooding birds began to desert their eggs. The Baird cormorants were the first to go. Many of the Brandt cormorants lingered on the edge of the rock while I walked about among

[1] As the subspecies *P.p. resplendens* of the Pelagic Cormorant was formerly called.

the nests, only a few steps away. Finally all were driven to the water, where they formed a great raft. They began to return as soon as I left the top of the rock.   1922

PELAGIC CORMORANT   *Phalacrocorax pelagicus*

P.p. pelagicus   (Pelagic Cormorant)

Throughout the whole length of the Aleutian chain we found this small, slender cormorant sitting in little groups on the rocks about the promontories or flying out to meet us and to satisfy their curiosity by circling about our boat; they seemed far from timid. Here they breed in colonies on the highest, steepest and most inaccessible rocky cliffs, safe from the depredations of foxes and men and shrouded in the prevailing fogs of that dismal region. The nest is placed on some narrow ledge on a perpendicular cliff facing the sea; it is made mainly of seaweeds and grasses, is added to from year to year and becomes quite bulky.

These cormorants have few enemies to contend with, except the winged robbers of their eggs and young. Mr. George Willett (1912) writes that on St. Lazaria Island [Alaska]:[1]

Owing to the depredations of the crows,[2] very few of these birds succeed in raising an entire brood, and I believe there are many who are unable to raise a single young. When frightened from the nest, they very foolishly fly a considerable distance to sea and often remain for several minutes at a time. This opportunity is quickly seized by the crows, and in an almost incredibly short time the cormorants' nest is empty.

Doctor Stejneger (1885) refers to a wholesale destruction of this species in the Commander Islands [Soviet Far East], as follows:

During the winter of 1876-77 thousands and thousands were destroyed by an apparently epidemic disease, and masses of the dead birds covered the beach all around the islands. During the following summer comparatively few were seen, but of later years their number has again been increasing, though people having seen their former multitude think that there is no comparison between the past and the present. From Bering Island the reports are similar, with the addition that the stone foxes would not eat the corpses.

The natives in the vicinity of Bering Sea depend largely on the flesh of these cormorants at certain seasons for food; their skins were formerly used for clothing and their nuptial crests and plumes served as ornaments. Mr. L. M. Turner (1886) writes:

[1] Now a national wildlife refuge.
[2] The Northwestern Crow, *Corvus caupinus.*

During severe weather of the winter and fall these birds resort to the high rocky ledges or the single rocks which jut from the sea. Some of the rocks are fairly covered with these birds, and these appearing like a lot of black bottles standing on the rock. The natives of all parts of the country use the flesh of this bird for food. Some of the Aleuts, especially those of Attu, prize the flesh more than any other bird. They formerly obtained many of these birds with a kind of net which was thrown over the birds when sitting on the shore rocks, being driven there by the severity of a storm, so that the birds could not remain on the outer rocks without being washed off.

P.p. resplendens   (Baird's Cormorant)

The following quotation from Mr. C. I. Clay (1911) will illustrate the remarkable diving ability of this species:

We were one and one-half miles southwest from Trinidad, Humboldt County, California, and about one-half mile off shore. Mr. Francisco had set a net the night before near a blind rock and in twenty fathoms of water. We were taking in the net when a Brandt cormorant came to the surface in its meshes, then a second one and a third. Although the Baird cormorants were common everywhere on the ocean there were none in the net. On closely questioning the fisherman, he informed me Brandt cormorants were caught almost daily in from five to thirty fathoms of water while using the deep water nets, but were never taken in over forty fathoms of water, while the Baird cormorant (I had taught him the difference between the two species) were often taken in as much as eighty fathoms of water.

Referring to the behavior of Baird cormorants, Mr. W. Leon Dawson (1909) writes:

Cormorants plunge into the wildest waters as fearlessly as sealions, and they carry on their fishing operations about the shoulders of booming reefs, which humans dare not approach. After luncheons, which occur quite frequently in the cormorant day, the birds love to gather on some low-lying reef, just above the reach of the waves, and devote the intervening hours to that most solemn function of life, digestion. There is no evidence that the birds discuss oceanic politics on these occasions; the benevolent assimilation of a twelve-inch cultus cod is presumed to be ample occupation for union hours.   1922

RED-FACED CORMORANT   *Phalacrocorax urile*

Walrus Island, one of the Pribilof group in Bering Sea, the home of the red-faced cormorant, is without exception the most interesting bird island I have ever seen. Although situated only seven miles to the eastward of St. Paul Island, it is well isolated and protected by the prevailing fogs and storms of that forbidding region, for it is only during the calmest weather that a landing may be effected on its rugged shores. It is a small, low, rocky islet of less than five acres in area, not over a quarter of a mile long, and less than eighty yards wide, formed mainly of flat volcanic rock and lava in a series of shelves and low cliffs extending in an irregular outline down to and into the water.

The day we landed, July 7, 1911, was perfectly calm and the sea was as smooth as glass; we stepped out of our dory onto a flat shelf of rock as easily as if it were a wharf. As we walked out among the murre colonies they scarcely moved enough to allow us to pass and it was not until we almost stepped on them that they decided to leave and went pouring off in swarms down into the water. They soon returned and circled about the island, a constant, steady stream of whirling birds. A cloud of great white gulls were hovering overhead screaming constantly and downy young gulls were running about in the grass. The lively little auklets were chattering beneath the rocks or scrambling out from under them to fly off to sea. Grotesque puffins, disturbed in their burrows, made ludicrous attempts to escape by bounding along the ground in an effort to fly. Amidst all the noise and confusion the stolid red-faced cormorants sat unmoved upon their nests, on the wide shelves of rock projecting from the low cliffs, their rich glossy black plumage glistening with metallic tints of purple, blue, green, and bronze, offset by the brilliant scarlet face and the gular sac of clear smalt blue, a striking feature in the scene, a picture of dignified indifference.

The nests are placed on broad flat ledges of rock on the steepest cliffs, where they are often inaccessible, though on Walrus Island the cliffs are so low that the nests are easily reached. Other writers have stated that they are exceedingly filthy about their nests, but my experience was quite to the contrary; the nests that I saw were the handsomest, neatest, and cleanest cormorants' nests that I had ever seen. The nests were large, well built, and securely plastered onto a firm foundation; some were made almost wholly of green grass and sods, evidently gathered in the center of the island; others were made partially or wholly of various pretty seaweeds, sea ferns (Sertularidae) and sea mosses, fresh and neat in appearance and of various shades of brown, pink, and purple, probably obtained at considerable depths by diving; some of the nests were profusely decorated with gulls' feathers.   1922

DARTERS   Family Anhingidae

ANHINGA   *Anhinga anhinga*

In the swamps and marshy lakes of Florida, where the shores are overgrown with rank vegetation and the stately cypress trees are draped with long festoons of Spanish moss, or in the sluggish streams, half-choked with water hyacinths, "bonnets" and "water lettuce," where the deadly mocassin lurks concealed in the dense vegetation, where the gayly colored purple gallinules patter over the lily pads and where the beautiful snowy herons and many others of their tribe flourish in their native solitudes, there may we look for these curious birds. We may expect to find them sitting quietly, in little groups, in the tops of some clump of willows on the marshy shore or on the branches of some larger trees overhanging the water, with their long necks stretched upwards in an attitude of inquiry or held in graceful curves if not alarmed; perhaps some may have their wings outstretched in the sun to dry, a favorite basking attitude. If alarmed by the sudden appearance of a boat one may be seen to plunge headlong into the water, straight as a winged arrow, and disappear; soon, however, a snake-like head and neck may be seen at a distance rapidly swimming away with its body entirely submerged.

One of the favorite pastimes of a flock of water-turkeys[1] is to indulge in aerial exercise by rising from their roost, mounting high in the air and soaring in circles gradually upwards until almost out of sight, suggesting in their movements the flight of the Buteos. After gazing in admiration at such a spectacle the observer may be suddenly surprised to see one after another of the birds fold its wings and dart downwards, swift as an arrow.   1922

FRIGATE-BIRDS   Family Fregatidae

MAGNIFICENT FRIGATE-BIRD   *Fregata magnificens*

The flight of the man-o'-war-bird[2] is an inspiration; the admiring observer is spellbound with wonder as he beholds it and longs for the eloquence to describe it; but words are powerless to convey the impression that it creates. It is the most marvelous and most perfect flying machine that has ever been produced, with seven or eight feet of

[1] As this species was formerly called.
[2] As this species is sometimes called.

alar expanse, supporting a four-pound body, steered by a long scissor-like tail. It is not to be wondered at that such an aeroplane can float indefinitely in the lighest breeze. I shall never forget an exhibition I once saw among the Florida keys. We had anchored for the night near a small mangrove key, a famous roosting place for this species, and saw that it was black with hundreds of the birds sitting on the low trees. As we rowed toward it they all arose into the air and hung over it in a dense cloud, as thick as a swarm of insects. Gradually they spread out, floating without the slightest effort on motionless wings, separating into three great flocks and then into five flocks. By counting and carefully estimating the flocks, we concluded that there were between 1,000 and 1,200 birds in all. For over an hour we watched them as they floated out over us in a leisurely, dignified manner and slowly drifted away. At times they seemed to be almost stationary and never once did we detect a flap of the long, half-flexed wings, though it was almost calm. Like painted birds upon a painted sky they faded into the shadows of the night.

The active flight of the frigate-bird and its control of its powers is fully as wonderful as its passive sailings. While floating high in the air, almost out of sight, its keen eye detects some morsel of food in the water below it; with wings half closed it shoots downward like a meteor, and so accurately does it gauge its speed and distance that, just as it seems as if it must plunge like a falling arrow into the water, it checks its momentum with a marvelous twist of its great wings and lightly picks up the morsel from the surface with its bill without wetting a feather. It indulges in some startling, playful antics in the air, performs much of its courtship on the wing, and caresses its mate as gracefully in mid-air as on the ground. It strikes terror into its victim by darting at him at such speed that it is useless for him to attempt to escape; over, under, and around him at will, as if playing with his powers of flight; it is mere sport for the man-o'-war, the swift frigate, to overtake the fastest flier, and when the poor victim drops its fish, the frigate bird quickly catches it and, perhaps, tosses it in the air, drops and catches it again as if it enjoyed the game.

HERONS, STORKS, IBISES, FLAMINGOS, AND ALLIES— ORDER CICONIIFORMES

HERONS AND BITTERNS   Family Ardeidae

GREAT WHITE HERON   *Ardea occidentalis*

The Bay of Florida, including Barnes Sound, which is really a part of it, is a practically triangular body of water, approximately thirty-five miles long and twenty-five miles wide. Throughout its whole area the water is exceedingly shallow, averaging not over three feet in depth; the bottom is covered with white, soapy, slimy mud, which makes the water generally turbid and mostly opaque. At low tide many square miles of mud flats are exposed, leaving only an intricate maze of winding channels open to navigation in shallow draft vessels, and even at high tide a thorough knowledge of the channels is necessary to avoid running aground in a boat drawing over two feet of water.

These mangrove keys or islands, particularly the larger ones, are favorite resorts of the great white heron, and here we found them in abundance. The broad mud flats covered with shallow water form their feeding grounds. As we cruised along the main channels we could see the great white birds standing in the water several miles away, often at a long distance from any land, dignified and motionless, until induced to move by the rise and fall of the tide or by our approach, when they would leisurely depart for some more distant shoal. In such situations a near approach was impossible; two hundred or three hundred yards was about as near as we could come. Sometimes as many as a dozen or fifteen birds were in sight at one time, generally scattered about, singly or in small groups, and often in company with brown pelicans, with which they seem to be on good terms.

When not fishing, the great white herons could be seen perched in small groups on the red mangroves which form the outer boundaries of nearly all the keys, their pure white plumage standing out in marked contrast against the dark green foliage, making them clearly visible at a distance of several miles, one of the most striking features of this mangrove archipelago. But the keenness of their vision and their extreme shyness afforded them all the protection necessary, for every attempt to sail up to them proved a failure; a fleeting picture of great white birds was all we ever saw, as, with slowly measured wing strokes, with heads drawn over their shoulders and long legs stretched out straight behind, they flew away to some far distant key.   1925

GREAT BLUE HERON   *Ardea herodias*

The great blue heron, or "blue crane" as it is often called, is the largest, the most widely distributed, and the best known of the American herons.

In its native solitudes, far from the haunts of man, it may be seen standing motionless, in lonely dignity, on some far distant point that breaks the shore line of a wilderness lake, its artistic outline giving the only touch of life to the broad expanse of water and its background of somber forest. Or on some wide, flat coastal marsh its stately figure looms up in the distance, as with graceful, stealthy tread it wades along in search of its prey.

In Alexander Wilson's (1832) time these herons nested in the primeval cedar swamps of New Jersey, which have long since disappeared as virgin forests; referring to their nesting haunts, he says:

These are generally in the gloomy solitudes of the tallest cedar swamps, where, if unmolested, they continue annually to breed for many years. These swamps are from half a mile to a mile in breadth, and sometimes five or six in length, and appear as if they occupied the former channel of some choked up river, stream, lake, or arm of the sea. The appearance they present to a stranger is singular. A front of tall and perfectly straight trunks, rising to the height of fifty or sixty feet without a limb, and crowded in every direction, their tops so closely woven together as to shut out the day, spreading the gloom of a perpetual twilight below.

More modern conditions in that region are thus described in some notes sent to me by R. P. Sharples:

Down back of Delaware City [Delaware], near the Delaware & Chesapeake Canal, is a great swamp. It is many hundred acres in extent and is absolutely unfordable and impassable. In places are many trees growing out of the water and down below is a dense thicket shading the mud and ooze.

It is such a place as snakes and frogs and slimy things inhabit. Crawfish in immense numbers make their homes in it. But above is a bird paradise, and the thickets and the grasses and the trees are alive with them. In a small patch of maples a colony of great blue herons have built their nests. There were eighty-nine of the nests in the bunch and thirty-five of them were apparently in use when examined one day, the last of March 1912. The birds had just begun to lay their eggs and were very wild. Seventeen of the nests were seen in one big tree. These structures are made of small twigs, in a thin layer, so thin that the eggs can be seen from the ground at the foot of the tree. The nests are shallow platforms, and instead of being close to the trunk are generally out on the tops of the higher limbs, often being from eighty-five to one hundred feet from the ground. They are about three feet across and are very insecure resting places.   1925

GREEN HERON   *Butorides virescens*   (Townsend)

The green heron is equally at home in the salt water marshes and in the regions of fresh water. It is a day feeder but prefers the early morning and late afternoon, often taking a nap at midday. One of the familiar sounds and sights by salt creek or by river or pond is the frightened cry of this bird and its awkward flight over the water. The names "skeow" and "fly-up-the-creek" are expressive of these attributes. The classic names "chalk-line" and "shite-poke" express the commonly observed physiological effect of fright. This effect must incidentally serve a useful purpose in blinding the stealthily creeping pursuer, be it carnivore or savage.

The length of the neck of the green heron in life is a most variable one and this bird well deserves to be called "rubber neck." Early one May morning I watched unseen one of these birds with its neck drawn in creeping along the branches of a spruce. In the dim light it looked more like a mammal than a bird. Suddenly it elongated its neck and seized with its bill a twig of a near-by elm, but was unable to break it off. It tried another and another and finally succeeded in tearing the green twig off from its base. I watched another bird as it awoke from its morning nap and, as it stretched its neck to an equal length with its body and shook out its feathers, the general form and appearance of the bird went through a marvelous change. In short flights this heron may retain the elongated pose of the neck, but in longer ones it folds up and retracts that member.

When walking about, especially if it knows it is watched, the green heron nervously twitches its tail downwards and erects and depresses its crest. It is also able to remain perfectly still, especially when on the watch for game. A common posture assumed on the margin of a pond or sand flats at low tide is with the back and neck horizontal and the tarsi so nearly flat on the ground that the body is close to the same. The bird under these circumstances is easily mistaken for a log of wood. In this position it waits patiently, ready to pounce on the little fish that swim its way and it rarely misses its aim. At other times it approaches stealthily, putting down each foot with care and secures its prey with a quick stroke. That this stroke must be quick and accurate is evident when we consider the nature of some of its food, frogs, fish, and grasshoppers.   1925

LITTLE BLUE HERON   *Florida caerulea*

Dr. T. Gilbert Pearson (1922) describes its haunts very well as follows:

This species inhabits much of the extensive marshlands in our Southland. When traveling through the pine barrens of our South Atlantic and Gulf States, one will often come upon shallow ponds or small lakes whose margins and shallow reaches are more or less grown over with various water plants and scattered bushes; farther out the leaves of the water lilies are usually much in evidence. About the pond the bare grasslands, or prairies, extend from one hundred feet to many hundreds of yards. Here is the natural and favorite feeding ground of the little blue heron. Singly, or in small flocks, they may be seen wading slowly along in the shallow water or standing stationary with heads erect, watching the intruder from a distance. Sometimes these lakes contain islands covered with buttonwood or willow bushes, and these frequently are chosen as nesting sites for various herons of the neighborhood. Other favorite breeding places of the little blue heron are the small ponds in dense hammock lands that surround many of the lakes. Here, in the heavy semitropical forests, one may find quiet little ponds thickly grown with bushes, and such places the herons love.

The young are fed at first on regurgitated food; as thus described by Doctor Cordier (1923):

The actual act of feeding is, to say the least, a vicious and terrible affair. The parent bird stands by the nest in a seemingly indifferent mood, while the young are screaming and fighting for the best position. Each time the parent's bill is within reach, a young bird seizes it crosswise at the base and jerks violently, while there is much protesting noise from the other less fortunate youngsters. The old bird may, with stoical indifference, refuse to feed for some time, during which the young bird continues, with bull-dog tenacity, to pull and jerk at the parent's beak getting nearer and nearer to the tip. When the psychological moment for regurgitation arrives the partly digested fish is either forced down the throat of the nestling, or, perchance it may light on the interested photographer's head or camera outfit.

When the young birds have been fed the parent frequently stands by the nest for an hour or more, all the while uttering a contented note, much like that of a barnyard hen as she struts around the yard with her half-grown brood following her.   1925

REDDISH EGRET   *Dichromanassa rufescens*

In flight the reddish egret is very light, graceful, and easy, as well as strong and rather swift. In the white phase, with its long plumes, it somewhat resembles the American egret [common egret], but it appears shorter and stouter and its wing strokes are not so long and slow. Its particolored bill is a good field mark, as it is conspicuous at quite a distance. On the ground it walks with deliberate grace and elegance. It is an adept on balancing itself on the insecure perches it finds on the slender tops of the bushes, where it nests. It is interesting to watch it swaying in the strong breeze, which generally prevails on the Texas coast, maintaining its balance by slight adjustments of its supple frame; only occasionally are its broad wings brought into play.

A curious habit is referred to by Mr. Cahn (1923) as follows:

They will stand at the very edge of the nest sometimes by the hour, simply for the purpose of warding off the supposed attacks of neighboring egrets that are likewise amusing themselves by repelling imagined intrusions. Bristling, with every feather erect, they jab viciously at the object of their attack, or simply endeavor, by a full display of plumage, to overawe the innocent offender. Thus they pass the time defending their nests against entirely theoretical attacks of their neighbors, whose one idea often is simply to slip back to their eggs as unobtrusively as possible.   1925

COMMON EGRET   *Casmerodius albus*

Man has always been the arch enemy of the egrets. The destruction wrought by the plume hunters has been most cruel and wasteful; as the plumes are at the best during the breeding season, the birds were shot in their nesting rookeries, leaving the eggs to rot or the young to starve in the nests. No thought was had for the future and whole rookeries were systematically annihilated.

The slaughter began in Audubon's (1840) time. He speaks of "a person who, on offering a double-barreled gun to a gentleman near Charleston [South Carolina] for one hundred white herons fresh killed, received that number and more the next day." His friend Bachman brought home forty-six from a single day's shooting and said that "many more might have been killed, but we became tired of shooting them." And the slaughter continued with unabated fury in all parts of the world where egrets were to be found. Herbert K. Job (1905), writing at a time when the egrets were at about their lowest ebb, published some interesting figures to account for their disappearance. He writes:

When we know about the millinery plume trade, we understand the reason. In 1903 the price for plumes offered to hunters was $32 per ounce, which makes the plumes worth about twice their weight in gold. There will always be men who would break any law for such profit. No rookery of these herons can long exist, unless it be guarded by force of arms day and night. Here are some official figures of the trade from one source alone, of auctions at the London Commercial Sales Rooms during 1902. There were sold 1,608 packages of "ospreys," that is, herons' plumes. A package is said to average in weight thirty ounces. This makes a total of 48,240 ounces. As it requires about four birds to make an ounce of plumes, these sales meant 192,960 herons killed at their nests, and from two to three times that number of young or eggs destroyed. Is it, then, any wonder that these species are on the verge of extinction?

T. Gilbert Pearson (1912) published a long list of affidavits emphasizing the falsity of such propaganda,[1] among which the following, from an old plume hunter, is most striking:

My work led me into every part of Venezuela and Colombia where these birds are to be found, and I have never yet found or heard tell of any *garceros* [heronries] that were guarded for the purpose of simply gathering the feathers from the ground. No such a condition exists in Venezuela. The story is absolutely without foundation, in my opinion, and has simply been put forward for commercial purposes. The natives of the country, who do virtually all of the hunting for feathers, are not provident in their nature, and their practices are of a most cruel and brutal nature. I have seen them frequently pull the plumes from wounded birds, leaving the crippled birds to die of starvation, unable to respond to the cries of their young in the nests above, which were calling for food. I have known these people to tie and prop up wounded egrets on the marsh where they would attract the attention of other birds flying by. These decoys they keep in this position until they die of their wounds or from the attacks of insects. I have seen the terrible red ants of that country actually eating out the eyes of these wounded, helpless birds that were tied up by the plume hunters. I could write you many pages of the horrors practiced in gathering aigrette feathers in Venezuela by the natives for the millinery trade of Paris and New York.   1925

[Protection came just in time for this species, as for the snowy egret, and was successful. The species reoccupied much of its ances-

[1] That the plumes were picked up off the ground.

tral range; but it is now seriously threatened by drought, drainage, and real estate developments.]

SNOWY EGRET   *Leucophoyx thula*

Much that I have already written about the ruthless destruction of the American [common] egret applies with equal force to this smaller species. The little snowy egret was slaughtered in much greater numbers than its larger relative, because it was originally much more numerous and more widely distributed, because it was much less shy and so more easily killed, and because its short and delicate plumes were more in demand than the larger, stiffer plumes of the American egret. For these three reasons it suffered far more at the hands of the plume hunters and came much nearer being exterminated. But the same timely efforts stopped the slaughter before it was too late and saved the species, which is now increasing in protected localities.

The National Association of Audubon Societies in its campaign of education, circulated a great mass of literature on the subject. In its special leaflet No. 21 is a most striking picture of the horrors of the plume trade; it is a quotation from a paper by Mr. A. H. E. Mattingley, of Melbourne, Australia, published in *The Emu*[1] it reads as follows:

Notwithstanding the extreme heat and the myriads of mosquitos, I determined to revisit the locality[2] during my Christmas holidays, in order to obtain one picture only—namely, that of a white crane, or egret, feeding its young. When near the place, I could see some large patches of white, either floating in the water or reclining on the fallen trees in the vicinity of the egret's rookery. This set me speculating as to the cause of this unusual sight. As I drew nearer, what a spectacle met my gaze—a sight that made my blood fairly boil with indignation. There, strewn on the floating water weed, and also on adjacent logs, were at least fifty carcasses of large white[3] and smaller plumed egrets[4]—nearly one-third of the rookery, perhaps more—the birds having been shot off their nests containing young. What a holocaust! Plundered for their plumes. What a monument of human callousness! There were fifty birds ruthlessly destroyed, besides their young (about two hundred) left to die of starvation! This last fact was betokened by at least seventy carcasses of the nestlings, which had become so weak that their legs had refused to support them and they had fallen from the nests into the water below, and had been miserably

---

[1] Vol. VII, Oct. 1, 1907.
[2] An Australian heronry.
[3] *Herodias timoriensis.*
[4] *Mesophoyx plumifera.*

drowned; while, in the trees above the remainder of the parentless young ones could be seen staggering in the nests, some of them falling with a splash into the water, as their waning strength left them too exhausted to hold up any longer, while others simply stretched themselves out on the nest and so expired. Others, again, were seen trying in vain to attract the attention of passing egrets, which were flying with food in their bills to feed their own young, and it was a pitiful sight indeed to see these starvlings with outstretched necks and gaping bills imploring the passing birds to feed them. What a sickening sight! How my heart ached for them! How could anyone but a cold-blooded, callous monster destroy in this wholesale manner such beautiful birds—the embodiment of all that is pure, graceful, and good?

The same scenes were enacted many, many times in this country. Picture the cost of a plume! The mother bird lies dead on the ground, the plumes rudely torn from her bleeding back, her reward for her maternal devotion. The fatherless and motherless young stand in the nest; there is no one to feed them and they are growing weaker day by day. At length, too weak to stand or cry for food, they sink down in the nest, awaiting the end; death will be a blessed relief.[1]   1925

LOUISIANA HERON   *Hydranassa tricolor*

My first morning in Florida gave me many delightful surprises and some charming new acquaintances. I had been wandering through a fascinating old hammock admiring the picturesque live oaks, with their festoons of Spanish moss, the stately cabbage palmettos, so suggestive of the Tropics, and here and there a Spanish bayonet in full bloom, shedding its fragrance from a pyramid of white blossoms; the thickets of saw palmettos, the various orchids and air plants on the old trees were all new and interesting to me. Finally I came to a little, muddy pool in an open glade and sat down behind some saw palmettos to watch a little flock of yellowlegs feeding in the pool. A passing shadow caused me to look up and there on silent wings a larger bird was sailing down to alight in the pool, my first glimpse of a Louisiana heron at short range. It was totally unaware of my presence and within a few feet of me. Soon another came and then another, until there were five of them. What beautiful, dainty creatures they were, their slender forms clothed in bluish gray, blended drabs, purples, and white, with their little white plumes as a nuptial headdress. How agile and graceful they were as they darted about in pursuit of their prey. With what elegance and yet with what precision every movement was made. For harmony in colors and for grace in

[1] Similar scenes were enacted in the United States.

motion this little heron has few rivals. I could have watched and admired them for hours, but the rattle of a dry leaf, as I moved, ended my reverie, for they were gone. But I shall never forget my first impression of this elegant "lady of the waters."

In its courtship this dainty little heron is most attractive; though it lacks the wealth of glorious white plumes displayed by the American [common] and snowy egrets, and though it can not throw out the bristling array of plumage shown by the reddish egret, still it has a grace of action and beauty of plumage peculiar to itself. Perched on the topmost bough of some low tree or bush, the male bows to his mate, his long slender form swaying in the breeze, bending in long graceful curves and yielding to the pressure of the wind, as if he were a part of the tree itself. Like a "reed shaken by the wind" he bends, but does not break; and he never loses his balance. And now he dances along from branch to branch toward his mate, bowing and curtseying, with wings half spread. Many are the pretty attitudes that he assumes, with many graceful curves of his long slender neck. The plumes on his back are raised and lowered, like a filmy veil of ecru drab, and the pure white head plumes are raised and spread like a fan, in striking contrast to the blue and drab. It is a picture of irresistible beauty; his mate finally yields and the conjugal pact is sealed right there on the tree tops, without loss of poise.   1925

BLACK-CROWNED NIGHT HERON
Nycticorax nycticorax

The name, night heron, immediately suggests to my mind Sandy Neck and the famous rookery that has flourished and struggled alternately for over a century on that long chain of sand dunes that separates Barnstable Harbor from Cape Cod Bay. Many ornithologists have visited it and I have seen it many times in spring, summer, autumn, and winter. Several times it has been "shot out" and it has, within my memory, occupied three different parts of the neck a mile or more apart. Sandy Neck is about six miles long. Its northern or bay side is the continuation of a broad, flat, sandy beach, which extends for many miles along the north side of Cape Cod and terminates in a wide point of bare sand. On its southern or harbor side it is bordered by extensive salt meadows or marshes, covering several square miles and intersected by numerous creeks, channels, and ditches. The central portion consists of a series of picturesque sand dunes, some low and rolling hillocks and some high mountains of sand with steep sides and narrow crests, from which one may gain a comprehensive view of the long succession of barren, wind-swept peaks, protecting sheltered hollows filled with luxuriant vegetation. Here the largest colony of night herons, at least the largest of which I can find any record, in North America makes it summer home.

The young have a very bad habit of voiding their excrement and vomiting the contents of their crops, when frightened; the investigator is quite likely to receive some very unpleasant shower baths under such circumstances. It would be well for the observer to wear an old hat and an old suit of clothes, which can be thrown away or better still a complete suit of oilskins or overalls, which can be washed as soon as he comes out of the rookery, else he may carry home some unpleasant reminders.

Provided one can stand the nauseating odors or does not mind the filth, the briars and the insect pests, flies, mosquitos, and wood ticks, it is an exceedingly interesting experience to visit the Sandy Neck rookery in July. As he climbs to the crest of some commanding sand dune, he looks down upon a broad expanse of pines, mingled with oaks and thickets of underbrush and vines. The scene becomes a lively one, as hundreds of the gray, black-backed birds rise in great clouds, circle over the rookery in a bewildering maze and then drift away to settle in the tops of distant trees. The tops of the trees in the rookery are dotted with hundreds of young birds in the brown juvenal plumage, clearly outlined against the dark green of the pines; they are not yet able to fly but have climbed up out of the nests to bask in the sunshine and see the outside world. As he walks down into the rookery the excitement increases, the air is full of birds overhead, the trees are full of scrambling and fluttering young and the din of many voices adds to the pandemonium; the shrill piping notes of the youngest birds, the "yip, yip, yip," or the "yak, yak, yak" of the older young, and the various croaks and squawks of the adults create a volume of sound that is not soon forgotten.   1925

YELLOW-CROWNED NIGHT HERON
Nyctanassa violacea

This handsome and conspicuously marked heron has always been associated in my mind with the fresh-water swamps and bayous of our tropical and semitropical regions, where the deadly mocassin lurks under leafy shadows and the lazy alligator slumbers on muddy banks. We found it in Florida in the extensive marshes of the upper

St. Johns, living with the Louisiana and little blue herons on the willow islands and on the borders of the big cypress swamps; there were at least one or two pairs of these herons in nearly every rookery we visited. In Texas we found the yellow-crowned night heron common in the swamp and bayou forests along the banks of the Guadalupe River, in Victoria County. Its favorite haunts seemed to be in the bayous and stagnant backwaters, where the stately cypress grows, along with a heavy mixed forest of swamp tupelo, sweet and black gums, water oak, magnolia, and various willows. I understand that it lives under similar conditions in Louisiana and other Southern States.

But it has been found living under strikingly different conditions in other places. Mr. B. S. Bowdish (1902) "found it common on Mona, an island near Porto Rico, which seemed rather remarkable, as it is a dry, hot rock, with no sign of lagoon or swamp." Col. A. J. Grayson (1871) found it on Socorro Island, one of the Revillagigedo Islands,[1] of which he writes:

Upon this remote island, where there is a scarcity of fresh water, I was surprised to find this well-known species. Here its natural haunts are entirely wanting. Here there are no lagoons or mangrove swamps to skulk in during the day; and the croaking of frogs, its favorite prey, is not heard. All is dry and destitute of such localities suited to the nature of fresh-water birds. I saw solitary ones in the daytime perched upon the rocks in the interior of the island, and on one or two occasions were started from the dry grass, where they were concealed. Hardly a night passed that I did not hear the well-known *quak* of this heron as they came to our spring to drink. From the appearance of the male bird on examination and the presence of the young one shot they doubtless breed here to some extent.   1925

LEAST BITTERN   *Ixobrychus exilis*

The well known hiding pose, or reedlike attitude, of the least bittern is well described by Dr. Arthur A. Allen (1915), as follows:

I parted the flags and counted the eggs before I finally perceived that there, on the back of the nest and in perfectly plain sight, stood the female bird less than three feet from my eyes. Under other circumstances, I should not have called it a bird, such was the strangeness of the shape which it had assumed. The photograph showing the "reed posture" gives one but a poor conception of the bird's real appearance at this time. The feathers were fairly glued to the body, and the head and neck appeared no thicker than some of the dried reeds that composed the nest. The bill, pointing directly upward, widened barely appreciably into the head and neck, and the

[1] Off the west coast of Mexico.

feathers of the lower neck were held free from the body and compressed to as narrow a point as the bill at the other end. The neck appeared to be entirely separate from the body, which was flattened so as to become but a part of the nest itself. There was not a movement, not even a turning of the serpentlike eyes which glared at me over the corners of the mouth. Every line was stiff and straight, every curve was an angle. It mattered not that all about the vegetation was a brilliant green, while the bird was buffy brown. It was no more a bird than was the nest below it. I recalled the habit of the American bittern of rotating so as always to keep its striped neck towards the observer, and I moved slowly to another side of the nest. But this bird was not relying upon color of its neck to conceal it. It was quite as unbird-like from any angle, and it moved not a feather.

But this was not its only method of concealment, as was shown a few minutes later. I parted the flags directly in front of the bird, to see how close an approach it would permit. My hands came within twelve inches of it before it melted away over the back of the nest. Its movements were apparently very deliberate, and yet almost instantaneously it disappeared into the flags. It did not go far, and in a very few minutes it came back. Very slowly it pushed its vertical neck and upturned bill between the flags until it just fitted the space between two of the upright stalks at the back of the nest. No longer were the feathers drawn closely to the neck, which was at this time the only part visible. Instead, they were shaken out to their fullest expanse, and hung square across the base, instead of pointed. The dark feathers arranged themselves into stripes, and simulated well the shadows between the flags. Again I moved around the nest, and this time, instead of remaining motionless, the bird also rotated so as always to present its striped front to me and conceal its body. This was evidently a second and entirely different stratagem.   1925

AMERICAN BITTERN   *Botaurus lentiginosus*

The bittern is not an active bird. It spends most of its time standing under cover of vegetation, watching and waiting for its prey, or walking slowly about in its marsh retreat, raising each foot slowly and replacing it carefully; its movements are stealthy and noiseless, sometimes imperceptibly slow, so as not to alarm the timid creatures which it hunts. When standing in the open or when it thinks it is observed, it stands in its favorite pose, with its bill pointed upward and with its body so contracted that its resemblance to an old stake is very striking; the stripes on its neck, throat, and breast blend so well with the vertical lights and shadows of the reeds and flags, that it is almost invisible. Professor Walter B. Barrows (1913) has noted [in Ingham County, Michigan] an interesting refinement of this concealing action, which he has described as follows:

The bird, an adult bittern was in the characteristic erect and rigid attitude already described and so near us that its yellow iris was distinctly visible. Then, as we stood admiring the bird and his sublime confidence in his invisibility, a light breeze ruffled the surface of the previously calm water and set the cat-tail flags rustling nodding as it passed. Instantly the bittern began to sway gently from side to side with an undulating motion which was most pronounced in the neck but was participated in by the body and even the legs. So obvious was the motion that it was impossible to overlook it, yet when the breeze subsided and the flags became motionless the bird stood as rigid as before and left us wondering whether after all our eyes might not have deceived us. It occurred to me that the flickering shadows from the swaying flags might have created the illusion and that the rippling water with its broken reflections possibly made it more complete; but another gentle breeze gave us an opportunity to repeat the observation with both these contingencies in mind and there was no escape from the conclusion that the motion of the bittern was actual, not due to shadows or reflections, or even to the disturbance of the plumage by the wind itself. The bird stood with its back to the wind and its face toward us. We were within a dozen yards of it now and could see distinctly every mark of its rich, brown, black, and buff plumage, and yet if our eyes were turned away for an instant it was with difficulty that we could pick up the image again, so perfectly did it blend with the surrounding flags and so accurate was the imitation of their waving motion. This was repeated again and again, and when after ten or fifteen minutes we went back to our work, the bird was still standing near the same spot and in the same rigid position, although by almost imperceptible steps it had moved a yard or more from its original station.   1925

STORKS AND WOOD IBISES
Family Ciconiidae

WOOD IBIS   *Mycteria americana*

In flight the wood ibises are splendid birds and one never tires of watching them, as they fly along in flocks, high over the tree tops flapping their long wings or scaling at intervals, all in perfect unison. Even more interesting are the spectacular aerial evolutions in which these birds so often indulge. Rising in a flock, they soar in wide circles, mounting higher and higher, crossing and recrossing in a maze of spirals, until they are almost beyond vision in the ethereal blue. Then suddenly they dash downward and repeat the operation or else drift away on motionless wings until lost to sight. They are easily recognized at a great distance, great white birds with jet black flight feathers, with long necks and heavy bills and with long legs extended far beyond their short black tails.

Distance lends enchantment to this species; the sign of the cross, so boldly written in black and white on the distant sky, one stands and admires; but not so with the awkward, ungainly fowl that we see perched on a tree in a hunched-back attitude of uncouth indolence. Its behavior on the ground is well described by Doctor Coues (1874) as follows:

The carriage of the wood ibis is firm and sedate, almost stately; each leg is slowly lifted and planted with deliberate precision, before the other is moved, when the birds walk unsuspicious of danger. I never saw one run rapidly, since on all the occasions when I have been the cause of alarm, the bird took wing directly. It springs powerfully from the ground, bending low to gather strength, and for a little distance flaps hurriedly with dangling legs, as if it was much exertion to lift so heavy a body.   1925

IBISES AND SPOONBILLS
Family Threskiornithidae

GLOSSY IBIS   *Plegadis falcinellus*

Mr. Baynard's (1913) observations in Florida give us information on the home life of this species. He writes:

Glossy ibis bred on Orange Lake for four years of the five since I first saw it there.

The following observations were made during a period of eight weeks, during which time I had two pairs of these birds under daily surveillance. In looking for a suitable place to put up my photographic blind I stumbled onto these two pairs just beginning to build their nests, the second for the season, as all of the first built nests had been abandoned after being looted by the fish crows which swarmed in the rookery. Both parent birds aided in the construction of the nest, and I could not see that one bird did any more of the work than the other. I did note, however, that in one case the female selected the site and in the other the male did the selecting. Both nests were built at a height of about ten feet in thick elder bushes, and about three feet from the tops of the bushes, as plainly shown in the accompanying photographs. The nests were ready for eggs at the end of the second day, although the nests were not finished by any means. Glossy ibis have the same characteristics as the white ibis in that they continue to add to their nest even up to the time that the young are able to leave it, so that by the time the eggs are ready to hatch the nest will be almost double the size that it was when the first egg was laid. An egg was laid each day until one nest contained four and the other three. Incubation did not start until after the last egg had been laid a full day. After the first egg was laid, however, the nest was never without one or the other of the pair close by, something that was very necessary in this rookery on account of the thieving fish crows. During the period of incubation, which lasted in each case exactly twenty-one days, I noticed that the female did most of the incubating; the male, however, put in about six hours out of the twenty-four covering the eggs. The female sat all night and until about 8:30 or 9:00 a.m., when the male came in from his morning hunt for food; on his approach to the nest he would give his call when about fifty feet away and his mate would immediately answer and spring up from the nest and pass him in the air sometimes twenty-five feet from the nest. The male would always fly directly to the highest twig above the nest and after about five minutes of careful preening his feathers he would give three or four calls in a medium tone and spring down to the nest, stand a few minutes examining the eggs and then go stalking through the bushes until he found a twig that suited him, break it off with his bill and take it back to the nest and after placing it on top settle down to a three hour job of incubating, getting off the nest, however, usually once during that time and getting another twig to add to the nest. The female would return and give her bleating note about fifty feet from the nest when the male would stand up and wait for her to alight in the bush over the nest, then would ensue about fifteen minutes of as neat courting and billing and cooing as one will ever see being done by a pair of doves. This loving disposition toward each other seems to be characteristic of the glossy ibis, as every pair that I have observed have done it. The white ibis will occasionally do it, but not for any such length of time as the glossy. They will stand erect and seem to rub their bill against the other one, all the time making cooing (guttural, I must admit) notes of endearment, they will preen each others feathers and act just like a couple of young humans on their honeymoon; these loving scenes continued until the young were able to fly, never seeming to diminish at all. This trait I certainly admire, and while it is known to exist in birds that mate for life, is seldom seen in birds that are supposed to mate only for a season.   1925

WHITE-FACED IBIS   *Plegadis chihi*

The name "black curlew" has been well applied to this species, for at a distance in flight it certainly appears very dark colored; its long curved bill stretched out in front and its legs extended backward give it the shape of a curlew. It can be easily recognized at any distance. Its flight is strong, direct, swift and well sustained. When traveling in flocks, it flies in long, diagonal lines, sometimes with the birds abreast, usually with steady, rapid wing strokes, but varied occasionally with short periods of scaling.

Dr. Frank M. Chapman (1908) was privileged to see flocks of from ten to forty of these birds perform a surprising evolution; he writes [Los Barros, California, May 22, 1903]:

In close formation, they soared skyward in a broad spiral, mounting higher and higher until, in this leisurely and graceful manner, they had reached an elevation of at least five hundred feet. Then, without a moment's pause and with thrilling speed, they dived earthward. Sometimes they went together as one bird, at others each bird steered its own course, when the air seemed full of plunging, darting, crazy ibises. When about fifty feet from the ground, their reckless dash was checked and, on bowed wings, they turned abruptly and shot upward.

George Willett and Antonin Jay (1911) visited a large breeding colony of white-faced glossy ibises[1] in San Jacinto Lake, in Riverside County, California, on May 28, 1911, which they describe as follows:

In nearly every patch of tules was a nest or two of this species, and in the patch farthest west which covered about a half acre, there must have been at least two hundred nests. They were built on bent down tules, and were composed of tule stalks and lined with marsh grass. They were situated from two to six feet above the water, the average height being about four feet. About half the nests examined contained young and most of the others held badly incubated eggs. A very few fresh sets were found but the height of the nesting season was past. The sets almost invariably consisted of three or four eggs. In one or two instances sets of two incubated eggs were noted and three nests contained five eggs each, two nests six eggs each, and one nest had seven. It is probable that sets numbering more than five eggs were deposited by more than one bird. In fact they invariably showed two different types of eggs. The color of the eggs evidently fades with incubation, as the heavily incubated eggs are a much lighter blue than the freshly laid ones. This is probably the largest breeding colony of these birds in southern California west of the mountains.   1925

WHITE IBIS   *Eudocimus albus*

The sluggish upper waters of the St. Johns River in Florida are spread out into extensive marshes, broad lakes, and small ponds, choked with water hyacinths, "lettuce," and "bonnets," and dotted with floating boggy islets or more substantial islands overgrown with willow thickets. Here we found a paradise for water birds, many miles from the haunts of man, in which Florida[2] ducks and various species of herons and gallinules were breeding in security. It was a joy to watch the graceful aerial evolutions of the stately wood ibises

[1] As this species was then called.
[2] As the subspecies *fulvigula* of the Mottled Duck was formerly called.

and to mark the morning and evening flights of the white ibises between their feeding ground and their rookeries in distant swampy
thickets. Sometimes in large, loose flocks and sometimes in long,
straggling lines, they were always recognizable by their snowy whiteness and their rapid wing beats. Wherever we went in southern
Florida we frequently found them on inland lakes and streams, feeding in the shallow, muddy waters, or flying out ahead of us as we
navigated the narrow creeks in the mangrove swamps. Once I surprised a large flock of them in a little sunlit, muddy pool in a big
cypress swamp; they were feeding on the muddy shores, dozing on
the fallen logs or preening their feathers as they sat on the stumps
and the branches of the surrounding trees; what a cloud of dazzling
whiteness and what a clatter of many black-tipped wings, as they
all rose and went dodging off among the trees.

The flight of the white ibis is strong, direct, and rather swift, with
rapid strokes of the wings and varied with occasional shorter periods
of sailing. When flying in flocks the birds flap their wings or scale
in unison, but the scaling or sailing periods are much shorter than
with pelicans or cormorants. On their morning and evening flight
they usually fly very low and in large flocks, close to the water, over
lakes, or along water courses, rising just over the tree tops when necessary. The long curved bill, the pure white plumage of the adults,
with their black wing-tips, and the parti-colored plumage of the
young, are all good field marks, by which the species can easily be
recognized at any reasonable distance. Occasionally a flock of white
ibises rises high in the air to indulge in interesting aerial evolutions
for sport or exercise.

When frightened and forced to fly away from their feeding grounds
or nests, they are apt to alight in large numbers on some convenient
tree, preferably a large dead one with bare branches; they often
perch for long periods on such favorite trees; preening their plumage
or dozing, standing on one leg, in an upright attitude, with the head
drawn down on the shoulders and the bill resting on the breast. A
large tree full of white ibises is a pretty sight, especially if there are
a few roseate spoonbills scattered among them, as is often the case.

1925

ROSEATE SPOONBILL   *Ajaia ajaja*

This unique and beautiful species is one of the many which have
paid the supreme penalty for their beauty and been sacrificed by the
avaricious hand of man, who can never resist the temptation to de-

stroy and appropriate to his own selfish use nature's most charming creatures. He never seems to realize that others might like to enjoy an occasional glimpse at a group of these gorgeous birds, clearly outlined in pink and white against a background of dark green mangroves; nor does he appreciate how much a Florida landscape is enhanced by the sight of a flock of "pink curlews" fading away over the tree tops, until the glow of rose-colored wings is lost in the distant blue of the sky. All his sordid mind can grasp is the thought of a pair of pretty wings and the money they will bring when made into ladies' fans!

Dr. Frank M. Chapman (1914) writes:

In 1858, when Dr. Henry Bryant visited Pelican Island, on Indian River, he found not only brown pelicans, but also roseate spoonbills nesting there. But even at that early date these beautiful and interesting birds were prey for the plumer, some of whom, Dr. Bryant writes, were killing as many as sixty spoonbills a day, and sending their wings to St. Augustine to be sold as fans. From that time almost to this, "Pink Curlews," as the Floridan calls them, have been a mark for every man with a gun. Only a remnant was left when the National Association of Audubon Societies protested against the further wanton destruction of bird life, and through its wardens and by the establishment of reservations, attempted to do for Florida what the State had not enough foresight to do for itself.

Writing at the time when the destruction of plume birds was flourishing, W. E. D. Scott (1889) says:

The record in regard to the species in question is even more shocking than that of the flamingo. The roseate spoonbill was ten years ago an abundant bird on the Gulf Coast of Florida, as far north at least as the mouth of the Anclote River. The birds bred in enormous rookeries in the region about Cape Romano and to the south of that point. These rookeries have been described to me by men who helped to destroy them, as being frequently of many acres in extent and affording breeding grounds to thousands of roseate spoonbills. The birds bred in January and were in the best plumage late in November and in December. They do not seem to have bred north of Charlotte Harbor, so far as I am able to ascertain, but immediately after the breeding season was finished, and as soon as the young were able to shift for themselves, there was a great dispersal of the birds to the northward, particularly along the coast, though they were common at points in the interior. All this is changed. I have spent the past four winters and two summers in Florida. My old hunting grounds have all been carefully retraversed, some of them many times, and the roseate spoonbill is almost as great a stranger to me as to my fellow workers who live the year round in Massachusetts.[1]   1925

[1] Protection has, temporarily at least, saved this species in Florida, but it is still very rare.

FLAMINGOS   Family Phoenicopteridae

AMERICAN FLAMINGO   *Phoenicopterus ruber*

I have never been privileged to see this gorgeous bird in its natural surroundings. But, having visited some of its former haunts in southern Florida, it is not difficult to picture in imagination the thrill of pleasure which others have enjoyed in their first sight of even a distant flock of these magnificent birds, perhaps a mile or more away across a broad, flat, shimmering waste of whitish marl, a glowing band of brilliant pink against a background of dark-green mangroves.

Dr. Frank M. Chapman (1908) describes it very well when he says:

There are larger birds than the flamingo, and birds with more brilliant plumage but no other large bird is so brightly colored and no other brightly colored bird is so large. In brief, size and beauty of plume united, reach their maximum of development in this remarkable bird, while the open nature of its haunts and its gregariousness seem specially designed to display its marked characteristics of form and color to the most striking advantage.

The flamingo is no longer to be found, except possibly as a rare straggler, on the North American Continent, but in Audubon's time it was fairly abundant in extreme southern Florida.[1] Even in those days it was relentlessly pursued and was becoming quite shy. Gustavus Wurdemann (1861), in a letter written to the Smithsonian Institution in 1857, wrote:

The flamingo is known to but a very few inhabitants of this state, because it is confined to the immediate neighborhood of the most southern portion of the peninsula, Cape Sable, and the keys in its vicinity. It was seen by the first settlers at Indian River, but abandoned these regions immediately, and never returned thither after having been fired upon.

In the same letter he refers to a flock of five hundred flamingos seen near Indian Key, in the Bay of Florida, and graphically describes his experiences in chasing and capturing, with a native hunter, some hundred or so of these beautiful birds, which were molting and unable to fly.

[1] "The . . . population in the Florida Bay area increased to 11 birds this summer and appears to have become established"—*Audubon Field Notes*, October, 1959. The famous flock of captives at the Hialeah Race Track near Miami, Florida, is the largest population of this species in the United States today.

Evidently this flock of flamingos, or its descendants, was able to survive in this remote and inaccessible portion of Florida long after the species had disappeared from other sections. It was supposed to breed somewhere in that vicinity, but the breeding grounds were never found. W. E. D. Scott (1887) reported that the last birds were killed in Tampa Bay in 1885 and that they disappeared from Cape Romano and all points north of that at about that time. But in February, 1890, he found a large flock frequenting a bay eighteen miles east of Cape Sable, about which he (1890) writes as follows:

It was some 9 or 10 miles from our anchorage to the mouth of the first of the three bays I have mentioned—a long way to go in a skiff. But both of our boats were soon manned and we began the details of the exploration. Rounding the point opening the first or more westerly of the bays, we found that it was about a mile and a half in width and some 3 miles deep into the land, with a decided bend to the west. No birds were to be seen till this bend was in turn opened, and there, still a mile or more away, was presented a truly wonderful sight. Stretched out for fully three-quarters of a mile, and about three hundred yards from the mainland shore, was a band of rosy, firelike color. This band was unbroken, and seemed to be very even, though curving with the contour of the shore. Now and again a flame or series of flames seemed to shoot up above the level of the line. This proved when examined through the glass to be caused by one or more birds raising their heads to look about or to rest themselves, for when first noticed all were feeding, with their heads most of the time buried in the shallow water, searching the mud for the small shellfish which appear to be the favorite food at this point.

Presently some of the birds saw the boats, and the alarm was given. Slowly the line began to contract toward the center, and the birds were soon in a compact body, appearing now like a large field of red upon the water, and the resemblance to flames was much increased by the constant movements of the heads and necks of the different individuals. In a few moments they began to rise and soon they were all in full flight, passing out of the bay and over the point of land to the east in long lines and in V-shaped parties, recalling to mind the flight of wild geese. If the color on the water was novel, that of the flock while in the air was truly surprising, a cloud of flame-colored pink, like the hues of a brilliant sunset. As far as we could descry the birds, the color was the great conspicuous feature. Looked at through the glass, while in flight, the individuals composing the flock were seen to be mostly adults. I saw only a small division of the lighter colored immature birds. These seemed to have their own particular position in the flock, and on this and subsequent occasions, when seen, these younger individuals were always alone. As nearly as could be estimated there were at least 1,000 birds in this flock; and of these all but about fifty appeared to be adults.

Twelve years later, on March 26, 1902, Dr. Reginald Heber Howe, Jr. (1902) "observed a flock of from five hundred to one thousand birds in a little bay to the east of Cape Sable," probably in the same locality. This was about the last of the flamingo in Florida, for in the following year, 1903, I spent parts of April and May in this vicinity, visiting Indian Key, where Audubon saw his first flock, and exploring the coast and islands from Cape Sable to a bay called Snake Bight, which I judge from their descriptions to be the place where Scott and Howe saw the two flocks referred to above.   1925

SWANS, GEESE, AND DUCKS—
ORDER ANSERIFORMES

SWANS, GEESE, AND DUCKS   Family Anatidae

WHISTLING SWAN   *Olor columbianus*

I had lived to be nearly fifty years old before I saw my first wild swan, but it was a sight worth waiting for, to see a flock of these magnificent, great, snow-white birds, glistening in the sunlight against the clear blue sky, their long necks pointing northward toward their polar home, their big black feet trailing behind, and their broad translucent wings slowly beating the thin upper air, as they sped onward in their long spring flight. If the insatiable desire to kill, and especially to kill something big and something beautiful, had not so possessed past and present generations of sportsmen, I might have seen one earlier in my life and perhaps many another ornithologist, who has never seen a swan, might have enjoyed the thrill of such an inspiring sight. No opportunity has been neglected to kill these magnificent birds, by fair means or foul, since time immemorial; until the vast hordes which formerly migrated across our continent have been sadly reduced in numbers and are now confined to certain favored localities. Fortunately the breeding grounds of this species are so remote that they are not likely to be invaded by the demands of agriculture; and fortunately the birds are so wary that they are not likely to be exterminated on migrations or in their winter resorts.

Considering its size and weight, a swan rises from the water with remarkable ease and celerity; it runs along the surface for fifteen or twenty feet, flapping its wings and beating the water with its feet alternately, until it has gained sufficient headway to launch into the air; like all heavy-bodied birds it must face the wind in rising. When well awing it flies with considerable speed and power, with the long neck stretched out in front and the great black feet extending beyond the tail; the wing beats are slow, but powerful and effective. It has been said to fly at a speed of one hundred miles an hour; probably no such speed is attained, however, except when flying before a heavy wind; it undoubtedly flies faster than it appears to on account of its great size, and it certainly flies faster than any of the ducks and geese. When traveling long distances swans fly in V-shaped wedges, in the same manner as geese and for the same reason; the resistance of the air is less, as each bird flies in the widening wake of its predecessor; the leader, of course, has the hardest work to do, as he "breaks the trail," but he is relieved at intervals and drops back into the flock to rest. On shorter flights they fly in long curving lines or in irregular flocks. They usually fly rather high, and when traveling are often way up above the clouds.   1923

TRUMPETER SWAN   *Olor buccinator*

This magnificent bird, the largest of all the North American wild fowl, belongs to a vanishing race; though once common throughout all of the central and northern portions of the continent, it has been gradually receding before the advance of civilization and agriculture; when the great Central West was wild and uncultivated it was known to breed in the uninhabited parts of many of our Central States, even as far south as northern Missouri; but now it probably does not breed anywhere within the limits of the United States, except possibly in some of the wilder portions of Montana or Wyoming;[1] civilization has pushed it farther and farther north until now it is making its last stand in the uninhabited wilds of northern Canada.

Prof. Wells W. Cooke (1906) says:

In early times it probably bred south to Indiana, Wisconsin, Iowa, Nebraska, Montana, and Idaho; it nested in Iowa as late as 1871, in Idaho in 1877, in Minnesota in 1886, and in North Dakota probably for a few years later. It is not probable that at the present time the trumpeter nests anywhere in the United States, and even in Alberta no nests seem to have been found later than 1891. The vast wilderness of but a generation ago is now crossed by railroads and thickly dotted with farms. The species is supposed still to breed in the interior of British Columbia at about latitude 53°.   1923

CANADA GOOSE   *Branta canadensis*

The common wild goose is the most widely distributed and the most generally well known of any of our wild fowl. From the

[1] Vigorous conservation measures have saved a small number of these birds in the United States. The Fish and Wildlife Service reported a 1958 population of 735 birds of which 310 were in the Red Rock Lakes National Wildlife Refuge in sw. Montana. Some of these breed; 147 cygnets were hatched during 1958 in the United States.

Atlantic to the Pacific and from the Gulf of Mexico nearly to the Arctic coast it may be seen at some season of the year, and when once seen its grandeur creates an impression on the mind which even the casual observer never forgets. As the clarion notes float downward on the still night air, who can resist the temptation to rush out of doors and peer into the darkness for a possible glimpse at the passing flock, as the shadowy forms glide over our roofs on their long journey? Or, even in daylight, what man so busy that he will not pause and look upward at the serried ranks of our grandest wild fowl, as their well-known honking notes announce their coming and their going, he knows not whence or whither? It is an impressive sight well worthy of his gaze; perhaps he will even stop to count the birds in the two long converging lines; he is sure to tell his friends about it, and perhaps it will even be published in the local paper, as a harbinger of spring or a foreboding of winter. Certainly the Canada goose commands respect.

The Canada goose is one of the earliest of the water birds to migrate in the spring. Those which have wintered farthest south are the first to feel the migratory impulse, and they start about a month earlier than those which have wintered at or above the frost line, moving slowly at first but with a gradually increasing rate of speed. Prof. Wells W. Cooke (1906) has shown, from his mass of accumulated records, that beginning with an average rate of nine miles a day, between the lowest degrees of latitude, the speed is gradually increased through successive stages to an average rate of thirty miles a day during the last part of the journey. Following, as it does, close upon the heels of retreating ice and snow, the migration of these geese may well be regarded as a harbinger of spring; for the same reason it is quite variable from year to year and quite dependent on weather conditions.

The first signs of approaching spring come early in the far south, with the lengthening of the days and the increasing warmth of the sun; the wild geese are the first to appreciate these signs and the first to feel the restless impulse to be gone; they congregate in flocks and show their uneasiness by their constant gabbling and honking, as if talking over plans for their journey, with much preening and oiling of feathers in the way of preparation; at length a flock or two may be seen mounting into the air and starting off northward, headed by the older and stronger birds, the veterans of many a similar trip; flock after flock joins the procession, until the last have gone, leaving their winter homes deserted and still. The old ganders know the way and lead their trustful flocks by the straightest and safest route;

high in the air, with the earth spread out below them like a map, they follow no coast line, no mountain chain, and no river valley; but directly onward over hill and valley, river and lake, forest and plain, city, town, and country, their course points straight to their summer homes. Flying by night or by day, as circumstances require, they stop only when necessary to rest or feed, and then only in such places as their experienced leaders know to be safe. A thick fog may bewilder them and lead them to disaster or a heavy snowstorm may make them turn back, but soon they are on their way again, and ultimately they reach their breeding grounds in safety.   1923

BRANT   *Branta bernicla*

Brant do not ordinarily fly in V-shaped flocks, like Canada geese, but in long undulating lines, spread out laterally in straight company-front formation, or in a curving line, or in an irregular bunch, and without a definite leader. When migrating overland they fly high, but when traveling along the coast they usually fly within a few feet of the water. Their flight is apparently slow and heavy, but it is really swifter than it seems. A flock of oncoming brant is a thrilling sight to the expectant gunner; he can recognize afar the long wavy line of heavy black birds; as they draw near, the white hind parts show up in marked contrast to the black heads and necks; and soon he can hear their gabbling, grunting notes of greeting to his well-placed decoys. They are naturally shy birds, and we seldom got a shot at the passing flocks when anchored off the shore in small boats. But on their feeding grounds they are more fearless and will decoy well to live or even wooden decoys around a well-concealed blind. Brant can swim well, but do not dive unless hard-pressed. They prefer to skulk and hide by stretching the neck out on the water or in the grass. They are very fond of sand and like to rest on sandy points and sand bars.

From the standpoint of the epicure the brant is one of our finest game birds, in my opinion *the* finest, not even excepting the far-famed canvasback. I can not think of any more delicious bird than a fat, young brant, roasted just right and served hot, with a bottle of good Burgundy. Both the bird and the bottle are now hard to get; alas, the good old days have passed.

On Monomoy [Cape Cod, Massachusetts] our brant shooting is done from boxes located on favorable points or sand bars near the feeding grounds. The box is well made and water-tight, six feet long, four feet wide, and four feet deep; big enough for three men; it is sunken into the sand deep enough to be covered at high tide; numerous bags, sometimes fifty or sixty, of sand are piled around it to hold it in place; and if it is in a grassy place, which helps to conceal it, the sloping sides of the pile may be thatched with marsh grass woven into the meshes of poultry netting, held in place by stakes and weighted with sand. Unless there is a natural sand bar near the box, one must be made, on which the live decoys are located and where the wild birds may alight. Live decoys[1] are preferable, but brant will come to good wooden decoys if properly placed; a supply of both is desirable. The brant feed at low tide away off on the eelgrass beds; but as the rising tide covers the grass too deeply, they are driven to seek other feeding grounds or sanding places, and in flying about will often come to the decoys. The best shooting then is for a short time only at about half-flood tide and again at about half ebb, while the birds are moving. The morning tides are considered the best, so it is often quite dark when we tramp down through the marsh to our box, heavily laden with decoys, guns, and ammunition and encumbered with rubber boots and oilskins, for it is cold and wet work. We set out the decoys, bale out the box, and sit low on a wet seat, our eyes just above the rim of the box, and scan the flats for distant flocks of brant. Occasional shots at passing birds or small bunches on their way seem like fair sport. But when a large flock swims up to the decoys on the rising tide or flies up and settles on the bar among them, it is exciting enough, but it seems like wanton slaughter to fire a battery of guns at a given signal into a dense mass of birds. Perhaps a dozen or a score of birds are killed or wounded and we jump out of the box and go splashing off through the mud and water to retrieve the cripples. When the rising tide finally drives us out of our box, we may have a large bunch of birds to lug back to the club house, but have we given them a fair show for their lives?

1923

BLACK BRANT   *Branta nigricans*

The spring migration of the black brant in northern Alaska and the circumstances surrounding it have been so attractively portrayed by Dr. E. W. Nelson (1881) that I can not refrain from quoting parts of what he says about it, as he observed it at St. Michael, Alaska; he writes:

[1] Now illegal.

The long reign of ice and snow begins to yield to the mild influence of the rapidly lengthening days; the middle of May is reached, and the midnight sky over the northern horizon blushes with delicate rose tints, changing to purple toward the zenith.

At length, about the 20th of May, the first barn swallow arrives and then we begin to look for the black brant, the *"nimkee,"* as it is called by the Russians, the *"luk-lug-u-nuk"* of the Norton Sound Eskimo. Ere long the *avant-courier* is seen in the form of a small flock of 10 or 15 individuals which skim along close to the ice, heading directly across Norton Sound to the vicinity of Cape Nome, whence their route leads along the low coast to Port Clarence where, I am told by the natives, some stop to breed; but the majority press on and seek the ice-bordered northern shore of Alaska and even beyond to unknown regions far to the north.

The 22d of May a native came in bringing a lot of geese and reporting plenty of black brant up the "canal."

Preparing the tent and other paraphernalia, two of us, accompanied by a couple of natives, started out the next morning with a sled and team of five large dogs, driven tandem, just as the sun gilded the distant hilltops and gave a still deeper tint to the purple haze enveloping their bases. The sharp, frosty air and the pleasurable excitement of the prospective hunt, after months of inactivity, causes an unusual elation of spirits, and with merry jests we speed along until, in a short time, we approach a low, moundlike knoll rising in the midst of innumerable lakelets. A strange humming, for which we were at first unable to account, now becomes more distinct, and we perceive its origin in the united notes of scores of flocks of brant which are dispersed here and there over the half bare ground. Some sit along the edges of the snow banks or upon the ground, still sleeping, while others walk carelessly about or plume themselves in preparation for the work before them. Their low, harsh, guttural *gr-r-r-r, gr-r-r-r* rises in a faint monotonous matinal whose tone a week later may waken the weird silence in unknown lands about the Pole.

Reaching the knoll before mentioned, we pitch our tent, and after tieing the dogs to keep them within bounds we separate to take positions for the morning flight. Each of the party is soon occupying as little space as possible behind some insignificant knoll or tuft of grass that now and then breaks the monotonous level. The sun rises slowly higher and higher until at length the long, narrow bands of fog hovering over the bare ground are routed. Now we have not long to wait, for, as usual at this season, the lakes, which are frozen over nightly, open under the rays of the sun between 7 and 9 in the morning and start the waterfowl upon their way. The notes, which until now have been uttered in a low conversational tone, are raised and heard more distinctly and have a harsher intonation. The chorus swells and dies away like the sound of an aeolian harp of one or two heavy bass strings, and as we lie close to the ground the wind whispers among the dead plants in a low undertone as an accompaniment; but while we lay dreaming the sun has done its work; the lakes have opened, and suddenly a harsh *gr-r-r-r, gr-r-r-r, gr-r-r-r* causes us to spring up, but too late, for, gliding away to the northward, the first flock goes unscathed. After a few energetic remarks upon geese in general and this flock in particular, we resume our position, but keep on the alert to do honor to the next party.

Soon, skimming along the horizon, flock after flock is seen as they rise and hurry by on either side. Fortune now favors us, and a large flock makes directly for the ambush, their complicated and graceful evolutions leading us to almost forget why we are lying here upon our face in the bog with our teeth rattling a devil's tattoo in the raw wind. On they come, only a few feet above the ground, until, when 20 or 30 yards away, we suddenly rise upon one knee and strike terror into the hearts of the unsuspecting victims. In place of the admirable order before observed, all is confusion and, seemingly in hope of mutual protection, the frightened birds crowd into a mass over the center of the flock, uttering, the while, their ordinary note raised in alarm to a higher key. This is the sportsman's time, and a double discharge as they are nearly overhead will often bring down from 4 to 10 birds. Scarcely have the reports died away when they once more glide along close to the ground; the alarm is forgotten; order is again restored, and the usual note is heard as they swiftly disappear in the distance. Thus they continue flying until 1 or 2 o'clock in the afternoon when, after a pause of three or four hours, they begin again and continue until after sundown. 1923

BARNACLE GOOSE   *Branta leucopsis*

The breeding grounds of the barnacle goose have only recently been found; the following quotation from A. L. V. Manniche (1910) seems to indicate that the species breeds abundantly in northeastern Greenland.[1] He writes:

June 8 and 9, 1908, I got my first opportunity to study the barnacles in their real nesting territory. Up to this time the geese had led a comfortable and by me unsuspected existence in a lonely marsh and moor territory far up country—10 to 15 kilometers from the nearest salt water—east of Saelsoen, imposing by its extent and grandness of scenery. This territory, the farthest extent of which is in a northerly direction, comprises an area of some 20 square kilometers; on the north it is bordered by a mountain range, the lower slopes of which are covered by a vegetation more luxuriant than I saw in any other place in northeast Greenland.

To the east and north the marshes lose themselves in barren stony plains sprinkled with sandy spots and a few deep lying fresh-water basins

---

[1] Casual along east coast of North America in winter.

bare of all vegetation. To the south the steep and barren mountain of Trekroner rises to a height of 360 meters in small terraced projections.

In the marsh and moor itself the vegetation was extremely luxuriant; as well the alpine willow as other plants reached here a relatively gigantic size. All over the snow had melted, though it was early in the season, and the place offered an increased allurement to the swimmers and waders by the countless ponds of melting snow. The influence of the powerful sunlight on the dark turfy soil surely accounts for the unusually early melting of the snow in this place.

At my arrival the barnacles were standing in couples or in small flocks in the ponds or they were grazing near these; some were high up the mountain slopes. Almost all the geese used to leave the marsh every day at certain times and disappeared southwards toward the high middle part of Trekroner. I set out in this direction, thinking that a larger lake was lying near the mountain, and that the geese retired to this after their meal. I really found a pair of larger fresh-water basins and saw in these a few geese, which being frightened flew farther toward the mountains. Having come within a distance of one kilometer from Trekroner I solved the riddle. The barnacles were swarming to and fro along the gigantic mountain wall like bees at their hive, and I heard a continuous humming, sounding like a distant talk. I took a seat at the foot of the mountain and observed the behavior of the geese for some hours. Using my field glass I could without difficulty notice even the smallest details.

While some of the geese would constantly fly along the rocky wall and sometimes mounted so high in the air that they disappeared on the other side of the rocks, the majority of the birds were sitting in couples upon the shelves of the rocky wall, some of which seemed too narrow to give room for the two birds—much less for a nest. It was only on the steep and absolutely naked middle part of the mountain wall that the geese had their quarters and in no place lower than some 200 meters from the base of the cliff. As the wall was quite inaccessible, I had to content myself by firing some rifle balls against it in order to frighten the birds and thus form an idea of the size of the colony. The birds which were "at home" then numbered some 150 individuals.   1923

EMPEROR GOOSE   *Philacte canagica*

The handsomest and the least known of American geese is confined to such narrow limits, both in its breeding range[1] and on its migrations, that it has been seen by fewer naturalists than any other goose on our list.

---

[1] Breeds in North America "in the coastal areas of northwestern Alaska from Point Barrow to the mouth of the Kuskokwin River (apparently not going inland more than 10 miles)"—1957 *A.O.U. Check-List.*

Dr. Edward W. Nelson (1913) writes:

At the border of the Yukon delta, Esquimos familiar with the country were employed to lead us to the desired nesting ground of the emperor goose. Nearly half a day's journey among the maze of ice-covered channels of the delta brought us to a low, flat island, where our guide assured me many *na-chau-thluk* would soon arrive to rear their young. It was a bare, desolate spot, with only a few scattered alders on the upper side of the islands, and an unbroken view out over the frozen sea to the west. A tent was put up on a slight rise and, after a stock of driftwood had been gathered, the guides took the sledge and left me with my Esquimo companion to await the arrival of the birds. Later, when the ice went out, they returned for me with kyaks.

A few white-fronted and cackling geese[1] gave noisy evidence of their presence, but it was not until May 22 that the Esquimo brought in the first emperor goose—a male in beautiful spring plumage. After this, small flocks came in rapidly until they were plentiful all about us. They arrived quietly, skimming along near the ground, quite unlike the other geese, which appeared high overhead with wild outbursts of clanging cries, which were answered by those already on the ground. The river channels and the sea were still covered with ice, and the tundra half covered with snow, at the time of the first arrivals.

Almost at once after their arrival on the islands, the emperor geese appeared to be mated, the males walking around the females, swinging their heads and uttering low love notes, and incoming flocks quickly disintegrated into pairs which moved about together, though often congregating with many others on flats and sand bars. The male was extremely jealous and pugnacious, however, and immediately resented the slightest approach of another toward his choice; and this spirit was shown equally when an individual of another species chanced to come near. When a pair was feeding, the male moved restlessly about, constantly on the alert, and at the first alarm the pair drew near one another, and just before taking wing uttered a deep, ringing *u-lugh, u-lugh;* these, like the flight notes, having a peculiar deep tone impossible to describe.

At low tide, as soon as the shore ice disappeared, the broad mud flats along shore were thronged with them in pairs and groups numbering up to 30 or 40 individuals. They were industriously dabbling in the mud for food until satisfied, and then congregated on bars, where they sat dozing in the sun or lazily arranging their feathers. By lying flat on the ground and creeping cautiously forward, I repeatedly approached within 30 or 40 yards of parties near shore without their showing any uneasiness.

The first of June they began depositing eggs in the flat marshy islands bordering the sea all along the middle and southern part of the delta. The nests were most numerous in the marshes, a short distance back from

[1] As the subspecies *minima* of the Canada Goose was formerly called.

the muddy feeding grounds, but stray pairs were found nesting here and there farther inland on the same tundra with the other species of geese and numerous other waterfowl. Near the seashore, the eggs were frequently laid among the bleached and wave-torn scraps of driftwood lying along the highest tide marks.

The nests I examined usually contained from 3 to 5 eggs, but the full complement ranged up to 8.   1923

WHITE-FRONTED GOOSE   *Anser albifrons*

The flight of the white-fronted goose is similar to that of the Canada goose, for which it might easily be mistaken at a distance. It flies in V-shaped flocks, led by an old gander, and often very high in the air. Its flight has been well described by Neltje Blanchan (1898) as follows:

A long clanging cackle, *wah, wah, wah, wah,* rapidly repeated, rings out of the late autumn sky, and looking up, we see a long, orderly line of laughing geese that have been feeding since daybreak in the stubble of harvested grain fields, heading a direct course for the open water of some lake. With heads thrust far forward, these flying projectiles go through space with enviable ease of motion. Because they are large and fly high, they appear to move slowly; whereas the truth is that all geese, when once fairly launched, fly rapidly, which becomes evident enough when they whiz by us at close range. It is only when rising against the wind and making a start that their flight is actually slow and difficult. When migrating, they often trail across the clouds like dots, so high do they go— sometimes a thousand feet or more, it is said—as if they spurned the earth. But as a matter of fact they spend a great part of their lives on land; far more than any of the ducks.

On reaching a point above the water when returning from the feeding grounds the long defile closes up into a mass. The geese now break ranks, and each for itself goes wheeling about, cackling constantly, as they sail on stiff, set wings; or, diving, tumbling, turning somersaults downward, and catching themselves before they strike the water, form an orderly array again, and fly silently, close along the surface quite a distance before finally settling down upon it softly to rest.

The peculiar laughing cry of this bird has given it the name of "laughing goose." Its cries are said to be loud and harsh, sounding like the syllable *wah* rapidly repeated; the note is easily imitated by striking the mouth with the hand while rapidly uttering the above sound.   1923

SNOW GOOSE   *Chen hyperborea*

C.h. hyperborea   (Lesser Snow Goose)

The breeding grounds of the snow goose are so far north that we know very little about them in their summer home. They are known to us mainly as winter residents or as migrants.

Walter E. Bryant (1890), in comparing their status then with past conditions in California, writes:

There has not, so far as I am aware, been a very marked decrease in the number of geese which annually visit California, but the area over which they now feed in considerably less than in 1850. In the fall of that year, my father, while going from San Francisco to San Jose, met with acres of white[1] and gray[2] geese near San Bruno. They were feeding near the roadside, indifferent to the presence of all persons, and in order to see how close he could approach he walked directly toward them. When within 5 or 6 yards of the nearest ones they stretched up their necks and walked away like domestic geese; by making demonstration with his arms they were frightened and took wing, flying but a short distance. They seemed to have no idea that they would be harmed, and feared man no more than they did the cattle in the fields. The tameness of the wild geese was more remarkable than of any other birds, but it must be understood that in those days they were but little hunted and probably none had ever heard the report of a gun and few had seen men. This seems the most plausible accounting for the stupid tameness of the geese, 40 years ago. What the wild goose is to-day on the open plains of the large interior valleys of California those who have hunted them know. By 1853 the geese had become wilder and usually flew before one could get within shotgun range, if on foot, but in an open buggy or upon horseback there was no difficulty. There was a very marked contrast between the stupidly tame geese after their arrival in the fall and the same more watchful and shy birds before the departure in spring of the years 1852 and 1853. This is an important fact, showing not only the change in the instinct occurring within three years, but the more remarkable change, or it may be called the revival of the instinct of fear, which was effected within a few months.

The following quotations from Grinnell, Bryant, and Storer (1918) will give a fair idea of present conditions in California:

There has been a more conspicuous decrease in the numbers of geese than in any other game birds in the State. Many observers testify that there is only 1 goose now for each 100 that visited the State 20 years ago, and some persons aver that in certain localities there is not more than 1 to every

[1] This species.
[2] Presumably White-fronted Geese.

1,000 which formerly occurred here. Not only have these birds been slaughtered for the market, but gangs of men have been paid to destroy them where they were feeding in grain fields. Until 1915 they were afforded no protection whatever.   1923

BLUE GOOSE   *Chen caerulescens*

The blue goose is one of the few North American birds which we know only as a migrant and a winter resident, and within the narrowest limits. It has generally been regarded as a rare species, but it is really astonishingly abundant within the narrow confines of its winter home on the coast of Louisiana.

The feeding habits of the blue goose have been well described by W. L. McAtee (1910), as follows:

In the Mississippi Delta the blue geese rest by day on mud flats bordering the Gulf. At the time of my visit (January 29 to February 4, 1910) these were entirely destitute of vegetation, a condition to which the geese had reduced them by their voracious feeding. Every summer these flats are covered by a dense growth of "cut grass" (the local name for *Zizaniopsis miliacea*), "goose grass" (*Scirpus robustus*), "oyster grass" (*Spartina glabra*), "Johnson grass" (*Panicum repens*), and cat-tails or "flag grass" (*Typha angustifolia*), and every fall are denuded by the blue geese, or brant, as they are called in the Delta. The birds feed principally upon the roots of these plants, but the tops of all are eaten at times, if not regularly. Each goose works out a rounded hole in the mud, devouring all of the roots discovered, and these holes are enlarged until they almost touch before the birds move on. They maintain themselves in irregular rows while feeding, much after the manner of certain caterpillars on leaves, and make almost as clean a sweep of the area passed over.

In the Belle Isle region the method of feeding is the same except that the birds feed by day, but the places frequented are what are locally known as "burns"; that is, areas of marsh burned over so that new green food will sooner be available for the cattle. These pastures, for the most part, are barely above water level, so that the holes dug by the geese immediately fill with water. Continued feeding in one area produces shallow, grass-tufted ponds, where formerly there was unbroken pasture. Some of these ponds are resorted to for roosting places, in which case the action of the birds' feet further deepens them, and veritable lakes are produced, which the building-up influence of vegetation can not obliterate for generations, and never, in fact, while the geese continue to use them.   1923

ROSS' GOOSE   *Chen rossii*

The smallest and the rarest of the geese which regularly visit the United States is this pretty little white goose, hardly larger than

our largest ducks, a winter visitor from farthest north, which comes
to spend a few winter months in the genial climate of California.

Whither it goes when it wings its long flight northeastward across
the Rocky Mountains in the early spring no one knows,[1] probably
to remote and unexplored lands in the Arctic regions.

Absolutely nothing seems to be known about its breeding habits
in a wild state.[1] Probably nothing will be known until some of the
vast unexplored areas in the Arctic regions are better known. But
these regions are so inaccessible that their exploration would involve
more time, greater expense, and more enthusiasm than even the
valuable results to be attained are likely to warrant. Therefore this
and several other similar problems are likely to remain for a long
time unsolved.

For all that we know about the nesting habits of the Ross goose,
we are indebted to F. E. Blaauw (1903) who has succeeded in breeding this species in captivity on his place at Gooilust in Holland. He
writes:

At a meeting of the British Ornithologists' Club on March 20, 1901, I
exhibited an egg of the rare Ross's snow goose (*Chen rossi*) laid in
captivity by a solitary female kept by me at Gooilust. A year later, through
the courtesy of Doctor Heck, of Berlin, I received a second specimen of this
species, which fortunately proved, as I hoped it would, to be a male. The
birds soon paired, and in the beginning of May, 1902, the female made a
nest under a bush in her inclosure. The nest was, as is usual with geese, a
small depression in the soil, lined with dry grass and grass roots.

Toward the end of the month the female began to lay, and on the 30th,
when the full complement of 5 eggs had been deposited, she began to
sit, having in the meantime abundantly lined her nest with down from her
own breast. The two birds had always been of a very retiring disposition,
but after the female had laid her eggs the male, who nearly always kept
watch close by the nest, became quite aggressive. He would fearlessly
attack anybody that approached.   1923

BLACK-BELLIED TREE DUCK

Dendrocygna autumnalis

This species is to be found in only a very limited area north of the
Rio Grande.

Colonel Grayson, in his notes, quoted by Mr. Lawrence (1874),
says:

[1] Now known to breed "along the Perry River, northeastern Mackenzie, inland
from the shores of Queen Maud Gulf, and on Boas River, Southampton Island"—
1957 *A.O.U. Check-List.*

This duck perches with facility on the branches of trees, and when in the cornfields, upon the stalks, in order to reach the ears of corn. Large flocks of them spend the day on the bank of some secluded lagoon, densely bordered with woods or water flags, also sitting among the branches of trees, not often feeding or stirring about during the day. When upon the wing they constantly utter their peculiar whistle of *pe-che-che-né*, from which they have received their name from the natives. (The other species is called Durado.) I have noticed that this species seldom lights in deep water, always preferring the shallow water edges, or the ground; the cause of this may be from the fear of the numerous alligators that usually infest the lagoons.

When taken young, or the eggs hatched under the common barnyard hen, they become very domestic without being confined; they are very watchful during the night, and, like the goose, give the alarm by their shrill whistle when any strange animal or person comes about the house. A lady of my acquaintance possessed a pair which she said were as good as the best watchdog; I also had a pair which were equally as vigilant, and very docile.   1923

FULVOUS TREE DUCK   *Dendrocygna bicolor*

Messrs. Grinnell, Bryant, and Storer (1918) introduce this species in a few well-chosen words as follows:

The term tree duck, as applied to the fulvous tree duck, seems to be an almost complete misnomer for the bird. As regards structure this species seems to be more closely related to the geese than to the ducks, and, at least in California, it seldom nests in trees but chooses the extensive tule marshes of our interior valleys. Birds apparently belonging to the same species of tree duck that occurs in this State are found in South America, in southern Uruguay and Argentina, and also in South Africa and in India—a very striking case of what is known as interrupted or discontinuous distribution. In North America the chief breeding ground of the species is in Mexico, but a considerable number of birds breed in the southwestern United States. The latter contingent is migratory, moving south for the winter season.

Referring to the migration in South America, W. H. Hudson (1920) writes:

This duck . . . is found abundantly along the Plata[1] . . . and northwards to Paraguay. . . . It is to some extent a migratory species, appearing in spring in Buenos Aires in very large numbers, to breed in the littoral marshes and also on the pampas. They migrate principally by night, and do not fly in long trains and phalanxes like other ducks, but in a cloud;

[1] River Plate.

and when they migrate in spring and autumn the shrill confused clangor of their many voices is heard from the darkness overhead by dwellers in the Argentine capital. 1923

MALLARD   *Anas platyrhynchos*

With the first signs of the breaking up of winter, the hardy mallards, the leaders in the migrating hordes of wild fowl, leave their winter homes in the Southern States and push northward whenever they can find water, about the margins of the ponds, in open spring holes, and among the floating ice of rivers and streams, flushed with the spring torrents from melting snow banks.

The annual molts and plumages of the adult consist of a double molt of all the contour feathers, into the eclipse plumage in the summer and out of it again in the fall; the flight feathers are molted but once, while the drake is in the eclipse plumage, in August. Thus instead of a nuptial plumage, worn in the spring and summer, and a winter plumage, worn in the fall and winter, we have a full plumage, worn in the winter and spring, and an eclipse, or a concealing, plumage, worn for only a month in the summer, but with much time consumed in the two transitional molts. The same thing takes place, to a greater or a lesser extent, with nearly all of the ducks; the eclipse plumage is much more complete in the surface-feeding ducks than in the others, and it is more strikingly illustrated in the mallard than in any other species. It seems remarkable, indeed, that such a brilliant and conspicuous plumage, as that of the mallard drake, should disappear entirely and be completely replaced with an entirely different plumage, which only an expert can tell from that of the somber, mottled female; but such is the case; the wings and the larger scapulars, which are molted only once, are all that remain to distinguish the male. I have seen males molting into the eclipse plumage as early as May 10, but usually the molt does not begin until the latter part of that month. I have seen drakes in full eclipse plumage as early as July 20, but usually it is not complete until August. It is worn for about a month, the earliest birds beginning to molt out of it in August. Some birds regain their full plumage in October, but some not until November or even later. 1923

MEXICAN DUCK   *Anas diazi*   (Huber)

In the valley of the Rio Grande River from El Paso, Texas, north to Albuquerque, New Mexico, this northern form of the *diazi* group makes its home. Whether on the mud flats in the river, the numerous alkali ponds, or cat-tail swamps through the valley this duck is ever watchful and wary of man.

The flight of the New Mexican[1] duck is similar to that of the mallard, but it is a stronger and somewhat faster flyer. It was during the very heavy wind storms lasting two or three days that occur in March in southwestern New Mexico that I noticed the greater strength of flight of this species over the mallard. One could easily distinguish an individual of this species in a flock of mallards by its darker color and conspicuous pyrite yellow bill.

During the months of April and early May 1920, I watched the courtship of several pairs of these ducks along the Rio Grande River west of Las Cruces, New Mexico. In April, two, three, and sometimes five New Mexican ducks could be seen on the mud flats in the middle of the river, as often with flocks of mallards as alone. When with a flock of mallards they would stay together and not mix with the former. The male could be seen bowing to the female and occasionally pecking and pulling at her wing feathers. When in the water the male would swim close to the female he had chosen, generally behind her, swim close up and pull at her feathers quacking all the while. If another (presumably a female) came too close he would swim rapidly at the intruder until she was driven to a safe distance. Returning to his prospective mate he would bob his head up and down a number of times quacking contentedly. Early in May these ducks were evidently mated as they were always seen in pairs or single birds [sic].

On May 7, 1920, while watching a pair of the ducks on a mud flat in the middle of the Rio Grande River west of Las Cruces, New Mexico, I witnessed a very interesting performance. Both ducks took flight simultaneously, rising in the air at an angle of about 30°. They were flying slowly, their wings seeming to raise higher than in ordinary flight, both quacking incessantly. They passed the point where I was concealed about four hundred feet away and about three hundred feet high, the male (as I afterward learned) directly above the female. Making a large circuit over the land the male all the while keeping his position directly above the female, they swung again over the river coming head up into the light wind, whereupon they set their wings and descended to the water, the female slightly in the lead. Immediately upon alighting copulation occurred.   1923

---

[1] As this species was formerly called.

BLACK DUCK   *Anas rubripes*

Whereas this is only one of the many birds which interest ornithologists and bird protectionists, it is the bird of all others which interests the wild-fowl gunners of the eastern states.

The methods employed for shooting black ducks are many and varied, but they all depend on the strategy and skill of the hunter in outwitting one of the keenest of game birds.

This method is practiced in Massachusetts. On the shore of a pond frequented by migrating waterfowl, or on an island in it, a permanent camp is built, known as a "duck stand," at which one or more of the gunners live constantly all through the shooting season. This consists of a small house or shanty equipped with sleeping bunks for several men, a stove for cooking and for heating it and shutters to prevent the lights showing through the windows at night. Along the shore is built a fence or stockade just high enough so that a man can shoot over it; there are portholes cut in the fence so that several men can shoot through it without being seen. The house and the fence are completely covered with branches of freshly cut pine and oak with the leaves on them, which renders the whole structure practically invisible from the lake. The stand is built where there is a beach or a point in front of it, or where a sandy beach can be artificially made. Various sets of wooden decoys or "blocks," as they are called, are anchored at some distance out in the lake. A large supply of live decoys, semidomesticated black ducks, mallards and Canada geese, are kept in pens, inside or behind the enclosure, and a few are tethered on the beach, anchored in the water near it or allowed to roam about. Sometimes a few are kept in elevated pens back of the stand, so arranged that the pens can be opened by pulling a cord and allowing the ducks or geese to fly out and meet the wild ones. With all this elaborate equipment ready for action the gunners, I can hardly call them sportsmen, spend their time inside the house, smoking, talking, playing cards, or perhaps drinking, while one man remains outside on the watch for ducks. Should a flock of wild ducks alight in the pond, he calls the others and they all take their places at the portholes, with heavy guns, ready for the slaughter. The quacking of the decoys gradually tolls the wild birds in toward the beach or perhaps the fliers are liberated at the critical moment. Each gunner knows which section of the flock he is to shoot at and waits in anticipation until the birds are near enough and properly bunched, when the signal is given to fire. If the affair has been well managed most of the flock have been killed or disabled on the water, but, as the frightened survivors rise in hurried confusion, a second volley is poured into them and only a few escape. The wounded birds are then chased with a boat and shot. There is no method of duck shooting which is more effective and deadly; with gunners constantly on the watch and decoys always ready to call a passing flock, very few ducks get by without an attempt being made on their lives, and often these attempts are only too successful. Probably before many years this form of duck shooting will be prohibited by law,[1] as too destructive, and the more sportsmanlike method of shooting flying birds from open blinds will give the ducks some chance for their lives.   1923

MOTTLED DUCK   *Anas fulvigula*

In the central and southern portions of Florida this duck is an abundant resident bird. I have met with it frequently in the various portions of Florida that I have visited. On the islands in Indian River, where there were muddy ponds surrounded by marshes, we usually found a pair of these ducks, which were probably breeding there but had their nests too well concealed in the luxuriant growth of tall, thick grass for us to find them. We saw them occasionally in the inland lakes of southern Florida, but we found them most abundant in the extensive marshes of the upper St. Johns River; here they found ample feeding grounds and playgrounds among the dense tangles of vegetation, pond lilies, bonnets,[2] water hyacinths, water lettuce, and other aquatic plants; the dense clumps of taller growth and the impenetrable saw-grass sloughs offered them concealment from their enemies; and they found safe sleeping and resting places in the centers of the larger bodies of water.

The period of incubation is probably the same as with the black duck, twenty-six to twenty-eight days. It is performed wholly by the female, although the male does not entirely desert her. Mr. C. J. Maynard (1896) writes of the behavior of the mother and young [on the Indian River, Florida]:

The eggs were deposited during the first and second weeks of April; then about the 1st of May, I would frequently see flocks of little downy ducklings following the female, but unless I took care to conceal myself,

[1] Live decoys now are illegal.
[2] Water-Lilies.

I did not enjoy watching these little families long, for as soon as the parent became aware of my presence, she would emit a chuckling note, when away they would scamper, helter-skelter, into the nearest grass, where it was impossible, upon the most careful search, to discover a single young. I once surprised a brood, when they were some distance from any place of shelter, for they had ventured out upon the mud of a creek, at low tide, and I chanced to come out of the high grass, just in front of them. The old duck appeared to comprehend the situation at once, for she came directly toward me, driving her brood before her, hoping to engage my attention by a display of bravery, while the young escaped into the sheltering vegetation behind me; but placing my gun on the ground, I stooped down and grasped two of the little fellows, as they were running past. The diminutive ducklings uttered shrill cries when they were captured, which drove their parent nearly frantic, for regardless of possible consequences, she dashed about in front of me, with ruffled feathers and half-closed wings, often coming within a foot of me, at the same time, quacking loudly. This outcry attracted the attention of the drake, but he did not approach very near, merely circling about, some 50 yards distant, quacking softly. Leaving the old female to care for the remainder of the brood, I carried my captives into camp and placed them in a box, the sides of which were about a foot and a half high, but young as they were, they managed to escape. 1923

GADWALL   *Anas strepera*

The arrival of the ducks on their breeding grounds in the great wildfowl nurseries of northwest Canada is a spectacular performance. I shall never forget the sights I saw, one cold, rainy day, June 13, 1905, as I walked down toward the great sloughs at the head of Crane Lake, Saskatchewan; hundreds of ducks arose from the wet meadows, from the sloughs, and from an island in the lake, flying around in great loose flocks; a great cloud of them rose, like a swarm of mosquitoes, from the mouth of Bear Creek; most of them were gadwalls, but there were also large numbers of canvasbacks, redheads, shovellers, and blue-winged teal, as well as lesser numbers of lesser scaups, mallards, baldpates, and ruddies, with a few Canada geese; the air seemed to be full of ducks, flying in all directions in bewildering clouds; I have never seen so many ducks before nor since. This was the center of their abundance in one of the greatest duck-breeding resorts I have ever seen. Probably all of the ducks had arrived on their breeding grounds at that time, but evidently many of them had not mated and others had not finished laying.

On June 17, 1905, Mr. H. K. Job and I made a careful census of the ducks breeding on the island, referred to above, by dragging a long rope over it as thoroughly as we could and by noting and recording the nests found by flushing the birds. The island was about three hundred or four hundred yards in length by about one hundred yards in width, fairly high at one end and everywhere covered with a thick growth of grass, through which were scattered on the higher portion numerous small clumps and in some places large patches of rose bushes, offering ideal conditions as a breeding ground for ducks. There were several small ponds near the center of it lined with fringes of cat-tails and bulrushes. On the lower portion of the island the grass was shorter, and where it extended out into a point the ground was bare. A colony of common terns occupied this point, which was also the favorite resort of a flock of white pelicans, which may have bred here later in the season. Marbled godwits, Wilson phalaropes, and spotted sandpipers were breeding here, as well as western savanna sparrows.[1]

A pair of crows had a nest in the only tree on the island, a small willow, and they must have fared sumptuously on stolen duck's eggs. A pair of short-eared owls had a nest on the island containing young in various stages of growth. We were unable to drag the whole island, as the rose bushes were too thick in many places, but in the course of two hours' work we recorded sixty-one nests, as follows: mallard, five nests; gadwall, twenty-three nests; baldpate, three nests; green-winged teal, two nests; blue-winged teal, ten nests; shoveller, seven nests; pintails, eight nests; and lesser scaup duck, three nests.   1923

PINTAIL   *Anas acuta*

Northward, ever northward, clearly indicated on the distant sky, points the long slim figure of the pintail, in the vanguard of the spring migration, wending its way toward remote and still frozen shores. Vying with the mallard to be the first of the surface-feeding ducks to push northward on the heels of retreating winter, this hardy pioneer extends its migration to the Arctic coast of the continent and occupies the widest breeding range of any North American duck, throughout most of which it is universally abundant and well known.

The courtship display of the shy pintail is not often seen, for even on their remote northern breeding grounds the males are ever alert and are not easily approached. The performance resembles that of the teals, where several drakes may be seen crowding their attention

[1] As the subspecies *anthinus* of the Savannah Sparrow was formerly known.

on a single duck, each standing erect on the water proudly displaying his snowy breast, with his long neck doubled in graceful curves until his bill rested upon his swelling chest and with his long tail pointed upwards; thus he displays his charms and in soft mewing notes he woos his apparently indifferent lady love until she expresses her approval with an occasional low quack.

A more striking form of courtship, and one more often seen, is the marvelous nuptial flight, which Doctor Nelson (1887) has so well described as follows [near St. Michael, Alaska]:

Once, on May 17, while sitting overlooking a series of small ponds, a pair of pintails arose and started off, the male in full chase after the female. Back and forth they passed at a marvelously swift rate of speed, with frequent quick turns and evolutions. At one moment they were almost out of view high overhead and the next saw them skimming along the ground in an involved course very difficult to follow with the eye. Ere long a second male joined in the chase, then a third, and so on until six males vied with each other in the pursuit. The original pursuer appeared to be the only one capable of keeping close to the coy female, and owing to her dextrous turns and curves he was able to draw near only at intervals. Whenever he did succeed he always passed under the female, and kept so close to her that their wings clattered together with a noise like a watchman's rattle, and audible a long distance. This chase lasted half an hour, and after five of the pursuers had dropped off one by one the pair remaining (and I think the male was the same that originated the pursuit) settled in one of the ponds.   1923

COMMON TEAL   *Anas crecca*

This well-known and widely distributed Palaearctic bird has always appeared on our check list as an occasional visitor or straggler.

Of its flight and vocal powers, Mr. Millais (1902) writes as follows:

During the day the teal is one of the most silent and inactive of birds. It will sit for hours motionless, apparently lost in a brown study or with the head buried in the scapulars. Out on the estuary a pack rests on the tidal heave without a sign of movement until night comes and with it the desire for food. In the daytime, during the early autumn, even in our much disturbed islands, teal are sometimes extremely tame, and will permit the approach of man within a few yards before flying away, and there are always certain holes in the large bogs where teal may be found and closely approached with certainty unless they have been previously disturbed. On being flushed they shoot up straight into the air, sometimes very rapidly, and often swaying slightly and rendering themselves a by no means easy mark—in fact, I once heard a friend, who had ineffectually expended 100 cartridges in one day, declare that *rising* teal were far more difficult to kill than snipe.[1] Be that as it may, I can remember certain windy days when *driven* teal were wild and "dodgy," and were quite as difficult to bag as the snipe with whom they flew. Teal can suddenly turn in the midst of a straight forward flight and either dive downward, or, what is far more difficult for the gunner to accept, shoot straight upward, and only present as a target a practically invulnerable stern. It is a pretty sight on a sunny day to watch a flock of teal about to settle; they wheel and swing almost as much as flocks of dunlins, the dark backs and the light breasts alternately shining; and it is not until they have thoroughly surveyed their prospective resting place and its approaches that they come to a halt. Whilst on the wing one male occasionally utters his low double whistle, but teal are silent birds at all times, and the female rarely calls unless frightened, such as when the brood is threatened, when she emits a subdued little "quack." 1923

GREEN-WINGED TEAL   *Anas carolinensis*

Following close on the heels of the pintail and the mallard, the hardy little green-winged teal is one of the earliest migrants to start in the spring for its northern breeding grounds.

From the sportsman's viewpoint the green-winged teal is an important member of the long list of American wild fowl. Its abundance assures him plenty of sport; its swift flight, with its sudden turnings and rapid twistings, tests his marksmanship to the limit; and its plump little body, fattened on the best of grains, nuts, and succulent herbs, provides a dainty morsel for the table.

That keen sportsman, Dr. F. Henry Yorke (1891), describes the departure of the late flight, in the following words:

The last issue of bluewings had collected, circled high in the air, and, following their instinctive impulse, had traveled southward. The second issue of mallards had come and gone, after staying with us a short time. The pintails, widgeons, green-winged teal (first issue), redheads, canvasbacks, and bluebills[2] had also departed, and Grass Lake was almost "duckless." Even the mudhens[3] had almost disappeared, and only a few scattered individuals, or small flocks of belated widgeons or pintails could be seen. Once in a while a few mallards turned up, but they were old, wary birds, "not to be caught with chaff." The only chance we could get was when a "stranger" flock of mallards came in, drifting down from the last issue, just preceding the frosts.

A week like this about the end of October is not an unusual occurrence.

[1] Common Snipe.
[2] Scaup.
[3] American Coots.

The sun shines warm after the cold nights, and the hazy atmosphere of our "Indian summer" induces idleness to a very reprehensive degree. But there was nothing to do, and we waited for a blast from old Boreas to awaken the ducks and put new life into ourselves.

Suddenly the herald of winter was heard. A fierce storm of rain or snow swept down from the North, where the icy grip of winter already held the lakes, and all nature was awake again. The laggard ducks came streaming in, mallards, pintails, and widgeon. Bluebills rushed down the flyways, and the game little green-winged teal, whipping and pitching in all directions, made his second appearance. This time the ducks meant business. While the weather was more uncertain, they came and returned, loth to leave their happy nesting grounds in the far north; but now Jack Frost was after them, and they were bent on a long and inevitable journey, although some of them, dropping here and there, would stay until they were absolutely frozen out before they betook themselves to the mild clime and the open waterways of the sunny South.   1923

BLUE-WINGED TEAL   *Anas discors*

The little blue-winged teal is a favorite with the sportsman; it comes at the beginning of the season, when he is eager to try his skill at one of the swiftest of ducks; it decoys readily, especially to live decoys;[1] it flies in large, compact flocks, which offer tempting shots as they twist and turn or swing and wheel in unison; it is unsuspicious of its hidden foe, is easily killed with small shot and makes a fine table bird. We used to look for it about the full of the moon in September and could always count on finding plenty of birds in the shallow ponds, marshes, and grassy creeks; but, unfortunately, it has been steadily decreasing since the early eighties and is now quite scarce in Massachusetts. In the good old days, when these birds were abundant, they were an easy mark for the youthful gunner, as they huddled together in a compact flock on the water, and a large number could be killed at a single discharge of the old muzzle-loader.

Mr. Dwight W. Huntington (1903) pays the following tribute to their speed:

After some days' shooting at the sharp-tailed grouse, I went one day to a famous duck pass in North Dakota, when the teal were flying from the Devils Lake to a smaller one to breakfast. As soon as I had made my blind, they began to come singly and in pairs, sometimes three or four together or a small flock, and although they came in quick succession and the shooting was fast enough to heat the gun, I believe it was an hour or more before I killed a bird. I was almost in despair, when I fired at a

[1] Now illegal.

passing flock, holding the gun a yard or more before the leading birds, and at the report a single teal, some distance behind the others, fell dead upon the beach. I at once began shooting long distances ahead of the passing ducks, and before long I had a large bag of birds.

A few days afterwards an officer from the garrison near by, a good shot in the upland fields and woods, went with me to my duck pass to shoot at teal. We made our blinds some two gun shots apart and soon began to shoot. The birds came rapidly as before, and my friend gave them two barrels as they passed, but was entirely out of ammunition before he killed a bird. His orderly came to my blind for shells, and with them I sent a message to shoot three times as far ahead as he had been doing, and he was soon killing birds.   1923

CINNAMON TEAL   *Anas cyanoptera*

The "western champion," as Dawson (1909) has aptly called this species, holds a unique position among American ducks, for it is the only member of the family that is confined to the western part of the continent with its center of abundance west of the Rocky Mountains and the only member of the family which has a regular breeding range in South America separated from that in North America by a wide gap of about two thousand miles.

On the authority of Mr. A. M. Shields, of Los Angeles, Mr. Fred A. Schneider (1893) has published the following interesting account of the behavior of the young:

After being hatched, the mother duck (joined by her mate) escorts the young brood to the nearest body of water and manifests the greatest solicitude for the welfare of the little fellows, giving a signal upon the slightest approach of danger, which is followed by the almost instant disappearance of the entire brood, as if by magic. If on the shore they disappear in the grass; if in the water, they dive, and that is generally the last seen of them, for the time being at least, as they swim under water for great distances until reaching the edge of the stream or pond, when they imperceptibly secrete themselves among the water moss or grass. I once watched a little fellow as he made his way under the clear water. He went straight for a little bunch of floating moss, and by gazing intently I could just distinguish the least possible little swelling of the moss; a small hump, as it were, about the size of a marble. He had come to the surface (as intended) under the patch of moss, and his head and bill were responsible for the little hump in the moss.

Possibly one thing more than anything else helps the little fellows to disappear in such marvelously quick time and before you can realize it. The old duck flutters and falls around you just out of your reach and most successfully imitates a fowl badly winged, hardly able to rise from the ground. Her actions are bound to more or less avert your attention for a moment at least, and it is just that moment that the little fellows disappear, as the mother duck undoubtedly intended. After a short time, when the little ones are all securely hidden, the mother, feeling no further anxiety, gracefully recovers from her crippled condition, flies off a few hundred yards, and there awaits your departure, when she returns to her family, who soon gather around her one by one till they are all assembled and everything goes on as though nothing had happened—until the next intruder appears, when "Presto! change!" and the same actions are repeated. 1923

EUROPEAN WIDGEON   *Mareca penelope*

This is an old-world species which has occurred frequently as a straggler on both coasts of North America, as well as in the interior.

Mr. Millais [1902] gives the following interesting account of the feeding habits of the widgeon:

In a regular feeding ground, generally some long open stretch of mud covered with *Zostera marina* [eel grass], it is interesting to see the careful manner in which widgeon approach it. The first little pack will come flying up against the wind and alight on the water, at about two or three hundred yards from the shore, after having previously swung round once or twice to ascertain that no enemy is approaching. This generally takes place when the tide is half ebbed. Out on the water they remain packed close together and very quiet till the first green fronds of their favorite food are observed floating on the surface away inshore. Then the whole gathering begins slowly going shorewards, till at last one bird bolder than the rest swims in and commences picking at the floating weed. Even then they are subject to sudden fears, and, when about to follow their leader, will often suddenly put up their necks and swim rapidly out, the cocks whistling loudly. Once, however, they have reached the food, their taste for more generally asserts itself, and precautions against surprise are somewhat relaxed, as they one and all move in to still shallower water and commence to turn upside down so as to pull up the *Zostera* and eat the root, by far the most succulent part.

Sometimes widgeon, which are both conservative as to their beats and modes of life, will pay little attention to a vegetable diet, but live almost exclusively on animal food. Such I find to be the case with the birds living on the sandy coast near the town of Dornoch in Scotland, where all conditions are purely marine. The widgeon here feed by day and live entirely on small cockles. This renders their flesh poor, bitter, and quite uneatable. I have shot a good few of them there and found all to be the same, whilst birds from the other side of the same firth, and living on the *Zostera* beds to the west of Tain, were fat and as good as widgeon generally are. In spring widgeon are great grass eaters, and later on, like teal[1] and garganey,[2] they devour an enormous quantity of flies. One day in Iceland I observed with a telescope a small party of male widgeon whose wives were engaged in domestic affairs, paddling along the edge of a small lake near Myvatn, and picking the flies off the stones in hundreds. This particular insect, a sort of stinging house fly, is very nutritive and tastes like a piece of sugar. As you are obliged to eat plenty of them yourself, for they are always getting into your mouth, you soon get used to them, and swallow them with equanimity, and it is a common sight to see the Icelandic children of the Myvatn district picking these natural lollipops off their faces and eating them by dozens.   1923

AMERICAN WIDGEON   *Mareca americana*

The baldpate[3] is not one of the earliest migrants; the ice has long since disappeared and spring is well under way before it starts, and many of the birds do not arrive in their breeding grounds in the Northern States until the latter part of May.

Blanchan (1898) says:

The gentlemen hidden behind "blinds" on the "duck shores" of Maryland and the sloughs of the interior and with a flock of wooden decoys floating near by, or the nefarious market gunner in his "sink boat" and with a dazzling reflector behind the naphtha lamp on the front of his scow, bag by fair mens and foul immense numbers of the baldpates every season, yet so prolific is the bird, and so widely distributed over this continent, that there still remain widgeons to shoot. That is the fact one must marvel at when one gazes on the results of a single night's slaughtering in the Chesapeake country. The pothunter who uses a reflector to fascinate the flocks of ducks that, bedded for the night, swim blindly up to the sides of the boat, moving silently among them, often kills from twenty to thirty at a shot.

On the Pacific coast it winters abundantly as far north as Puget Sound, though according to Bowles (1909) it is not so common there as formerly; he says:

During fall, winter, and spring it is most numerous of all ducks in Washington, save possibly the bluebills [scaups] and scoters. Large numbers of them congregate upon the tide flats of Puget Sound, and the bird is abundant also on the interior waters. Constant persecution, however, has greatly reduced their ranks, as is the case with the entire duck family, and possibly for this reason their migratory habits have undergone

---

[1] Common Teal.
[2] A European pond duck, *Anas querquedula.*
[3] As this species is sometimes called.

a marked change. Eight or ten years ago they used to appear in enormous flocks during the first week in October, at which period I have seen on the Nisqually Flats, near Tacoma, what was estimated at about 500,000, all in the air at one time. For the past two or three years, however, no widgeon to speak of have appeared before November or December, and then in such greatly reduced numbers as to give rise to serious fear, not only as to the abundance, but as to the existence of future generations.   1923

SHOVELER   *Spatula clypeata*

The little shoveller[1] is one of the best known and most widely distributed ducks in the world; by its peculiar spatulate bill and by the striking color pattern of the drake it is easily recognized; it is universally common over nearly all of the continents of North America, Europe, and Asia, wandering south in winter to northern South America and Africa and even to Australia. It is essentially a freshwater duck at all seasons, never resorting to the seacoasts except when forced to by stress of weather; it is a bog-loving species, fond of inland sloughs, marshes, streams, and ponds, where it can dabble in the shallows like a veritable mud lark. It is always associated in my mind with the shallow pond holes and sluggish creeks which are so characteristic of the wet, grassy meadows of the prairie region, where pairs of these handsome birds are so frequently seen jumping into the air, surprised by a passing train or wagon.

Mr. T. Gilbert Pearson (1916) says:

Shovellers feed mostly at night, especially in places where they are much pursued by gunners. I have often seen dozens of flocks come from the marshes at sunrise and fly out to the open water, far from any place where a gunner might hide. There, if the weather is fair and not too windy, they will often remain until the shades of night and the pangs of hunger again call them back to the tempting marshes. They do not gather in enormous flocks like some other ducks. I have never seen over 40 in one company, and very often they pass by in twos and threes. In hunting them the fowler usually conceals himself in a bunch of tall grass or rushes, on or near the margin of an open pond, and, after anchoring near-by 20 or 30 wooden duck dummies called decoys, sits down to wait the coming of the birds. Sometimes the ducks fly by at a distance of several hundred yards. It is then that the hunter begins to lure them by means of his artificial duck call. *Quack-quack, quack-quack,* comes his invitation from the rushes. The passing birds, unless too intent on their journey to heed the cry, see what they suppose to **be** a company

[1] As this bird's name was formerly spelled.

of mallards and other ducks evidently profiting by a good feeding place, and, turning, come flying in to settle among the decoys. It is just at this moment, with headway checked and dangling feet, that they present an easy mark for the concealed gunner.   1923

WOOD DUCK   *Aix sponsa*

While wandering through the dim cathedral aisles of a big cypress swamp in Florida, where the great trunks of the stately trees towered straight upward for a hundred feet or more until the branches interlaced above so thickly that the sunlight could not penetrate, we seemed to be lost in the gloom of a strange tropical forest and far removed from the familiar sights and sounds of the outside world. Only the frequent cries of the omnipresent Florida red-shouldered hawk[1] and an occasional glimpse of a familiar flycatcher or vireo, migrating northward reminded us of home. But at last the light seemed to break through the gloom, as we approached a little sunlit pond, and there we saw some familiar friends, the center of interest in a pretty picture, framed in the surroundings of their winter home, warmed by the genial April sun and perhaps preparing to leave for their northern summer home. The sunlight filtering through the tops of the tall cypresses which surrounded the pool shone full upon the snowy forms of fifty or more white ibises, feeding on the muddy shores, dozing on the fallen logs, or perched upon the dead stumps or surrounding trees; the air seemed full of them as they rose and flew away. But with this dazzling cloud of whiteness there arose from the still waters of the pool a little flock of wood ducks, brilliant in their full nuptial plumage, their gaudy colors flashing in the sunshine, as they went whirring off through the tree tops. What a beautiful creature is this Beau Brummel among birds and what an exquisite touch of color he adds to the scene among the water hyacinths of Florida or among the pond lilies of New England!

The period of incubation is from twenty-eight to thirty days. This duty is performed wholly by the female, but the male is more or less in attendance on her during this period and returns to help her care for the young. The young are provided with sharp claws which they use in climbing from the nest up to the entrance of the cavity, a distance of often three to four feet and sometimes as much as six or eight feet. Much has been written about how the female conveys the young from the nest to the water in her bill, between her feet or even on her back, and several writers claim to have seen the first

[1] As the subspecies *alleni* of the Red-shouldered Hawk was formerly called.

method employed. I am inclined to think that this method of convey-ance is used only when circumstances make it necessary; if the nest cavity is not too high, or if it overhangs the water, or if there is soft open ground below it, I believe that the young are usually coaxed or urged to jump or flutter down and are then led by the old bird to the nearest water; certainly such is often the case.

Mr. E. G. Kingsford (1917) has seen the wood duck carry its young to the water and thus relates his personal experience:

Early in July, 1898, while tented on the bank of the Michigamme River, township 43, north range 32 west, section 1, Iron County, Michigan, I had the good fortune to see it done. The nest was in a hollow pine that stood directly back of the tent and about 200 feet from the water, and the hole where the old duck went in, was 50 or 60 feet from the ground. After seeing the old duck fly by the tent, to and from her feeding grounds up the river many times during the time of incubation, one morning before sunrise she flew by from the tree to the river with a little duck in her beak which she left in an eddy a short distance upstream. She then made 10 or 12 trips to the nest and each time took a little duck in her beak by the neck to the water, where they all huddled in a little bunch. It was all done in a few minutes, and she evidently took them to the water very soon after they hatched, as they were only little balls of down. In going to and from work, we passed the little bunch many times. On our approach the old duck would fly away and leave the little ones huddled in a bunch near the shore where the water was quiet.   1923

REDHEAD   *Aythya americana*

Mr. J. H. Bowles (1909) gives the following attractive account of the nesting habits of the redhead in Washington:

They are essentially lovers of shoal bodies of fresh water, and in summer resort in considerable numbers to the larger lakes of central Washington for the purpose of rearing their young. One of their favorite breeding grounds may be found at Moses Lake, a beautiful body of water situated in the north central part of the State. At this place, in the summer of 1906, it is certain that at least 150 pairs remained to nest. Paddling our canoe along the margin of the lake, close to its heavy fringe of cat-tails, we would flush a pair or two at intervals of every hundred feet. As is customary with all waterfowl during the nesting season, they were remarkably tame, allowing such a close approach as to give an excellent view of the handsome nuptial plumage of the male.

Leaving the canoe and plunging at random into the sea of rushes, fortune may favor us sufficiently to permit of our happening upon one of their nests. This is a heavy, deep basket of rushes placed in the thickest of the growth, either upon a small muddy island left by the receding water, or built up amongst the flags upon the matted dead stems which cover the surface of the lake in these places. It is a structure of such beauty as to cause the bird student to pause almost breathless upon its discovery. The mother duck has heard his noisy approach long since and departed, first carefully spreading over the eggs a heavy blanket taken from the lining of the nest. This consists entirely of down of the most delicate shade of white faintly tinged with gray, which the duck plucks from her own breast. A faint glimpse only can be obtained of the 12 or 14 greenish-drab eggs which seem completely to fill the nest, but let the sun be shining brightly with the dense green rushes for a background, and be sure that fatigue, soaked clothing, mosquitoes, and a dozen other discomforts will instantly vanish from remembrance at the sight.

Redheads are abundant on the Chesapeake,[1] where they are shot in large numbers with the canvasbacks from the batteries; when feeding on wild celery their flesh is of fine flavor. They are very popular as game birds on the lakes and sloughs of the Mississippi Valley; they travel about in large flocks and are easily decoyed to wooden decoys set near the hunter's well-concealed blind or sink box. A net set on poles around the gunner's boat or duck float may be rendered quite inconspicuous by weaving branches or grass into it so that it will match its surroundings; the ducks do not seem to notice it and very good shooting may be had from such a blind.   1923

RING-NECKED DUCK   *Aythya collaris*

Although usually classed with the scaup ducks and resembling them in general appearance, this species seems to be more closely related to the European tufted duck than to any American species. Wilson figured and described it under the name, "tufted duck," supposing it to be identical with that species.

Although the ring-necked duck feeds largely in the shallow water of the marshes, it is nevertheless a good diver and can, if necessary, dive in deep water. Its feet are large and powerful, it dives with its wings tightly closed and swims below the surface very rapidly by the use of feet alone. It swims lightly and rapidly on the surface and rises readily from the water, making a whistling sound as it does so. Its flight is swift and vigorous and it is as lively as the other scaup ducks in all its movements. It flies mostly in small flocks of open formation, rather than in close bunches or lines, so that it does not offer such tempting shots as the other bluebills.[2] While on its feeding

---

[1] Not in 1959, when the whole North American population was much reduced.
[2] The gunners' name for Scaup.

grounds it is also usually more scattered and more often flushed singly or in pairs.

Dr. F. Henry Yorke (1899) says:

The feeding grounds are more inshore than those of the bluebills [scaups], and they feed more upon seeds such as frog bit, duck and pond weed, being very fond of bulbs of the nonscented water lily, upon which they will gorge themselves and get exceedingly fat; at that time they are counted a delicacy for the table. The playgrounds are in open pieces of water surrounded by weeds and lily pads, in buck brush, willows, and wild rice. The roosting grounds are in buck brush, the edges of timber, down smartweed, and flags.

The methods employed for shooting the "ringbills" as they are called, are the same as for the "bluebills." Blinds are set in their fly ways or passes, to and from their feeding grounds, where they decoy well to wooden decoys and where large numbers are killed. Although not so universally abundant as some other species and not so well known, this is one of the most abundant ducks of the South Atlantic and Gulf States in winter. On the coast of Louisiana these ducks spend the night out on the Gulf, but come into the ponds to feed at daybreak. They come in small flocks of from three or four to ten or twelve, flying with great speed, and drop at once without circling, into the pond they have selected. They seem to have certain favorite feeding ponds, for while one pond will yield excellent sport, the gunner in an adjoining pond may not get a shot. They are naturally not shy and are not easily driven from their favorite feeding grounds. Mr. Arthur H. Howell (1911) writes that on Big Lake, Arkansas, "in November and December it is often the most abundant duck, and gunners there frequently kill as many as fifty birds in a few hours. A few remain all winter."   1923

CANVASBACK   *Aythya valisneria*

The coast region of Virginia and North Carolina with its numerous estuaries and tributary streams has always been the most famous winter resort of canvasbacks, and many other species of wild fowl, in North America. Vast hordes of canvasbacks, redheads, scaup ducks, as well as geese and swans formerly frequented these waters, attracted by the mild climate and the abundance of food. Several generations of gunners, by persistent and constant warfare, have seriously reduced the numbers of these hosts of wildfowl, but the birds are still sufficiently plentiful to attract sportsmen in large numbers and to keep alive the various gunning clubs which now control nearly all of the best shooting grounds. Some of the more destructive methods of killing ducks, such as night shooting and wholesale slaughter with swivel guns, have been prohibited by law. Netting ducks in gill nets sunken a short distance below the surface proved very destructive, but was abandoned as the ducks caught in this way became water soaked and of inferior flavor.

One of the oldest and most sportsmanlike methods of shooting ducks on Chesapeake Bay is known as point shooting. The sportsman lies concealed in a blind, with a retriever to pick up his birds, and waits for passing flocks to come near enough for a shot. The best flight is early in the morning, between dawn and sunrise, when the ducks are flying to their feeding grounds; they usually fly around the points rather than over them; but if the wind is favorable, they often come within gunshot. This kind of shooting requires considerable practice and hard shooting guns, for the canvasbacks fly swiftly, often high in the air and are hard to kill, all of which makes it attractive to the true sportsman. Similar shooting is obtained on narrow sand bars where the ducks fly directly overhead; this is even more difficult. Canvasbacks are also shot over decoys at the points, from blinds on the flats, and from water holes in the ice on the rivers.

An interesting ancient method of shooting canvasbacks was by tolling them in with a small dog, especially trained for the purpose. Some quiet place was selected where a large flock of canvasbacks was bedded a short distance offshore and where the hunters could conceal themselves in some suitable ambush near the water. A small dog was kept running up and down the beach after sticks or stones, with a white or red handkerchief fluttering from some part of his body, which would so arouse the curiosity of the ducks that they would raise their heads and swim in toward shore to study the cause of such peculiar actions. Often their discovery of the hidden danger came too late, for as they turned to swim away they would receive a broadside from a battery of guns and large numbers would be killed. Tolling is now prohibited in many places.

The old-fashioned dugout, in which the hunter lay concealed with his boat covered with eelgrass has been entirely replaced by the modern surface boat or battery, an ingenious contrivance from which more canvasbacks are shot than by any other method. It consists of a stout wooden box, just long enough and deep enough to effectually conceal a man while lying down, surrounded by a broad wooden platform, attached to its upper edge; the platform is also surrounded with frames covered with canvas; it is so constructed and ballasted that the platform floats flush with the surface of the water and the box is entirely below it; the platform is constantly awash, but the water is kept out of the box by projecting flanges. The battery is towed out to the shooting grounds and anchored with two hundred or more wooden decoys anchored around it. The gunner is entirely out of sight, except from overhead, as he lies flat in the bottom of the box until the birds are near enough, when he rises and shoots. An assistant is needed with a sailboat, launch, or skiff to pick up the birds.

1923

GREATER SCAUP   *Aythya marila*

The feeding grounds of the scaup duck are mainly in fairly deep water at a safe distance from the shore where their food is obtained by diving; they are expert at this and can remain under water for fifty or sixty seconds. Where food is plentiful they often feed in large companies, diving separately, indiscriminately, or all in unison; they show no particular system in their manner of diving and are not very careful about posting sentinels to watch for dangers; sometimes the whole flock will be below the surface at the same time, so that an approach is fairly easy. In their summer homes in freshwater lakes and ponds they more often feed on or near the surface, where they live on fish fry, tadpoles, small fishes, small snails and other mollusks, flies, and water insects; they also eat some vegetable food, such as the buds, stems, roots, and seeds of floating and submerged water plants. Dr. F. Henry Yorke (1899) has identified the following genera of water plants in the food of this duck: *Vallisneria, Lymnobium, Zizania, Piper, Elymus, Iris, Nuphar, Nymphaea, Myriophyllum, Callitriche,* and *Utricularia.*

During the winter on the seacoast its food consists of surface-swimming crustaceans, crabs, starfish, and various mollusks; small mussels, obtained by diving in the mussel beds, form the principal part of its animal food at this season; but it also eats considerable vegetable food, such as the buds and root-stocks of wild celery (*Vallisneria*), and the seeds and succulent shoots of *Zostera marina* [eelgrass]. In the Chesapeake Bay region the scaup ducks feed on the roots of the wild celery with the canvasbacks and redheads, where they are quite as expert as any of the diving ducks in obtaining these succulent roots; consequently they become very fat and their flesh, which is ordinarily undesirable, acquires an excellent flavor.

Mr. Walter H. Rich (1907) says that on the coast of Maine—

most of the bluebills [scaups] are killed from the "gunning float," the gunner clad in a white suit and the little craft itself "dressed down" to the water's edge with snow and ice to represent a floating ice cake. It is no wonder that the poor victims are "deluded" for it needs sharp eyes and close attention to make out anything dangerous in an object so harmless in appearance. There is commonly little trouble in approaching within easy range of a flock if the gunner is skilled in handling his craft, but to get within shot reach is not all, for any duck which can last out the New England winter will carry off a good load of shot, as the bird must have an abundance of vitality and an extra-heavy suit of underwear to endure the climate. Both of these our hero has.   1923

LESSER SCAUP   *Aythya affinis*

Unlike the larger scaup duck, this species is more essentially an inland species, showing a decided preference for the smaller lakes, ponds, marshes, and streams, whereas its larger relative seems to prefer the larger lakes in the interior and the seacoast in winter.

Although they arrive on their breeding grounds fairly early, they are very deliberate about nesting preparations and are among the later breeders. All through the extensive western prairies these little ducks may be seen, throughout May and the first half of June, swimming about in pairs in the little marshy creeks, sloughs, and small ponds; they are apparently mated when they arrive and seem to enjoy a protracted honeymoon. In the Devils Lake region in North Dakota we found the lesser scaup duck nesting abundantly in 1901 and examined a large number of nests. On the small islands in Stump Lake, now set apart as a reservation,[1] we found sixteen nests of this species in one day, June 15, and all of the eggs proved to be fresh or nearly so. The nests were almost invariably concealed in the taller prairie grass, but some nests were located under small rosebushes and one was placed against the side of a small rock surrounded by tall grass, but in a rather open situation. The nest consisted of a hollow scooped in the ground, profusely lined with very dark down mingled with a little dry grass and occasionally a white feather from the breast of the bird. The females seemed to be very close sitters; we always flushed the bird within ten feet of us or less; but when once flushed they seemed to show no further interest in our proceedings. The males apparently desert the females after incubation has begun and flock by themselves in the sloughs or small

[1] Stump Lake National Wildlife Refuge.

ponds. Lesser scaup ducks occasionally lay in other duck's nests; we found one of their eggs in a gadwall's nest and one in a white-winged scoter's nest; but we found no evidence that other ducks ever lay in the scaup's nests.

In southwestern Saskatchewan the lesser scaup duck was not so abundant as in North Dakota, but still quite common; we found six nests in situations similar to those described above; three of these were on that wonderful island in Crane Lake, more fully described under the gadwall. In Manitoba, about Lake Winnipegosis, we found a few nests one of which was in a different situation from any other we had seen; it was built like a canvasback's nest in the water near the edge of a clump of bulrushes (*Scirpus lacustris*), but it contained the dark down and the characteristic eggs of the lesser scaup. Nests have been reported by other observers in such situations, but the nest is usually placed on dry ground. MacFarlane (1891) found over a dozen nests of this species near the northern limit of the wooded country on the east side of the Anderson River [Northwest Territories, Canada], of which he says:

They were usually found in the midst of a swamp—a mere hole or depression in the center of a tuft of turf or tussock of grass, lined with more or less down, feathers, and hay.   1923

COMMON GOLDENEYE   *Bucephala clangula*

With the breaking up of winter in Massachusetts, when the February sun has loosened the icy fetters of our rivers and the ice cakes are floating out of our harbors, the genial warmth of advancing spring arouses amorous instincts in the breasts of the warm-blooded goldeneyes.

Dr. Charles W. Townsend (1910) writes:

One or more males swim restlessly back and forth and around a female. The feathers of the cheeks and crest of the male are so erected that the head looks large and round, the neck correspondingly small. As he swims along, the head is thrust out in front close to the water, occasionally dabbling at it. Suddenly he springs forward, elevating his breast, and at the same time he enters on the most typical and essential part of the performance. The neck is stretched straight up, and the bill, pointing to the zenith, is opened to emit a harsh, rasping double note, *zzee-at*, vibratory and searching in character. The head is then quickly snapped back until the occiput touches the rump, whence it is brought forward again with a jerk to the normal position. As the head is returned to its place the bird often springs forward kicking the water in a spurt out behind, and displaying like a flash of flame the orange-colored legs.

Mr. Charles E. Alford (1921) writes:

Though the habit of lying more or less prone upon the water is common to most females of the Anatidae when they desire to pair, the duck golden-eye carries this performance beyond all normal bounds; her behavior on such occasions being, indeed, scarcely less amazing than that of the drake. With neck outstretched and her body quite limp and apparently lifeless, she allows herself to drift upon the surface exactly after the manner of a dead bird. When first I witnessed this maneuver I was completely de-ceived, for she remained thus drifting toward the shore, and with the male swimming round her for fully 15 minutes before actual pairing took place. This occurred on February 2, 1920, a beautiful springlike day, the whole of that month being unusually mild and sunny [in western Canada].

During the four years that I lived on the coast our most interesting winter sport was whistler[1] shooting. Long before daylight we braved the winter's cold and pushed out our skiff to our blind among the ice cakes. We wore white nightgowns over our clothes, white caps and gloves, and sometimes had our gun barrels whitewashed, for the goldeneyes are very wary birds and it is necessary to remain motion-less and invisible to be successful. The wooden decoys are placed, as soon as it is light enough to see, in some convenient open space, preferably off the mouth of some fresh-water creek. The blind is made of ice cakes or snow, high enough to conceal the gunners. With the coming of the daylight birds begin to move; large gray gulls are seen flapping slowly up the bay to feed on the mud flats; a flock of black ducks flies out from an open spring hole where it has been feeding all night. The winter sunrise is beautiful, as the rosy dawn creeps up from the cold, gray sea and sends a warm glow of color over floating ice and banks of snow. Our eyes are trained seaward to catch the first glimpses of incoming whistlers. At last a black speck is dimly discerned in the distance against a pink cloud; on it comes straight toward the blind, and we recognize it as an old cock whistler, the advance guard of the morning flight; he circles, sets his wings and scales down over the decoys; in our eagerness we betray our-selves by a sudden movement; he sees us and scrambles upward into the air to escape, but is is too late, the guns speak and the first kill is scored. Soon a small flock of five birds comes in, the shrill whis-tling of their wings sending a thrill of pleasure through our chilled veins; they scale down toward the decoys, but see the blind, wheel,

---

[1] As this species is called by the gunners.

and fly off without offering us a shot; they settle in the water away off among the floating ice and it is useless to stalk them. We have been too conspicuous to the keen eyes of the birds and must conceal ourselves better; so we pile up more ice around the blind and keep more quiet. Better luck follows in consequence, for the ducks decoy well, if their suspicions are not aroused, and during the next two hours we have good sport. By the time the early morning flight is over, an hour or two after sunrise, we have had enough of it and are glad to return home with a small ·bag of the keen-witted goldeneyes.

1923

BARROW'S GOLDENEYE *Bucephala islandica*

Dr. D. J. Elliot (1898) writes of its behavior:

I have found it at times quite numerous on the St. Lawrence near Ogdensburg [New York], and have killed a goodly number there over decoys, and some specimens, procured on these occasions, are now in the Museum of Natural History in New York. The two species[1] were associated together on the river, and I never knew which one would come to the decoys, but I do not remember that both ever came together, unless it might be the females, for, as I have said, it was difficult to distinguish them without an examination.

The birds would fly up and down the river, doubtless coming from, and going to, Lake Erie, stopping occasionally in the coves to feed, and floating down with the current for a considerable distance, when they would rise and fly upstream again. My decoys were always placed in some cove or bend of the stream where the current was least strong, for I noticed the birds rarely settled on the water where it was running swiftly. This duck decoys readily in such situations, and will come right in, and if permitted, settle among the wooden counterfeits. They sit lightly upon the water and rise at once without effort or much splashing. The flight is very rapid, and is accompanied with the same whistling of the wings so noticeable in the common goldeneye. In stormy weather this bird keeps close to the banks, seeking shelter from the winds. It dives as expertly as its relative, and frequently remains under water for a considerable time. The flesh of those killed upon the river was tender and of good flavor, fish evidently not having figured much as an article of their diet.

Mr. [M. P.] Skinner says, in his notes:

I usually find these ducks by ones and twos and small groups, but once I found a flock of 85 swimming in a compact group off the shore of Yellowstone Lake.[2] When in pairs, it is the female that takes alarm and

[1] This and the Common Goldeneye.
[2] Yellowstone National Park, Wyoming.

flushes first. They take great delight in "shooting the rapids"; nothing in the Gardiner River, at least, being too rough for them. They drop down over a fall 3 feet high, and at the bottom go out of sight in the foam and spray, but nevertheless keep right on swimming along. Should they tire of this boisterous sport, they are quick to take advantage of any eddy, or rest behind a boulder. As a rule these are the tamest of our ducks; on the reservoir and other roadside waters they are unalarmed even while the big autos go thundering past. If I approach a flock too closely, the Barrows swim away, or go coasting down the rapids, instead of flushing as the mallards do. But if they do flush, they go only a little way, come back, and drop down again into the water without hesitation or fear. 1923

BUFFLEHEAD   *Bucephala albeola*

The propriety of applying the name "spirit duck" to this sprightly little duck will be appreciated by anyone who has watched it in its natural surroundings, floating buoyantly, like a beautiful apparition, on the smooth surface of some pond or quiet stream, with its striking contrast of black and white in its body plumage and with the glistening metallic tints in its soft fluffy head, relieved by a broad splash of the purest white; it seems indeed a spirit of the waters, as it plunges quickly beneath the surface and bursts out again in full flight, disappearing in the distance with a blur of whirring wings.

The flight of the bufflehead is exceedingly swift and direct, generally at no very great elevation above the water, and is performed with steady and very rapid beats of its strong little wings. It rises neatly and quickly from the surface of the water and sometimes from below it, bursting into the air at full speed. When alighting on the water it strikes with a splash and slides along the surface. It generally travels in small irregular flocks made up largely of females and young males, with two or three old drakes.

It is one of the best of divers, disappearing with the suddenness of a grebe, with the plumage of its head compressed and its wings closely pressed to its sides. It can often succeed in diving at the flash of a gun and thus escape being shot. Under water it can swim with closed wings swiftly enough to catch the small fish on which it feeds so largely; but I believe that it often uses its wings under water for extra speed. It can also dive to considerable depths to secure its food from the bottom.

The following incident, related by Mr. Samuel Hubbard, Jr. (1893), shows that its diving powers are sometimes taxed to the limit:

A broad, sandy bay made in from the harbor, the upper end of which terminated in a shallow slough about 18 inches deep. I waded across and was proceeding toward the beach, when my attention was attracted by a small bufflehead duck (*Charitonetta albeola*) commonly called butterball. He was swimming around in the slough and obtaining his food in the way common to his kind, by diving and picking up that which came his way. With an admiring glance at his beautiful plumage, I was about to pass on, when one of those pirates of the air, a duck hawk (*Falco peregrinus anatum*) came in sight. Without hesitating an instant, he made straight for my little friend and swooped at him. His long talons came down with a clutch, but they closed on nothing, for the duck was under the water. Undaunted the hawk hovered overhead, and as the water was clear and shallow, he could follow every movement of his prey. Again the duck came up; the hawk swooped to seize him, each move being repeated in quick succession and each dive becoming shorter and shorter. It was evident that the poor little hunted creature was getting desperate, for the next move he made was to come out of the water flying. The hawk promptly gave chase. There was some clever dodging in the air, but the duck, frightened and tired, soon saw that his swift pursuer was getting the best of it, so he closed his wings tight against his body and dropped like a stone into the water and plunged out of sight. Now comes the beginning of the end. While he was under water he either saw the hawk hovering over him or else he became bewildered, for he came again out of the water flying. Like lightning the hawk struck; there was a muffled "squawk," and the tragedy was ended.   1923

OLDSQUAW   *Clangula hyemalis*

Oldsquaws, or long-tailed ducks, as I should prefer to have them called, are lively, restless, happy-go-lucky little ducks, known to most of us as hardy and cheery visitors to our winter seacoasts, associated in our minds with cold, gray skies, snow squalls, and turbulent wintry waves.

When migrating, oldsquaws fly high in the air in irregular flocks or in Indian file, but at other times they fly close to the water or a few feet above it, but almost never in a straight line; they twist and turn suddenly, showing the breast and belly alternately like shore birds, swinging in broad circles most unexpectedly. Their flight is so swift and erratic that it is very difficult to shoot them, but they are often very tame or stupid and are quite as likely to swing in toward a gunner's boat as away from it; then in turning they often bunch together so closely that a tempting shot is offered; I have seen as many as nine dropped out of such a bunch at one shot. I have seen them, when shot at, dive out of the air into the water, swim for a long distance under water, and then come out of the crest of a wave flying at full speed, as if they had never broken their flight. They can rise readily off the surface of even smooth water, and when alighting on it often drop in abruptly with an awkward splash. If there is a strong wind blowing they are more inclined to circle into the wind, glide down gently against it on set wings and alight with a sliding splash. Oldsquaws can generally be recognized at a long distance by their peculiar method of flight and by their striking color pattern, the white head and neck and the short, sharp-pointed, black wings being very conspicuous.

Toward spring they are particularly restless and active on the wing and often indulge in aerial evolutions, such as Mr. Mackay (1892) describes, as follows:

These ducks have a habit of towering both in the spring and in the autumn, usually in the afternoon, collecting in mild weather in large flocks if undisturbed, and going up in circles so high as to be scarcely discernible, often coming down with a rush and great velocity, a portion of the flock scattering and coming down in a zigzag course similar to the scoters when whistled down. The noise of their wings can be heard for a great distance under such conditions. In one such instance, at Ipswich Bay, Mass., a flock of several hundred went up twice within an hour. 1923

HARLEQUIN DUCK   *Histrionicus histrionicus*

The harlequin duck is a rare bird on the Atlantic coast of North America, where its chief summer home is in Labrador and Ungava.

Dr. C. Hart Merriam (1883) contributes the following:

While in Newfoundland last winter I learned that these birds, which are here called "lords and ladies," are common summer residents on the island, breeding along the little-frequented watercourses of the interior. I was also informed, by many different people, that their nests were built in hollow trees, like the wood duck's with us. Mr. James P. Howley, geologist of Newfoundland, has favored me with the following response to a letter addressed to him on this subject: "I received your note inquiring about the harlequin duck, but delayed answering it till the arrival of one of our Indians. It is quite true the birds nest in hollow stumps of trees, usually on islets in the lakes or tarns of the interior. They usually frequent the larger lakes and rivers far from the seacoast, but are also found scattered all over the country."

Mr. Millais (1913) describes the flight of this species as follows:

The beautiful markings of the male of this species are only noticeable when the observer is close at hand, so that they are not the easiest duck to identify except when in flight. The flight, at first somewhat laborious, is very rapid. The short, pointed wings are beaten swiftly, and the bird constantly swings from side to side, even more frequently than the long-tailed duck.[1] The elevation is moderately high, performed at an altitude similar to the goldeneye, but when passing up or down stream it zigzags and turns, to accommodate its line to every bend of the stream, however slight. The harlequin never thinks of cutting off corners, and it would seem that it imagines its life depends on keeping exactly over the water, however much it bends or twists. I have seen harlequins fly religiously above a bend in a stream that formed almost a complete circle in its course, and yet the birds did not cut across it to shorten their route.

I have watched harlequin ducks in flight many times and have shot quite a few of them, but I never noticed any swinging from side to side, as referred to above, and several writers have referred to their flight as straight. They usually fly close to the water and often in such compact flocks that a large number may be killed at a single shot. They also swim in close formation, sometimes with their bodies almost touching.

Walter H. Rich (1907) says:

If a shot is fired at a flock on the wing they will sometimes plunge from the air into the water and after swimming below the surface again take wing, coming up a hundred yards away—seeming, the instant they re-appear, to dash from the depths into the air at full speed, leaving the gunner inexperienced in their ways, and who perhaps had thought that by some miraculous chance he had killed the entire flock, to find that he doesn't care for that kind of duck after all. I passed through just such an experience once, and remember yet how disgusted and surprised I was when after steaming up to where the whole flock should have been dead—no duck—and what may have been their ghosts rising from their watery graves 60 yards away. 1923

LABRADOR DUCK   *Camptorhynchus labradorium*

What little there is known about the life history of this extinct species has already been published and repeatedly quoted by various writers. Probably nothing more of importance will ever be learned about its former abundance or its habits. It is doubtful if any more specimens will ever be brought to light. Therefore, in writing this obituary notice, it is necessary only to compile what has already been written in order to make its life history as nearly complete as possible.

[1] Oldsquaw.

Col. Nicholas Pike sent to William Dutcher (1891) the following interesting account of his experiences with the Labrador duck:

I have in my life shot a number of these beautiful birds, though I have never met more than two or three at a time, and mostly single birds. The whole number I ever shot would not exceed a dozen, for they were never plentiful. I rarely met with them. The males in full plumage were exceedingly rare; I think I never met with more than three or four of these; the rest were young males and females. They were shy and hard to approach, taking flight from the water at the least alarm, flying very rapidly. Their familiar haunts were the sandbars where the water was shoal enough for them to pursue their favorite food, small shellfish. I have only once met with this duck south of Massachusetts Bay. In 1858, one solitary male came to my battery in Great South Bay, Long Island, near Quogue, and settled among my stools. I had a fair chance to hit him, but in my excitement to procure it I missed it. This bird seems to have disappeared, for an old comrade, who has hunted in the same bay over 60 years, tells me he has not met with one for a long time.

Dr. D. G. Elliot (1898) saw a considerable number of Labrador ducks, mostly females and young males, in the New York markets between 1860 and 1870, but full plumaged males were exceedingly rare. The last specimen taken and preserved was shot on Long Island in the fall of 1875, purchased from J. G. Bell, by George N. Lawrence and presented by him to the Smithsonian Institution; it was a young male and possibly its parents or others of the same brood may have survived for a few years; but probably the Labrador duck became an extinct species at about that time.

There has been considerable speculation among ornithological writers as to the causes which led to the disappearance of this species, which was apparently as well fitted to survive as several other species of ducks. It was a swift flyer, rather shy and difficult to approach in its offshore resorts; it was essentially a maritime species and seldom resorted to inland bays or rivers, though Audubon said that it was known to ascend the Delaware River as far as Philadelphia; it was not particularly popular as a table bird and often proved a drug in the market, when other more desirable ducks were obtainable; for the above reasons it is fair to assume that it was not exterminated by gunners and never was shot in very large numbers. What evidence we have goes to show that it never was a numerous species and that it probably had a very limited breeding range. If this breeding range was, as it appears, restricted to the southeast coast of Labrador, its disappearance may easily be charged to the wholesale destruction of bird life which took place on that coast during the last century. Continued persecution on its breeding grounds, where its nests and eggs were apparently conspicuous and where both young and old birds were easily killed in summer, when unable to fly, is enough to account for it. That certain other species, which are known to have wider breeding ranges, survived the same persecution is no proof that the Labrador duck did not succumb to it.   1923

STELLER'S EIDER   *Polysticta stelleri*

This beautiful and oddly marked duck was first described by the Russian naturalist, Pallas,[1] who named it after its discoverer. Steller obtained the first specimens on the coast of Kamchatka, which is near the center of its abundance and not far from its principal breeding grounds in northeastern Siberia. Illustrating the abundance of this species on the Siberian coast of Bering Sea, Dr. E. W. Nelson (1883) writes:

The first night of our arrival was calm and misty, the water having that peculiar glassy smoothness seen at such times, and the landscape rendered indistinct at a short distance by a slight mistiness. Soon after we came to anchor before the native village this body of birds arose from the estuary a mile or two beyond the natives' huts and came streaming out in a flock which appeared endless.

Flocks of thousands were found about Cape Wankarem during our stay there the first of August 1881, and, in company with an equal number of king eiders and a few of the Pacific eider[2] were seen passing out and in each evening to and from the large estuary back of the native village. This village was built upon the spit cutting this estuary from the sea at this place, and lay directly in the track of flight followed by these eiders as they passed to or from the sea. As these flocks passed back and forth the birds were being continually brought down by the slings thrown into the midst of the passing birds by the natives; yet, notwithstanding this, the birds continued from day to day the entire season to pass and repass this place. Their heedlessness in this respect may be accounted for from the fact that these people were without guns of any kind, and were thus unable to frighten them by the noise of the discharge. The birds were easily called from their course of flight, as we repeatedly observed. If a flock should be passing a hundred yards or more to one side, the natives would utter a long, peculiar cry, and the flock would turn instantly to one side and sweep by in a circuit, thus affording the coveted opportunity for bringing down some of their number. These flocks generally contained

[1] Peter Simon Pallas, 1741-1811, was of German birth.
[2] As the Pacific subspecies, *v-nigra*, of the Common Eider was then called.

a mixture of about one-twentieth of the number of Pacific eiders, and the remainder about equally divided of Steller's and the king eiders. At times the entire community of these birds, which made this vicinity their haunt, would pass out in a solid body, and the flock thus formed exceeded in size anything of the kind I ever witnessed.   1923

COMMON EIDER   *Somateria mollissima* (Townsend)

S. m. borealis   (Northern Eider)

The flight of the northern eider is apparently slow, heavy, and labored, but in reality it is much stronger and swifter than it appears and exceedingly straight and direct. Its heavy head is held low, with the bill pointing slightly downward, a characteristic and diagnostic attitude. Eiders usually fly in small flocks, in Indian file, close to the water, often following the indentations of the shore line, but very seldom flying over the land.

Referring to the food value of eider's eggs to the Eskimos, Dr. Donald B. MacMillan (1918) writes:

How impatiently we awaited the discovery of those first golden nuggets in the nests. Can we ever forget those annual pilgrimages to the shrine at historic Littleton and Eider Duck Islands and McGarys Rock. Here, among a laughing, jolly company of men, women, and children, we pitched our tents among the nests; we boiled eggs, and we fried eggs, and we scrambled eggs, and we shirred eggs, and we did everything to eggs. In a few hours 4,000 delicious fresh eggs were gathered from one small island alone. Cached beneath the rocks, away from the direct rays of the sun, they remain perfectly fresh; they become chilled in August; and freeze hard as so many rocks in September—a much-appreciated delicacy during the long winter months. The shells are often broken and the contents poured or squirted from the mouth of the Eskimo into the intestinal sheath of the bearded seal or the walrus, a most nutritious sausage to be eaten on the long sledge trips.

The eider-down industry has never been so highly developed on the American side of the Atlantic as it has on the other side. It would undoubtedly prove a profitable industry and would also serve to protect the birds if properly conducted. The following account of how it is done in Iceland, written by C. W. Shepard, is published by Baird, Brewer, and Ridgeway (1884):

The islands of Vigr and Oedey are their headquarters in the northwest of Iceland. In these they live in undisturbed tranquility. They have become almost domesticated, and are found in vast multitudes, as the young remain and breed in the place of their birth. As the island (Vigr) was approached we could see flocks upon flocks of the sacred birds, and could hear their cooing at a great distance. We landed on a rocky, wave-worn shore. It was the most wonderful ornithological sight conceivable. The ducks and their nests were everywhere. Great brown ducks sat upon their nests in masses, and at every step started from under our feet. It was with difficulty that we avoided treading on some of the nests. On the coast of the opposite shore was a wall built of large stones, just above the high-water level, about 3 feet in height, and of considerable thickness. At the bottom, on both sides of it, alternate stones had been left out so as to form a series of square compartments for the ducks to nest in. Almost every compartment was occupied, and as we walked along the shore a long line of ducks flew out, one after the other. The surface of the water also was perfectly white with drakes, who welcomed their brown wives with loud and clamorous cooing. The house itself was a marvel. The earthen walls that surrounded it and the window embrasures were occupied by ducks. On the ground the house was fringed with ducks. On the turf slopes of its roof we could see ducks, and a duck sat on the door scraper. The grassy banks had been cut into square patches, about eighteen inches having been removed, and each hollow had been filled with ducks. A windmill was infested, and so were all the outhouses, mounds, rocks, and crevices. The ducks were everywhere. Many were so tame that we could stroke them on their nests; and the good lady told us that there was scarcely a duck on the island that would not allow her to take its eggs without flight or fear. Our hostess told us that when she first became possessor of the island the produce of down from the ducks was not more than 15 pounds in a year; but that under her careful nurture of 20 years it has risen to nearly 100 pounds annually. Most of the eggs are taken and pickled for winter consumption, one or two only being left in each nest to hatch.

S. m. v-nigra (Pacific Eider)

Turner (1886) writes:

The bird is very shy except when on land during boisterous weather. At that time the natives of the western islands of the Aleutian chain used small handnets to throw over the birds as they sat stupidly on the shore. A bright night with a hard gale of wind was the best time to secure them. The birds then sit in a huddle and many are caught at one throw of the net. The natives assert that the common hair seals catch these birds when on the water and drag them under to play with them; hence, these birds are constantly on the alert for seals and take flight as soon as a seal is discovered near.   1923

KING EIDER   *Somateria spectabilis*

To visit the winter haunts of the king eider on the New England coast, one must be prepared to brave the rigors of the cold, rough sea in the most exposed places; for these hardy birds do not come until wintry conditions have made offshore boating far from comfortable, and they prefer to frequent the outer ledges which at that season are almost always unapproachable. I can well remember a December morning on the coast of Maine, the first chance after a week of waiting for a day smooth enough to reach the outer islands, when we started long before daylight for a little eider duck shooting. Fifteen miles or more we had to go in our little launch to reach the ledges where we were to shoot.

We soon realized, as we began to reach the outer islands, that it was none too smooth; a heavy ocean swell was rolling in and breaking on the ledges; and the west wind, coming up with the sun, was stirring up a troublesome cross chop. As we approached Spirit Ledge, where we intended to do our shooting, all hope of landing was dispelled, for the waves were breaking over it with clouds of spray and all around it the submerged ledges were white with combing breakers. It was no place for us, this wild scene of ocean fury, but for the birds it held no terrors. There, just beyond our reach were hundreds of American eiders,[1] surf and white-winged scoters, flocks of oldsquaws, and a few of the black-backed king eiders; flocks were going and coming, settling in the water among the breakers or circling about the rocks. It was a wild and attractive scene, but we could only view it from a distance, and we were finally obliged to retire to a more sheltered ledge where we succeeded in landing and setting out our decoys in the lee. Here only occasional flocks, pairs, or single birds came in to us, as we lay concealed among the rocks while our boatman was anchored at a distance. Off around the outer ledges we could still see the flocks of eiders feeding in the surf, riding at ease among the angry waves, paddling backwards or forwards to avoid the breaking crests, or diving under a combing breaker. There were both old and young birds in the flocks, but the latter decidedly in the majority; the old birds were too shy to come to us, but we secured young males in various stages of plumage. Before long it became too rough to stay even here, and our boatman insisted on our leaving before it was too late; as it was we lost one oar and nearly lost our skiff; we were glad to leave the sea ducks alone in their glory.   1923

SPECTACLED EIDER   *Lampronetta fischeri*

Little is known about the habits of the oddly marked spectacled or Fischer eider, which occupies such a restricted breeding range in

[1] As the subspecies *dresseri* of the Common Eider was formerly called.

northwestern Alaska and northeastern Siberia. Few naturalists have ever seen it in life. Dr. E. W. Nelson (1887), to whom we are indebted for most of our knowledge of the habits of this species, says on this point:

Its restricted range has, up to the present time, rendered this bird among the least known of our waterfowl. Even in the districts where it occurs it is so extremely local that a few miles may lead one to places they never visit.

In Mr. Dall's paper upon the birds of Alaska he limits the breeding ground of the spectacled eider to the marshes between the island of St. Michael and the mainland. This, with the statement made to him by natives that they are never found north of St. Michael, is not borne out by my observations, for these eiders breed from the head of Norton Bay south to the mouth of the Kuskoquim, at least. St. Michael may be noted as the center of abundance. The spectacled eider is so restricted in its range and so local in its distribution, even where it occurs, that, like the Labrador duck and the great auk, it may readily be so reduced in numbers as to become a comparatively rare bird. A species limited in the breeding season to the salt marshes between the head of Norton Bay and the mouth of the Kuskoquim River occupies but a very small territory, and a glance at the map will show this coast line not to exceed 400 miles, even following its indentations. The width of the breeding ground will not exceed 1 or 2 miles, and there are long stretches where it does not breed at all.[1]

In addition to the natural struggle for existence the species has to contend against thousands of shotguns in the hands of the natives. The diminution in all the species of waterfowl breeding along the coast is more and more marked each season; and while this may mean a desertion of one region for another in the case of the great majority of geese and ducks, yet for such narrowly limited species as the spectacled eider, and to a less extent the Emperor goose, this diminution is but the beginning of extermination. Moreover, the present scarcity of large game along the coast is having great effect in causing the natives to wage a continually increasing warfare upon the feathered game.   1923

WHITE-WINGED SCOTER   *Melanitta deglandi*

The time-honored sport of coot[2] shooting has for generations been one of the most popular and important forms of wildfowl hunting on the New England coast. Next to the black duck, which undoubtedly

[1] According to the 1957 *A.O.U. Check-list,* however, it now "*Breeds* . . . on the arctic coast of northwestern Alaska to Point Barrow (occasionally to the Colville River) south in Bering Sea to St. Lawrence Island, and to the mouth of the Kuskokwim River."

[2] The gunner's name for a scoter.

stands first in the estimation of our sportsmen, there are probably
more scoters killed on our coasts than any other of the Anatidae.
Aside from the fact that the scoters are not of much value for the
table, coot shooting has much to recommend it; it is a rough and
rugged sport, testing the strength, endurance, and skill of an experienced boatman; the birds are strong fliers and hard to kill, requiring
the best of marksmanship, under serious difficulties, and hard-shoot-
ing guns; during good flights game is almost always within sight,
giving the sportsman much pleasant anticipation; and chances are
frequently offered to show his skill at difficult and long shots. I was
born and bred to be a coot shooter, inheriting the instinct from three
generations ahead of me, and I only wish that I could impart to my
readers a small fraction of the pleasure we have enjoyed in following
this fascinating sport.

Rudely awakened at an unseemly hour, soon after midnight it
seems, the party of gunners are given an early breakfast before starting out. It is dark as midnight as we grope our way down to the
beach, heavily laden with paraphernalia, launch our boats in a sheltered cove among the rocks, and row out onto the ocean. The crisp
October air is cool and fresh, as the light northeast wind comes in
over the ledges, fragrant with the odors of kelp and rockweed. There
is hardly light enough at first to see the line of boats, strung out
straight offshore from the point, but soon we find our place in the
line, anchor our several strings of wooden decoys, and then anchor our
dory within easy gunshot of the nearest decoys, which if correctly
placed are the smallest and most life-like; the largest decoys are
merely to attract the birds from long distances. Perhaps before our
decoys are set we have seen a few shadowy forms flitting past us in
the gloom, or heard the whistle of their wings in the dark, the begin-
ing of the morning flight; occasionally the flash of a gun is seen along
the line and the day's sport has begun. As the gray of early dawn
creeps upward from the sea we can clearly distinguish the long line of
boats, perhaps a dozen or fifteen, anchored at regular intervals, a
little less than two gunshots apart so that birds can not slip through
the line, and extending for several miles offshore, an effective barrier
to passing flocks. Every eye is turned northward, looking up the
coast and straining to discover the minute specks in the distance, as
the first flock appears several miles away. "Nor'ard," the warning
signal is passed along the line, as some keen eye has made the longed-
for discovery, and every gunner crouches in his boat to watch and
wait and hope for a shot. Soon we can make them out, an irregular,

wavering bunch of black specks, close to the water and well inshore. The boom of distant guns tells us that other gunners up the coast have seen them and perhaps taken their toll. On they come, now strung out in a long line headed straight for us, big black birds with flashing white wing patches, "bull white wings," as the males of this species are called; we shall surely get a shot. But no, they have seen us and swerved, flying along the line seaward; a shot from the next boat drops a single bird and they pass through the line beyond, dropping two more of their number.

A temporary lull in the flight gives us a chance to rest and admire the beauty of the scene around us; the delicate blush of dawn deepens and brightens as the gorgeous hues of sunrise spread from the eastern horizon over the broad expanse of sky and sea, a rapidly changing play of colors until the sun itself appears over the water and bright daylight gilds the ocean.

Although they are thus persecuted year after year throughout the whole length of their migration route, they do not seem to have diminished materially in numbers since the time of our earliest records, and vast numbers of them still migrate along our coast.   1923

SURF SCOTER   *Melanitta perspicillata*

The flight of the surf scoter is not quite so heavy as that of the white-winged scoter; it is a smaller, lighter, and livelier bird on the wing, but it so closely resembles the American scoter[1] in flight that the two can not be distinguished at any great distance. It rises heavily from the surface of the water and experiences considerable difficulty in doing so unless there is some wind, which it must face in order to rise. This necessity of rising against the wind is well understood by gunners, who take advantage of it to approach a flock of bedded birds from the windward, forcing the birds to rise toward the boat and thus come a little nearer. When once under way the flight is strong, swift, and well sustained. In calm weather or in light winds migrating birds fly high, but in windy or stormy weather they plod along close to the waves. They often fly in large flocks or irregular bunches without any attempt at regular formation, following the coast line, as a rule, but sometimes passing over capes or points to make short cuts.

As a diver the surf scoter is fully equal to the other sea ducks, depending on its diving powers in its daily pursuit of food and to

[1] As the subspecies *americana* of the Common Scoter was formerly called.

escape from its enemies in emergencies. It dives with an awkward splash, but very quickly and effectively, opening its wings as it goes under, and using them in its subaqueous flight. It can remain under for a long time and swim for a long distance without coming up; it is useless to attempt to chase a slightly wounded bird. Mrs. Florence Merriam Bailey (1916) has graphically described the ability of this species to dive through the breaking surf [near Venice, California]:

It was a pretty sight when, under a gray sky, the beautiful long green rolls of surf rose and combed over and the surf scoters came in from the green swells behind to feed in front of the surf and do skillful diving stunts to escape being pounded by the white waterfalls. As the green wall ridged up over their heads they would sit unmoved, but just as the white line of foam began to appear along the crest they would dive, staying under till the surf had broken and the water was level again. When diving through the green rollers near the shore the black bodies of the scoters, paddling feet and all, showed as plainly as beetles in yellow amber.   1923

COMMON SCOTER   *Oidemia nigra*

The Massachusetts method of "coot[1] shooting," in which I have often indulged, is described under another species, so I shall quote from Walter H. Rich (1907) as to the methods employed on the Maine coast; he writes:

Probably the least wary of the duck family, they may be approached quite readily as compared with other members of the tribe. Gunners use many methods for capturing the coots, but the greater number are killed over decoys. A string of "tolers" is set in a promising place just off some rocky point or ledge in the deep water, the gunner is well hidden, and if the birds are flying there is every prospect of good shooting, for the coot is one of the best of birds to decoy. Often in the early part of the season, before the birds have become shy from constant peppering, the gunner may set his decoys on a line from his boat, only keeping below the gunwale when the flocks are coming in. And they *will* come in. I have often seen them fly close enough to be struck with an oar—I may say that they make it an invariable rule to do this when the gunner has taken the shells out of his gun or laid it aside to pick up his decoys after a morning's cootless waiting in the cold. One oddity in the gentle art of duck shooting is the practice of "hollerin' coots"—that is, of making a great noise when a flock is passing by out of shot—when they will often turn and come to the decoys. The report of a gun sometimes has the same effect, but we New Englanders are too thrifty to waste powder and lead where our vocal organs will serve as well.

[1] The gunner's name for a scoter.

Next to decoying, the use of the "gunning float" is the most effective method of killing coots. The "gunning float" is a long, low craft, drawing but little water and showing only a foot or so above the surface when properly trimmed down with ballast. In the fall, for use in the open water, they are "trimmed" with "rockweed"; in the marshes with "thatch." In the spring and winter months the proper thing is snow and ice to represent a drifting ice cake. It takes sharp eyes to detect the dangerous one among the many harmless pieces of ice when the gunner, clad in his white suit, is working his cautious way along toward the feeding flocks. The deception is so complete that I have known that crafty old pirate, the crow, to almost alight on the nose of a float when it was being pushed after a flock of sea fowl. This float gunning is the method most used for all duck and goose shooting on the eastern New England coast line.   1923

RUDDY DUCK   *Oxyura jamaicensis*

This curious little duck is in a class by itself, differing in several peculiarities from any other North American duck. It is widely scattered over the most extensive breeding range of any of our ducks, from far north to far south and from our eastern to our western coasts. Its molts and plumages are unique, involving a complete seasonal change from the gaudy nuptial to the dull and somber autumn dress; even the seasonal changes in the oldsquaw are less striking. But its eggs furnish the greatest surprise of all; for, although this is one of our smallest ducks, it lays eggs which are about as large as those of the great blue heron or the wild turkey. In its appearance and behavior it is also unique and exceedingly interesting. One must see it on its breeding grounds, in all its glory, to appreciate what a striking picture is the male ruddy duck. In the midst of a sea of tall, waving flags a quiet, sheltered pool reflects on its glassy surface the dark green of its surroundings, an appropriate setting for the little gem of bird life that floats gently on its surface, his back glowing with the rich, red brown of his nuptial attire, offset by the pure white of his cheeks, his black crown, and above all his wonderful bill of the brightest, living, glowing sky blue. He knows he is handsome as he glides smoothly along, without a ripple, his saucy sprigtail held erect or even pointed forward till it nearly meets his upturned head; he seems to strut like a miniature turkey gobbler.

His mate knows that he is handsome, too, as she shyly watches him from her retreat among the flags, where perhaps she is already building her basketlike nest. As she swims out to meet him his courtship display becomes more ardent; he approaches her with his head stretched up to the full extent of his short neck and his eyes gleaming under two swollen protuberances above them like the eyes of a frog; with his chest puffed out like a pouter pigeon, he bows and nods, slapping his broad, blue bill against his ruddy breast; its tip striking the water and making a soft, clucking sound. Should a rival male appear upon the scene, he rushes toward him, they clash in an angry struggle, and disappear beneath the surface in desperate combat, until the vanquished one skulks away and leaves the victor to strut and display his charms with more pride than ever.   1923

HOODED MERGANSER   *Lophodytes cucullatus*

In the overflowed, heavily wooded bottoms of our great interior rivers, where rising waters have half submerged and killed the forest trees, this pretty little timberland duck finds a congenial home among the half-sunken snags, stumps, and dead trees, which offer suitable nesting hollows and where its striking color pattern matches its surroundings so well that it is easily overlooked.

Mr. J. Hooper Bowles has sent me the following interesting notes on his experience in inducing hooded mergansers to nest in boxes, near Tacoma, Washington:

I have never found a naturally located occupied nest of the hooded merganser, my rather limited experience being confined to nesting boxes that I put up for them. This was done through the kindness of Dr. G. D. Shaver, of Tacoma, Washington, who very kindly gave me entire use of his country estate near that city. The locality selected is a lake about half a mile in diameter, entirely surrounded by dense fir and deciduous woods, with a stream running in at one end and out again at the opposite end. At the head of the lake the stream runs through a large and heavily wooded swamp, in which I put up two of my boxes. A third was put up on a dead tree standing in the middle of the lake, a fourth on a tree at the outlet, a fifth on the side of the lake, and a sixth on a lone, giant fir tree that stands on a bare hillside some 300 yards from the water at the end of the lake. All are about 18 feet above the ground, or water, and seemed to cover as well as possible the nesting sites that might be suitable for these birds. Not to take up too much space, I will say that a set of 10 eggs was taken from one of the boxes in the swamp at the head of the lake, a brood being reared in the other box there. A set of 11 eggs was taken from the box on the tree in the lake, the bird using the box on the lone fir on the hillside for her second, and this time successful, attempt at rearing a brood for the season. The box on the side of the lake showed no signs of being visited, but down feathers on the entrance of the box at the outlet gave evidence that it had been thoroughly examined, although considered unsuitable for some reason. The birds are so exceedingly shy that I have never been able to see them enter their nests, but when leaving they come out at full flight, which would seem almost an impossibility under the circumstances. The eggs are just about the size, shape, and color of white billiard balls, and every bit as hard in their composition.   1923

COMMON MERGANSER   *Mergus merganser*

This large and handsome duck has always been associated in my mind with the first signs of the breaking up of winter. Being a hardy species, it lingers on the southern border of ice and snow and is the very first of our waterfowl to start on its spring migration.

Several writers state that the young mergansers are carried from a nest in a hollow tree to the water, in the bill of the parent bird. [Others say they drop by themselves.]

Mr. William S. Post (1914) has twice witnessed [such a] performance; the following is his account of it:

It was my good fortune to witness twice the emerging of a young brood of mergansers from an extreme situation of this kind, an old pileated woodpecker's hole about 40 feet high in the limb of a live elm, standing about 15 feet from the edge of the Tobique River in New Brunswick.

On June 18, 1910, I fished the famous salmon pool at the fork of the river, and having incidentally run the canoe close to the shore near where this old elm stands, I landed and rapped several times sharply on the tree with a stick, for I had been told that a wood duck—which on the Tobique means a golden eye—nested there the previous spring. The female merganser immediately flew out and, having circled about over the river, alighted on the water. After assuring myself of the identification, which caused me some astonishment on account of the size of the bird in proportion to the entrance of the hole, I returned to my fishing.

In a few moments I noticed a small bird drop down apparently from the hole, and in a few more seconds another and then a third. My first thought was that a bank swallow, of which there are many on the river, had flown up near to the hole and down again three times in succession. This caused me to stop fishing and to watch, when to my astonishment a small bird with white breast appeared in the hole, jumped out, and was followed by another, and again another. I then lost no time in reaching a point in the river opposite the tree, where I saw in the water against the bank, swimming around, a brood of 11 young ducks. I was much surprised, as I had been under the impression from what I had read that the old duck would certainly carry down the young from such an inaccessible position, and though I believe the young birds must have landed in the water, I was yet astonished that they could withstand the shock of such a drop, and I presumed that by rapping on the tree I had caused the old bird to leave in such fright that her fear had been communicated to the young and they had followed her example, and that the whole procedure was therefore an unnatural one.

The clubhouse is situated directly across the river, and on June 12, 1913, two years later [*sic*], I was sitting on the piazza when my attention was attracted by seeing something large drop from the top of this same elm into the water. I immediately saw that it was the old sheldrake[1] and that she was swimming around close to the shore.

In a few seconds another dropped from the hole to the ground and I could see it run down the bank and join its mother who was calling loudly and turning round and round in the water. This one was quickly followed by others in succession until there were seven. By this time I had called my guide and in company of one of the members of the club was crossing the river, provided with trout-landing nets.

The old bird seeing us immediately swam upstream and around the point with her brood and this was the last we saw of her. We landed and stood under the tree where we could hear distinctly more young ducks peeping in the hole. Looking up we saw one tottering on the edge, and before we could take stations where we could properly observe the actual drop, he had struck the ground close to my friend and made such rapid progress toward the water that he escaped in spite of landing nets. In a few seconds another, which proved to be the last, followed, falling on the other side of the tree, and I promptly made him captive. The first bird was in the water and had immediately dived. It is strange that he should have known enough to seek the water, and also to dive immediately.   1923

RED-BREASTED MERGANSER   *Mergus serrator*
(Townsend)

The red-breasted merganser, or sheldrake, as it is commonly called in New England, the "bec-scie" or "saw bill" of the Acadians, although often hunted, is generally classed as a fish duck and considered almost worthless. But there are other things in life besides bread and meat and dollars and cents, and the esthetic appreciation of this, as well as of many other "worthless" birds, is surely increasing.

The courtship of the red-breasted merganser is a spectacular performance. I (1911) have described it as observed at Ipswich [Massachusetts] as follows:

The nuptial performance is always at its best when several drakes are displaying their charms of movement, voice, and plumage, before a single duck, and each vies with the other in the ardor of the courtship. The drake begins by stretching up his long neck so that the white ring is

---

[1] Popular name for Merganser.

much broadened, and the metallic green head, with its long crest and its narrow red bill, makes a conspicuous object. At once the bill is opened wide and the whole bird stiffly bobs or teeters, as if on a pivot, in such a way the breast and the lower part of the neck are immersed, while the tail and posterior part of the body swing upward. This motion brings the neck and head from a vertical position to an angle of 45°. All the motions are stiffly executed, and suggest a formal but ungraceful curtsey.

This song, emitted when the bill is opened, is a difficult one to describe, but easily recognized when once heard, and remains long in the memory after one has heard it repeated over and over again by a number of merganser suitors. It is a loud, rough, and purring, slightly double note which I wrote down "da-ah," but the note is probably insusceptible of expression by syllables.

The bobbing and the love note may be given twice in rapid succession, although at times the performance is a single one, or may consist of an extensive bob, preceded by a slighter but similar one. The performance is, however, repeated at frequent or infrequent intervals, depending on the ardor and number of the suitors, and, no doubt, on the attitude of the modestly dressed lady.

Although the female merganser may remain passive and coyly indifferent, as is the habit of her sex, she sometimes responds by a bobbing which is similar to that of the male, but of considerably less range. That is to say, the neck is not stretched so straight up, and the breast is not so much depressed during the bob. She emits a single note at this time, which is somewhat louder than that of the male and is of a different quality as it is decidedly rasping. As nearly as I can remember this note is similar to the rough croaks I have heard given by these birds in Labrador when they were flying to and from their nests.

When the female responds in this manner she appears to be very excited, and the ardor of the drakes is correspondingly increased, if one may judge by the frequent repetition of the love antics and notes, and by the fact that they crowd about the duck. Every now and then she darts out her neck and dashes at the ring of suitors, just as the female English [house] sparrow does under similar circumstances.

The bobbing up of the stern of the male is the more conspicuous as the wings are then apparently slightly arched upwards, so that the white secondary feathers are very prominent. These show at all times as the male swims in the water, but in the female they are generally, but not always, invisible.   1923

VULTURES, HAWKS, AND FALCONS—ORDER FALCONIFORMES

AMERICAN VULTURES   Family Cathartidae

TURKEY VULTURE   *Cathartes aura*   (Tyler)

When death comes to any animal, its body becomes food for the vultures. As soon as the animal can no longer move, the meal is ready, and if a vulture finds a dead body, although it be warm from the life just flown, the bird begins at once to feed. But a large animal—a horse or a cow—cannot be finished, even by a company of voracious vultures, while the body is fresh. Putrefaction works fast and overtakes the birds, and the end of the meal becomes far advanced in decomposition. Also it often happens, owing to the position of the body, or because it is submerged, or because the hide is too tough for the vulture's beak to tear, that little or none of it is accessible to the birds. Then the vultures gather about the carcass, in large numbers if it be a big one, and wait patiently near at hand until time and decay, making it soft and ripe, shall fit it to their needs. Then they descend and strip it to the bone.

In any region, no matter how widely it may range, there is a limited number of places in which a bird as large as a turkey vulture can hide its nest. The vulture is a big bird; it must have room for its nest somewhere either inaccessible to predatory animals or where they cannot easily reach its eggs or young. There is the added danger that the odor of the food may proclaim the whereabouts of the nest after the eggs are hatched and the young birds have to be fed.

Many situations meet these requirements in some degree, notably on precipitous cliffs, of access only through the air, or in caves or hollow stumps, or in the midst of dense shrubbery where a narrow entrance limits the attack by enemies to one direction. In such locations the vulture lays its eggs on the ground, or on the bare stone of a cliff, or on the rotten chips in a hollow log with little or no attempt to make a nest.

When the nature of the vulture's food is considered, it seems almost inevitable that the young birds, in their earlier days, be fed by the process of regurgitation. Thus, one of the first associations that the nestlings learn is that of the odor of decomposing animal matter with appetite and good digestion.   1936

BLACK VULTURE   *Coragyps atratus*   (Townsend)

When a carcass of an animal is discovered, black vultures gather at the feast, which in many cases they must share and fight for, not only among themselves, but with turkey vultures and sometimes with eagles and dogs. Alexander Wilson's (1832) classic description of one of these feasts on a dead horse near Charleston, S. C., is well worth quoting:

The ground, for a hundred yards around it, was black with carrion crows[1], many sat on the tops of sheds, fences, and houses within sight; sixty or eighty on the opposite side of a small run. I counted at one time two hundred and thirty-seven, but I believe there were more, besides several in the air over my head, and at a distance. I ventured cautiously within thirty yards of the carcass, where three or four dogs and twenty or thirty vultures were busy tearing and devouring. Seeing them take no notice, I ventured nearer, till I was within ten yards, and sat down on the bank. Still they paid little attention to me. The dogs, being sometimes accidentally flapped with the wings of the vultures, would growl and snap at them, which would occasion them to spring up for a moment, but they immediately gathered in again. I remarked the vultures frequently attack each other, fighting with their claws or heels, striking like a cock, with open wings, and fixing their claws in each other's head. The females, and, I believe, the males likewise, made a hissing sound, with open mouth, exactly resembling that produced by thrusting a red hot poker into water; and frequently a snuffling, like a dog clearing his nostrils, as I suppose they were theirs. On observing that they did not heed me, I stole so close that my feet were within one yard of the horse's legs, and again sat down. They all slid aloof a few feet; but, seeing me quiet, they soon returned as before. As they were often disturbed by the dogs, I ordered the latter home: my voice gave no alarm to the vultures. As soon as the dogs departed, the vultures crowded in such numbers, that I counted at one time thirty-seven on and around the carcass, with several within; so that scarcely an inch of it was visible. Sometimes one would come out with a large piece of the entrails, which in a moment

[1] As he called this species.

was surrounded by several others, who tore it in fragments, and it soon disappeared. They kept up the hissing occasionally. Some of them, having their whole legs and head covered with blood, presented a most savage aspect. Still as the dogs advanced, I would order them away, which seemed to gratify the vultures; and one would pursue another to within a foot or two of the spot where I was sitting. Sometimes I observed them stretching their necks along the ground, as if to press the food downwards.   1936

CALIFORNIA CONDOR   *Gymnogyps californianus*

Far from the haunts of man, in the wilder portions of southern California, among the most rugged and rocky gorges and canyons of the less frequented mountain ranges, this magnificent vulture, the largest and grandest of its tribe, still survives. Here in the remote fastnesses of the untamed wilderness it still finds comparative freedom from the dangers of advancing civilization and may long continue to exist. To see one of these great birds in the solitude of its native haunts gives a thrill well worth the time and effort required. Few have enjoyed the experience, and many are not equal to the task.

The flight of the California condor is a superb exhibition of graceful ease and grandeur as it floats steadily along on its great wings, a powerful and skillful master of the air. On account of its great size its flight seems slow, but it really travels very fast; a mere speck in the distant sky rapidly develops into a great black bird, sweeping overhead with seven or eight strokes of its white-lined wings, curved upward at the tips, followed by prolonged periods of graceful sailing, until, all too soon, it disappears in the distance. From its perch on a tree or rock the bird launches itself with a few great flaps into a glorious sailing flight; but when rising from the ground it must run, hop, and flap along for fifty or sixty feet before taking the air, much like the take-off of an airplane. Then it soars in wide circles, mounting higher and higher on the ascending currents of warm air, until it is almost lost to sight in the ethereal blue. Illustrating its mastery of the air, Mr. Dawson (1923) relates the following incident, as witnessed by Claude C. L. Brown [near the San Juan Range, California]:

Just because the sails of this bird are so accurately trimmed for the utilization of light breezes, the craft itself is unable to make headway against a strong wind. Not even by flapping can the Condor negotiate a breeze above a certain intensity. What the bird does in such an emergency is best told by Brown, who was once present on a quite critical occasion ° ° ° Presently he descried four Condors approaching from the far northeast, but before they came up a smart breeze sprang up from the southwest, and presently it whistled over the peaks with increasing fury. The birds

were baffled on the very last mile of their approach. They tacked back
and forth, down wind, or struggled valiantly in the teeth of the gale, only
to be swept away again and again. The cold sea breeze had it in for them,
and though it was only midafternoon, it began to look to the observer like
a case of sleeping out that night. But off to the southeastward some twenty
or thirty miles, the Carisso plains lay baking in the sun. The focal point
of this great oven was sending up a huge column of heated air, as evidenced
by clouds slowly revolving at the height of a mile or so above the plain.
What followed can best be given in Mr. Brown's own words: "Presently
one of the Condors gave up the fight, sailed a mile or so to the eastward,
and, after circling to gain elevation, made away in a bee-line for the southeast. In a short time the other three went through the same manoeuver
and followed after their companion. I now brought my telescope into
action and I never took the glass off the birds although they became mere
specks in the sky. The Condors did not swerve from their course until
they entered the spiral cloud. Upon striking that ascending column of air
they rose rapidly, apparently without effort, as a balloon might rise, being
now and again lost to view in the fleecy folds of ascending vapor, until
within an incredibly short space of time they emerged above the clouds,
into a higher region of absolute clearness, say three miles above the earth.
Here they must have found themselves well above and quite free from the
lower currents of air which had plagued them, for now they sailed straight
to the westward, descended and—glided triumphantly homeward on the
wings of their ancient enemy, the southwest gale!

"I do not think that more than thirty minutes had elapsed from the time
the Condors gave up the fight till they were safely at roost in their rookery;
yet these birds must have traveled somewhere from fifty to seventy miles
to accomplish their purpose, and the whole performance took place without
the flap of a wing."   1936

KITES, HAWKS, AND HARRIERS
Family Accipitriidae

WHITE-TAILED KITE   *Elanus leucurus*

The flight of the white-tailed kite is light, airy, and graceful; often
it is a pretty fluttering flight with quick wing beats, or a stationary
hovering flight like a sparrow hawk; and at times it is quite swift. I
noticed that when the bird is soaring or scaling there is a bend in the
wing, as in the osprey. Dr. Pickwell (1930) describes it as "with
wings slightly raised and down-curving at the tips." Also he says:

The leg-dangling habit of the Kites is one of their most conspicuous
oddities. On the nesting territory the protesting birds flew here and there
nearly constantly, uttering their cries, beating the air slowly with short

strokes, the wings held up at a sharp angle above the back, the legs dangling from a point about the center of the body.

W. H. Hudson (1920) says of the South American form[1]:

Its wing-power is indeed marvellous. It delights to soar, like the Martins, during a high wind, and will spend hours in this sport, rising and falling alternately, and at times, seeming to abandon itself to the fury of the gale, is blown away like thistle-down, until, suddenly recovering itself, it shoots back to its original position. Where there are tall Lombardy poplar-trees these birds amuse themselves by perching on the topmost slender twigs, balancing themselves with outspread wings, each bird on a separate tree, until the tree-tops are swept by the wind from under them, when they often remain poised almost motionless in the air until the twigs return to their feet.

Although ordinarily gentle birds, these kites are often very pugnacious toward certain large birds, crows and hawks, that invade their territory. Several observers have seen them persistently drive away crows and the various Buteos. Dr. Pickwell (1930) writes:

In fact many of our records of Kites have come about because our attention has been drawn first to a large harried Buteo in the distance and glasses showed there not only Buteo but Kites above swooping down, one, then the other (Kites are nearly always in pairs), in huge parabolas reaching a hundred feet or more above the harried giant. Down one comes with a rush and swings up again. Immediately after, the other one drops, then up, and so around and around they alternate until the distance and blue swallows up Buteo and tormentors. This game is played the year around, in the breeding season and out.   1936

SWALLOW-TAILED KITE   *Elanoides forficatus*

This elegant bird seems to have largely withdrawn from its former wide range in North America and is now confined, in this country, mainly, if not wholly, to Florida and perhaps the other Gulf States.

I first made my acquaintance with this beautiful species in the Cape Sable region of extreme southern Florida. While crossing the narrow strip of prairie between Flamingo and Alligator Lake, we saw seven of these lovely birds sailing about over the prairie, soaring in circles high overhead, or scaling along close to the ground, like glorified swallows. They seemed to be quartering the ground systematically in the search for prey, for, as they circled, they gradually moved along over new ground. It was a joy to watch their graceful movements and a pity to disturb them, but my companion, the late Louis

[1] Subspecies *leucurus;* the North American form is *majusculus.*

A. Fuertes, and I both wanted specimens. We concealed ourselves in the long grass and had not long to wait before we had two of the birds down on the ground and five others hovering over them, after the manner of terns, uttering their weak squealing or whistling notes. We shot no more; they were too beautiful; and we were rapt in admiration of their graceful lines, the purity of their contrasting colors, and the beautiful grapelike bloom on their backs and wings, which so soon disappears in museum specimens. I shall never forget the loving reverence with which the noted bird artist admired his specimen, as he began at once to sketch its charms.

The flight of the condor or the eagle may be grand, majestic, but the flight of the swallow-tailed kite is beautiful in the extreme, unsurpassed in grace and elegance. Coues (1874), in his usual matchless style, describes it as follows:

Marked among its kind by no ordinary beauty of form and brilliancy of color, the Kite courses through the air with a grace and buoyancy it would be vain to rival. By a stroke of the thin-bladed wings and a lashing of the cleft tail, its flight is swayed to this or that side in a moment, or instantly arrested. Now it swoops with incredible swiftness, seizes without a pause, and bears its struggling captive aloft, feeding from its talons as it flies; now it mounts in airy circles till it is a speck in the blue ether and disappears. All its actions, in wantonness or in severity of the chase, display the dash of the athletic bird, which, if lacking the brute strength and brutal ferocity of some, becomes their peer in prowess—like the trained gymnast, whose tight-strung thews, supple joints, and swelling muscles, under marvellous control, enable him to execute feats that to the more massive or not so well-conditioned frame would be impossible. One cannot watch the flight of the Kite without comparing it with the thorough-bred racer. 1936

MISSISSIPPI KITE   *Ictinia misisippiensis*

As I have never seen this kite in life, I shall have to rely wholly on the observations of others. It is a bird of the Lower Austral Zone, being seen chiefly in the Southern States from South Carolina and northern Florida to Texas, Oklahoma, and Kansas.

Dr. E. W. Nelson (1877*b*) says:

Their power of sight is truly wonderful. I saw them repeatedly dart with unerring aim upon some luckless grasshopper, from an elevation of at least one hundred yards.

No less remarkable is their power of flight. . . . I repeatedly saw them dart down from a great height with such velocity that it would seem an impossibility for them to escape being dashed to pieces on the ground, but instead, when within a few feet of the earth, they would suddenly spread their wings and the reaction would lift them with almost equal rapidity to about one-half their former elevation. They were so shy that it was impossible to get within gunshot of them.

Although a gentle, inoffensive bird at ordinary times, it can put up a stiff fight when wounded. Wilson (1832) tells of one that fastened its claws so firmly in his hand that he had to cut the tendons in its leg to release its grip. It is brave too in the defense of its nest, driving away such predatory birds as crows and jays. It will even occasionally attack a man that is climbing to its nest, as Mr. Ganier (1902) relates [of an incident in Warren County, Mississippi]:

I had scarcely made half the distance when three or four Kites began to circle about on the level with the tree-top, and as I seated myself to rest on a branch, twelve feet below the nest, one of the birds began to dart at me. It was a very pugnacious fellow and would circle around within twenty feet of me until it would catch my eye; then, pausing for a moment, it would dart directly at me, to within six or eight feet of my face, when it would swoop suddenly upward, emitting at the same time a sharp shrieking cry. This performance was kept up until I descended, the birds darting closer as I reached the nest.   1936

EVERGLADE KITE   *Rostrhamus sociabilis*

The everglade kite has been well named "snail hawk," for it feeds exclusively on the meat of a large fresh-water snail (*Ampullaria depressa*), which formerly abounded all over the Everglades and is still abundant in some other fresh-water marshes and sluggish streams in Florida and in many places in South America. It is useless to look for this kite where these snails have been killed off by drainage or drought, as in southern Florida. Their presence can be detected by their pearly egg clusters on the sawgrass or reeds. The kites search for the snails in the open places in the marshes or in shallow ponds, beating slowly back and forth, low over the ground, after the manner of marsh hawks, or hovering over the water like a gull. When the snail is located the kite plunges down to secure it and flies with it in its claws to some favorite perch on a stump, post, low tree, or bush; often an old deserted nest is used as a feeding station. Here the snail is neatly extracted with the aid of the kite's long hooked beak, admirably suited for the purpose, and the shell is dropped unbroken. That the birds use the same perch regularly is shown by the large number of empty shells often found in such places, sometimes as many as two hundred or three hundred. There is no evidence to indicate that this kite ever eats anything but these mollusks.

Dr. John B. May (1935) quotes Herbert Lang (1924) as follows, regarding its methods of feeding, as observed at Georgetown, British Guiana:

The snails remain in the water during the hotter part of the day, but in the early morning and late afternoon are found at the surface or creeping about on the marsh vegetation. The Kite quarters back and forth low over the water, suggesting a sea gull at a distance. Often it hovers over one spot for a considerable interval, then dives down to pick up a snail which it carries in its talons to some favorite perching place in a bush or low tree. Here it stands for several seconds motionless, on one leg, holding the snail in the long claws of the other foot. Soon the snail, which had withdrawn into its shell when picked up, closing tightly its operculum, begins slowly to extrude its slimy body. Suddenly, like a flash the Kite grasps the body of the snail, between the operculum and the shell, in its blunt-edged but deeply hooked beak. The muscular contraction of the snail's body apparently detaches it from its attachment within the shell, and a moment later, with a shake of the Kite's head, the shell is tossed aside and the body swallowed, including the operculum.   1936

GOSHAWK   *Accipiter gentilis*

From the heavily forested regions of Canada, the main summer home of the goshawk, this bold brigand of the north woods, the largest, the handsomest, and the most dreaded of the *Accipiter* tribe, swoops down, in winter, upon our poultry yards and game covers with deadly effect. He is cordially hated, and justly so, by the farmer and sportsman; and for his many sins he often pays the extreme penalty. But, as Herbert Ravenel Sass (1930) says:

We do not live by bread alone. Beauty and courage, swiftness and strength mean something to us; and we shall find these qualities in high degree in the hawks of the Accipiter clan. Especially is this true of the largest and strongest of them, the goshawk, one of the deadliest, handsomest, bravest birds of prey in the world.

None will dispute the goshawk's title to a place among the Kings of Winter. . . . Proud and resolute of mien, with brilliant orange eyes through which the fierce spirit of the fiery-hearted warrior gleams at times like points of living flame—the goshawk ranks second to none in martial beauty and in fearlessness.

Dr. George M. Sutton (1925) who spent a whole day watching a goshawk's nest "was almost constantly attacked and screamed at by the female bird. For eight hours she remained at her post." He continues [Conrad, Potter County, Pennsylvania, May 19, 1925]:

Before my companions left me I crawled into a rudely constructed blind where I crouched motionless, hoping that I would not be detected by the hawks. The female bird drove the departing group of men to the edge of the woods and then returned, calmer for an instant or two, apparently, and then, spying me without the slightest difficulty, redoubled her fury and bore down upon me with savage intent. Intrepid and insistent she swooped at me from all directions and only the branches of the blind kept me from the direct blows of her feet although the protecting boughs cracked and snapped at each onslaught. My being alone doubtless increased her daring and she perched at a distance of only twelve feet and screamed in my face, her bright eyes glaring, and her powerful beak expectantly parted. . . . With the Sept camera in hand I photographed the attacking bird, and while I tried to steel my nerve to accept the blows of her feet without flinching, I found I could not. Every time, when I saw her glowing eyes, partly opened bill, and loosely poised feet descending upon me I ducked and raised my arms in spite of myself. Had I not worn a strong cap and a cloth about my neck no doubt her talons would have brought blood more than once; and it was evident that the claw of the hind toe was most powerful and effective, since that nail dug in and dragged as the bird passed on.

The most memorable thing about the day's experience was the method of attack of the female bird, which has partly explained to me the ease with which some of these birds capture their prey. When the Goshawk left her perch to strike at me her set wings and slim body were for several seconds almost invisible and the only actual movement perceptible was the increase in the size of her body as she swiftly approached. Three times at least I was looking directly at the approaching bird *and did not see her at all* because the lines of her wings and body so completely harmonized with the surroundings, and the front view was comparatively so small.

1936

SHARP-SHINNED HAWK   *Accipiter striatus*

The eggs of the sharp-shinned hawk are highly prized by collectors, as they are among the handsomest of American hawks' eggs and show almost endless variations in color and pattern. The set usually consists of four or five eggs, often only three, and rarely six or even seven or eight. If some of the eggs are taken during the laying period the hawk will keep on laying. C. L. Rawson, "J. M. W." (1882), took eighteen eggs from a single pair of birds in one season:

From the nest in a pine grove four eggs were taken the week ending May 23d. The next morning boys Crow-hunting tore down the nest. Before night a new nest resembling a Night Heron's was constructed in the same grove and three eggs taken the second week. By the middle of the third week two more eggs were taken, and a Pigeon's egg substituted, from which were taken successively as laid nine more eggs. The early morning of every alternate day was the rule for a fresh egg. The longest break in the series was from June 2d to June 6th. The seventeenth and last egg in the direct line was laid on June 21st, and when taken the nest was deserted, neither bird being seen for several days. On the 25th, the female ventured back, and apparently as an afterthought or a "positively the last" trial-egg, laid just one more.

Most wonderful flights have been seen at Point Pelee, Ontario, during September, where these hawks came along in such enormous numbers that it seemed at if all the hawks in Ontario had gathered at this point to cross Lake Erie. The flight begins about the first of September, but the heaviest flight lasts for only three or four days around the middle of the month, after which the numbers of hawks gradually decrease. Taverner and Swales (1907) have given a full account of it, from which I quote as follows:

After the coming of the first in the fall their numbers steadily increased until from six to a dozen can be noted in a day, which in most localities would be accounted common. Then there came a day, Sept. 11, 1905, and Sept. 15, 1906, when the morning's tramp found Sharp-shins everywhere. As we walked through the woods their dark forms darted away between the tree trunks at every few steps. Just over the tree tops, a steady stream of them was beating up and down the length of the Point, while in the air they could often be discerned at every height until the highest looked like a mote floating in the light. As concrete illustrations of the number present: in 1905 we stood in a little open glade and at various times of the day counted from twenty-five to thirty in sight at one time and [W.E.] Saunders writes, "When I saw the flight in 1882 it was probably even greater than in 1905. There were more Sharp-shins than one would suppose were in Ontario, and one day my brother and I stood thirty paces apart, facing each other, with double-barrel breech-loaders, and for a short time the hawks passed so thick that we had to let some go by unmolested because we could not load fast enough to fire at each as it came." A farmer told us of sitting in his front yard one afternoon and shooting fifty-six without leaving his chair. . . . Near the extreme end of the Point is a wooden observatory tower built by the U. S. Lake Survey for the purpose of making observations on the changes of the shore contour. It is about fifty feet high, and stands with its base in the red cedar thicket whilst the platform rises well above all surrounding foliage. On this vantage point Saunders and Taverner took their stand the 18th, and with watch in hand counted the Sharp-shins that passed, nearly all within gunshot. From 11:24 to 11:54, 281 passed us, 207 making for the end of the Point and 74 returning, making 133 that started across the lake within half an hour. As far as we could make out without remaining on the spot the whole time this rate was kept up all day and every day of the greatest abundance of the species.

1936

COOPER'S HAWK   *Accipiter cooperi*

If the sharp-shinned hawk is a blood-thirsty villain, this larger edition of feathered ferocity is a worse villain, for its greater size and strength enable it to do more damage. Furthermore, it is much more widely common during the breeding season, being one of our commonest hawks in nearly all parts of the United States. It is essentially *the* chicken hawk, so cordially hated by poultry farmers, and is the principal cause of the widespread antipathy toward hawks in general.

In my early bird-nesting days, thirty and forty years ago, this was one of our commonest nesting hawks; but for the past thirty years it has been steadily decreasing in numbers. This is perhaps due to constant persecution, but it is largely due also to the marked decrease in the numbers of small birds.[1] I have always considered this and the sharp-shinned hawk as competitive species, each intolerant of the other. I have frequently found one of these Accipiters nesting in the same tract of woods with one of the Buteos, but I have never found the two species of *Accipiter* nesting in the same tract; and several times I have known *cooperi* to replace *velox*[2] in a tract where the latter had repeatedly nested. It is a curious fact that the solitary vireo (*Lanivireo solitarius*) has so often been found nesting in pine woods occupied by a pair of Cooper's hawks as to suggest some significance in the ecology; I find six such cases recorded in my notes, and once the vireo's nest was within fifty feet of the hawk's nest; we have also noted that we never find the vireo in similar woods occupied by sharpshins; the reason seems obvious.   1936

RED-TAILED HAWK   *Buteo jamaicensis*

Two common hunting methods of the red-tailed hawk are the lofty soaring flight, from which its keen eyes detect its prey far below, and its slow flapping or sailing flight low over the fields and meadows, much after the manner of the marsh hawk or roughleg; a third, and perhaps the commonest, method is watchful waiting on some commanding perch on tree or post from which it can quickly pounce on any moving object that it sees. Much of its hunting must be in the forests, for many woodland mice and squirrels are included in its food. To capture such active animals as red or gray squirrels, it is

[1] Hardly the case now.
[2] Former specific name of the Sharp-shinned Hawk.

often necessary for these hawks to hunt in pairs; these lively animals can easily avoid the swoops of a single hawk by dodging around a tree; but, if there is a hawk on each side, the squirrel is doomed unless it can scamper into a hole. Col. N. S. Goss (1891) says that these hawks while "sailing often fill their craws with grasshoppers, that during the after part of the day also enjoy a sail in the air." Mr. Shelley says in his notes:

It is also a great experience to see these large Buteos alight in a newly hayed field to catch grasshoppers and crickets; as they hop along the wings are always maneuvered to give the bird a rising impetus and timed so that the feet no more than touch the ground when the insect is plucked and the bird is clear of the ground on the next bound for the insect ahead. More than anything else, this maneuver resembles the floppings of a hen with its head cut off, only more mathematical, to give a crude description.

Early in September, red-tailed hawks begin to drift southward from New England and other northern parts of their range. These fall flights are very spectacular and usually contain a variety of species; they are seen to best advantage on clear cool days with a northwest wind. These large mixed flights often contain hundreds of individuals, spread out over a wide area and continuing to pass for several hours. 1936

HARLAN'S HAWK *Buteo harlani*

Mr. Swarth (1926) says of the haunts of Harlan's hawk in the Atlin [British Columbia] region:

These dark-colored Buteos were seen by us almost daily through the summer and in all parts of the region that we visited. On May 21 several were observed soaring low over the snow-covered slopes on the east side of White Pass. During the next week, at Carcross, they were seen daily; apparently several pairs were settled on their nesting grounds near the town.

About Atlin these hawks were distributed throughout the lowlands; there were nesting pairs at intervals of a few miles in whatever direction one traveled. Although the species was thus relatively numerous, specimens were hard to obtain; the birds were remarkably wary.

The Harlan hawk is in the Atlin region mostly a bird of the timber. The sort of perch most often chosen is the top of one of the taller spruce trees, often in fairly dense woods but always with such a commanding view as to make approach unseen out of the question. With the exception of the dark colored hawks seen in White Pass early in the season and supposed to be of this species, none was observed in the open country above timber line. The abundance of ground squirrels might have been supposed to be an attraction to that region, too. They were extremely wary always, so much so that although both birds of a pair might circle about, screaming, as long as an intruder remained in their territory, it was generally impossible to approach within gun shot.　　　　　　　　　　1936

RED-SHOULDERED HAWK　　　*Buteo lineatus*

One of the delights of early spring, on one of the first balmy days of March, when the genial warmth of the advancing sun is thawing out the hibernating butterflies, the early wild flowers are showing signs of new life, and the first hylas are peeping in the marshy pools, is to walk through the now leafless woods, breathe the fresh fragrance of awakening spring, watch for the early migrating birds, and listen for the courtship cries of our favorite hawks, old friends of many years' standing. The blue jays can closely imitate their cries, but there is a difference we can recognize. And soon we see them soaring in the air in great circles high above the same old woods where they have nested for many years. We believe that they are mated for life, and we like to think that this is the same old pair that we have known so long. But probably it is only the continuation of a pair, for if one of a pair is killed, the survivor promptly brings a new mate into the territory, or feudal domain of the pair. These hawks are very noisy and conspicuous at this season, in marked contrast with their behavior at other seasons. Their loud, wild cries of *"kee-ah, kee-ah"* are frequently repeated as they circle overhead, their wings and tails broadly extended and stiffly held with only slight adjustments. Frequently they swing near each other and then far apart, or, mounting high in the air, one may make a thrilling dive downward toward the other. These evolutions are indulged in every year, even by mated pairs, and constitute, I believe, their principal courtship display.

The soaring flight of the red-shouldered hawk, oftenest seen during the early part of the nesting season, is much like that of the other large Buteos. It is powerful and graceful, often protracted to a great height and occasionally ending in a thrilling nose dive. Often, while hunting, it glides swiftly along on rigid wings just over the tops of the forest trees or even through the woods; again it glides low over the marshes or meadows in search of frogs or mice. Its coloration is concealing in the lights and shadows of the forest, where it can slip up unawares on the squirrels in the trees, or pounce down upon its humbler prey on the ground. When flying from its nest it swoops downward and flaps away in rather heavy flight, quite unlike the bulletlike dash of the Accipiters. On returning to its nest it flies low and glides up to it in an easy curve. When circling above the intruder at its nest and screaming, it does a great deal of flapping, interspersed with short sailings, and then it may glide off out of sight. As with all hawks, the feet are extended behind, a little below the tail.   1936

BROAD-WINGED HAWK   *Buteo platypterus*

In May, when the tender, freshly opened oak leaves are as big as a crow's foot, when the farmer goes out to sow his corn, and when the hosts of warblers are migrating through the treetops, then may we look for the home secrets of the broadwings. They are gentle, retiring, quiet birds of the deep forests. They are seldom seen in the open country except when migrating or soaring in great circles over their woodland homes.

The broad-winged hawk is generally considered a sluggish bird, quiet, gentle, unobtrusive, and unsuspicious; it is the tamest of all the hawks; one has no difficulty in approaching it, as it sits on some low limb in the woods calmly watching the intruder with apparent indifference. If forced to fly it flaps along through the trees, much after the manner of an owl, and alights again at no great distance. But above the treetops it is far from sluggish in its soaring flight, fully equal to the best of the Buteos in sailing on its broad wings. Mr. [Lewis O.] Shelley has sent me the following interesting notes on one of its spectacular flight maneuvers:

The soaring of the broad-winged hawk, in 1926, was watched on several occasions. A family group of six birds had been noted about a densely wooded tract and a hill known as Smith's Hill, where I often observed adults earlier in the year as they crossed over its rocky summit to hunt over the lower valleys to the west. Little time was available to spend with them, but with the young fledged and on the wing, their hunting excursion as a family unit was always a spectacular sight. A still more pleasing exhibition was when, toward the period of the fall migration, they met in what I considered a spirit of play. In this performance they resembled more than anything a batch of dry leaves lifted and tossed and whirled on a zephyr of brisk autumn wind. A low call would be given, believed to be from an adult, whereupon the birds if separated would congregate at the spot where the first bird wheeled and sailed and called some 200 feet in the air. Then, with the family together, more calls could be heard, growing fainter as the birds rose in their display. Slowly at first, but gradually gaining momentum, the six birds on set pinions soared in and out among each other, round and round in a radius not greater than a quarter mile, lifting and ducking, volplaning and diving steeply toward earth at varying angles, constantly rising, nevertheless, into the clear blue sky. As height was gained and maintained, the dives and sails became swifter, in the forms of arcs and a series of dips and rises; a lower bird rising above them all, only to side-skip, arc, dive, and rise again, another repeating the maneuver, then another, and another. As leaves on the wind current, there seemed no advantageous goal to their actions, except to rise, slowly at first and then with the gain of altitude, swiftly, up, up, and finally, lost to sight. Then in from 5 to 20 minutes they reappeared as tiny dots, by the aid of binoculars, as they shot down plummetwise, banked, regained altitude, but slowly lowering, in spectacular sweeps through the air, growing clearer until the entire physique could be made out, and, finally, on set wings, a sail that would take them to the summit of Smith's Hill and the dark wilderness fastness of the Fuller Wood beyond.   1936

SWAINSON'S HAWK   *Buteo swainsoni*

The food habits of Swainson's hawk are highly beneficial; it is one of the farmer's best friends, for it feeds almost entirely on injurious rodents and insects, with a minimum of birds and poultry. Dr. A. K. Fisher (1893) says that of eighteen stomachs examined, seven contained small mammals, rabbits, gophers, spermophiles, and mice, eight contained insects, three lizards, and three frogs. One stomach contained sixty-eight locusts and another fifty grasshoppers. None contained traces of birds or poultry. He quotes Dr. C. Hart Merriam as follows:

Driving along the crest of the plateau just south of the Umatilla River [Oregon], at about sundown, we were astonished to see a very large number of large hawks hopping about on the ground, catching grasshoppers. We counted about 150 of these hawks, and there must have been at least 200 in the immediate neighborhood. At first we took them to be roughlegs, but later ascertained that nearly if not all were Swainson's hawks (*Buteo swainsoni*). The period between sundown and dark in that region is so short that the birds were still catching grasshoppers when overtaken by darkness.

About 6 o'clock the next morning I visited the same place and was gratified to find the hawks engaged in making their breakfast of grasshoppers. They were scattered over a larger area than when we saw them the previous evening. Before 8 o'clock most of them had left the hills and settled down for the day in the poplar trees along the river bottom. Here I found the trees literally full of hawks, and counted as many as thirteen in one tree. Two of the three whose stomachs were examined contained grasshoppers and no other food. The third contained, in addition to grasshoppers, the head of a meadow mouse of the genus *Arvicola* (subgenus *Chilotus*). One contained 88 grasshoppers, another 96 and the third 106.

Assuming that each hawk captured 200 grasshoppers a day and that there were 200 hawks, the daily catch would be 40,000 grasshoppers. At this rate these hawks would destroy 280,000 grasshoppers in a week and 1,200,000 in a month. . . . When in southern California about a month later I was told by Mr. Edward Merriam that on three occasions he had noticed similar gatherings of hawks in San Diego County. Once he saw a flock of several hundred large hawks catching crickets in cracked adobe soil in the San Marcos Valley. At night the hawks came into the live oaks at the head of the valley to rest. He shot one and found its stomach packed full of large black crickets.   1936

ZONE-TAILED HAWK   *Buteo albonotatus*

The zone-tailed hawk is a Central American species that reaches the northern limit of its range in our Southwestern States. My acquaintance with it is limited to a brief visit to two of the picturesque canyons of the Catalina Mountains in Arizona. After a long drive over the rolling plains east of these mountains, we dipped down a sharp decline into Apache Canyon, where we pitched camp for a few days. This is one of the most picturesque canyons in Arizona. It is a broad, deep, rocky canyon, well watered by a stream of good clear water flowing over a wide stony bed. The sides of the canyon are rough and rocky, in some places very steep or even precipitous, and more or less overgrown with small giant cactus, hackberries, thorns, mesquite, and mountain misery. In the steep rocky walls are numerous small caves, crevices, and ledges where we found nests of the turkey vulture, golden eagle, raven, and canyon wren. The broad bed of the stream is heavily wooded with large picturesque sycamores and giant cottonwoods, with lofty spreading branches that reminded me of New England elms, towering over the tops of the other trees, including a variety of oaks, maples, and walnuts. In one of these big cottonwoods near our camp was an apparently new hawk's nest, fully one hundred feet from the ground, about which a pair of zone-tailed hawks showed considerable concern.

The next day, April 19, 1922, we explored Edgar Canyon, a few miles farther north in the same mountains.

While we were walking down the bed of the stream we were delighted to see a zone-tailed hawk fly from the leafy top of a tall cottonwood. Its nest was barely visible in the thick foliage near the end of a slender branch in the very top of the tree, at least sixty feet from the ground. The hawk began screaming and was soon joined by its mate; both birds circled about in the vicinity as long as we were there. There was no doubt about its identity, but, to make doubly sure, I shot the female; I could easily have shot both. The nest looked inaccessible, but we made a scoop out of a tripod leg, a handkerchief, and a piece of barbed wire; Mr. [F. C.] Willard made a spectacular and daring climb, tying the upper branches together with ropes, and getting near enough to the nest to scoop out the single fresh egg. When I skinned the bird the next day I found an egg in her oviduct fully formed and ready to be laid. The nest could not be closely examined on account of its position, but it was at least partially lined with green leaves.

After recording in my field notes the resemblance of the zone-tailed hawk to the turkey vulture in its flight, I was interested to read that several other observers had noted the similarity. Its flight is apparently lazy and sluggish; it usually holds its wings at an angle above its body when soaring, often carries its tail partially closed, and tilts its body from side to side after the well-known manner of the vulture; this is not a universal rule, however, for it often sails on flat wings with spread tail. The dark body and the lighter pattern of the primaries and secondaries, as seen from below, add to the resemblance. The white zones in the tail do not show at all angles and are conspicuous only from below.   1936

WHITE-TAILED HAWK   *Buteo albicaudatus*

The northern representative of this South American species extends its range into the United States only in the open and prairie regions of southern Texas.

Mr. Burrows (1917) writes:

This species feeds upon rabbits and wood rats, in fact I have found that its diet is largely confined to rabbits which are found in immense numbers in that section.[1] If the nest contains young birds it is sure to show that they are amply provided for by the amount of fur and the number of rabbits' feet found in and about the nest. . . . I have never found any evidence that they feed at any time upon other birds.

The bird will always leave the nest while the intruder is quite a distance away, often at a distance of a quarter of a mile, for as I said above the nest commands a broad expanse and the bird is always on the watch. When the female leaves the nest, the male bird usually joins her at once and the two often disappear and do not come in sight while the nest is being examined; at other times they mount high in the air, far above the reach of a shotgun and directly above the nest, where they will often stand poised in one spot for several minutes at a time coolly watching developments below. At such a time the birds always face the strong sea breeze which blows so steadily and strong that it is possible for them to appear perfectly motionless and stand suspended in mid-air.   1936

[1] Between the Nueces and the Rio Grande.

SHORT-TAILED HAWK   *Buteo brachyurus*

This in another South American hawk, tropical or subtropical in distribution, that appears in the United States only in Florida. It always has been extremely rare and local even there, and now I believe it has almost, if not quite, disappeared from that State. I saw it many years ago in the extensive mangrove swamps of extreme southern Florida, where there may be a few still left.

The latest and most complete account of the nesting habits of the short-tailed hawk is given by Herbert W. Brandt (1924) as follows:

Lake Istokpoga is the second largest lake in Florida, lying northwest of Lake Okeechobee in the central part of the state. It is roughly twelve to fifteen miles across and is entirely surrounded by a large cypress growth. To the south, reaching nearly to Lake Okeechobee, is a very dense impenetrable swamp, said to be one of the worst in Florida, and one through which very few white men have gone. It is in this swamp and in the big cypress bordering the lake that we found the Short-tailed Hawk.

During the latter half of March 1923, we spent considerable time watching these birds, and on the 29th of that month, Mr. [A.H.] Howell found a nest in the dense swamp, three hundred yards from the lake. The male bird would sit by the hour in a big cypress tree near the mouth of Istokpoga Creek, evidently using this tree as a lookout perch. Mr. Howell patiently watched this bird on a number of occasions, and finally, about five o'clock, on the evening of the 29th the Hawk left his perch, circled upward a couple of times and dived into the swamp about one hundred yards from the lookout tree. A careful search of the swamp, in the direction taken by the bird, resulted in locating a nest in the top of a tall, slender magnolia, and on rapping the tree the female flushed from the nest.

The following day, March 30, I took a set of two nearly fresh eggs from this nest, which was in a swamp magnolia up fifty-eight feet from the ground. The tree was one foot in diameter at the base and very heavily overgrown with poison ivy, making the ascent rather difficult. It stood in a dense jungle of small trees and undergrowth, with water and mud knee deep.

The nest was two feet in diameter and nearly a foot in height and was very large for the size of the bird.   1936

ROUGH-LEGGED HAWK   *Buteo lagopus* (Townsend)

To anyone who has been to the summer home of the rough-legged hawk in the North, or has seen it in its winter migrations, the mention of its name brings up visions of a splendid bird, one of the largest and finest of our hawks.

As a rule the rough-legged hawk is an unsuspicious **bird and can** be more easily approached than most hawks. Particularly is this the case when the observer is mounted or in a carriage or automobile.

The flight of the rough-legged hawk, although generally slow and leisurely, is graceful and indicative of skill and power. In soaring, the wings and tail are spread to their full extent; the first half-dozen primaries are spread out separately like fingers and curve upward at their tops. On motionless wings, if the air currents are favorable, this bird may often be seen soaring high over the land rising higher and higher until it becomes a mere speck in the sky.

In searching for mice they often fly slowly, alternately flapping and sailing, close to the ground or even fifty yards up in the air. They often quarter the ground like marsh hawks or harriers, frequenting open fields and pastures and marshy places.

It is not uncommon to see this hawk skimming close to the surface of water, and one I watched in February at Ipswich [Massachusetts] flew from the region of the dunes over the sea, swooping down for a moment close to the waves at the bar. The vicinity to water seems always to attract this species.

They frequently hang in one place by rapid vibration of the wings, turn the head from side to side in looking down, and often drop their long-feathered tarsi preparatory to pouncing on the prey, only to draw them up behind when they change their mind. At other times, when luck is propitious, they partially close their wings and drop like a plummet.   1936

FERRUGINOUS HAWK   *Buteo regalis*

This name, *regalis*, is a very appropriate one for this splendid hawk, the largest, most powerful, and grandest of our Buteos, a truly regal bird.

The ferruginous roughleg[1] appears sluggish at times, as it sits quietly on some low tree or fence post or even on the ground watching for its prey. At such times it is not particularly wary and can be approached within gun range if it thinks it is not observed. A rider on horseback or in an automobile has a better chance to approach the bird than a man on foot.

The ferruginous roughleg is a highly beneficial hawk and should be encouraged as a great destroyer of injurious rodents.

[Taverner (1926) writes:]

A conservative estimate of the requirements of a family of these large Hawks is surprising in its total. Two adults, from spring arrival to the birth

[1] As this species was formerly called.

of young, three months, consume not less than a gopher a day, 90 in all. After the young are out, four in the brood, and for two months at least, the family requirement can not average less than three gophers a day, or 180. Thereafter for one month, the six practically adult, though four are still growing, probably will require one gopher each day, or 180 more. A single gopher, under favourable circumstances, destroys at least one bushel of wheat. Supposing that one-tenth of this can be charged against the average gopher, we still have thirty-five bushels of wheat as the value of this one family of large Hawks for a single season. This can be translated into dollars and cents by multiplying the current price of wheat, and makes a sum that is well worth considering. 1936

GRAY HAWK   *Buteo nitidus*

One of the greatest delights of my days spent in the mesquite forest near Tucson, Ariz., was the frequent glimpses we had of this beautiful little hawk sailing gracefully over the treetops. Its mantle of pearly gray and its breast finely barred with gray and white were well contrasted with a tail boldly banded with black and white. The exquisite combination of soft grays, black, and white made it, to my mind, one of the prettiest hawks I had ever seen.

To me its flight seemed swift, active, and graceful, more like that of an *Accipiter* than a *Buteo*. It must be very swift on the wing for it catches the small lizards, which were very common in the mesquite forest and are the swiftest moving reptiles I have ever seen.

Major Bendire (1892) observed a flight maneuver in April, which was probably a courtship activity; he writes:

From that time on not a day passed without my seeing two or three pairs of these handsome little Goshawks[1] (which were readily recognized by their light color) engaged in sailing gracefully over the tree tops, now sportively chasing each other, or again circling around, the female closely followed by the male, uttering at the same time a very peculiar piping note, which reminded me of that given by the Long-billed Curlew in the early spring (while hovering in the air in the manner of a Sparrow Hawk), rather than the shrill cries or screams usually uttered by birds of prey. To my ear, there was something decidedly flute-like about these notes. After they were paired they became more silent. 1936

HARRIS' HAWK   *Parabuteo unicinctus*

Harris's[2] hawk has been referred to as a sluggish, heavy bird, slow of flight and not graceful, but there is much evidence to the contrary.

[1] This species was then known as the Mexican Goshawk.
[2] As the name of this species was formerly spelled.

No very slow or sluggish hawk could catch the lively creatures recorded in its food. I have seen it chasing a western redtail and it has been seen to attack and drive away the big ferruginous roughleg.[1] Vernon Bailey (1902) writes:

In southern Texas the rich rufous marks and swift, clear-cut flight of the Harris hawk soon become pleasantly familiar, for he is one of the hawks that are both common and tame on the coast prairies. He is so tame that as you drive by a telegraph pole on which he is perching he will sometimes stand calmly on one foot looking down upon you with a statue-like indifference. In the mesquite thickets you may meet one at close quarters as he dashes under the thorny bushes in quest of wood rats, ground squirrels, and the small game that abounds in these dwarf forests; and sometimes, as happened one day when we drove along the Nueces River, you will see him sitting on a low branch feasting on a wood rat captured at the door of its stick house close by. If you chance near the hawks' nest a long harsh Buteo-like scream may make you look up to find one or both anxious birds circling overhead.

The following is from some notes sent by Maj. Allan Brooks to Dr. John B. May:

Harris's hawk is a dual personality, a sort of Jekyll and Hyde character. A casual acquaintance with this species will probably show one, or more probably a pair, of these hawks sitting in the top of a tree that rises above the general scrub, sitting quietly like Buteos apparently taking little interest in their surroundings as they soak up the morning sun. Presently they will take flight, mounting into the air in easy spirals, higher and higher into the blue, and that will probably be the last you will see of them. But to see this hawk in action one has to be afield early while the mists still hang over the *resacas*. Then Mr. Hyde appears, a flutter of wings as a flock of teal rise in confusion with a dark shape striking right and left among them with all the dash of a goshawk. If unsuccessful, the next attack may be on a group of small herons, one of which may be singled out and followed until killed. Very often a pair of these hawks combine to secure their quarry, and I have seen a snowy heron shared amicably after it had fallen a victim to one of these raptores. In action and flight it combines many of the characteristics of the Buteos, marsh hawk, and goshawk.   1936

BLACK HAWK   *Buteogallus anthracinus*

From an extensive range in South and Central America this well-named, coal-black hawk crosses our southern border to a limited extent from the Lower Rio Grande, in Texas, to southern Arizona. Gerald B. Thomas (1908) says that in British Honduras, where this

[1] As the Ferruginous Hawk was then called.

"is by far the most abundant hawk of the region," its favorite haunt is the long stretches of sand dunes and savannas studded here and there by clumps of palmetto and gnarled pines [where] the ground is honeycombed by thousands of holes of various sizes, the abode of countless numbers of huge land crabs.

He continues:

In the evening, as soon as the sun is down, they come out from their holes by thousands, hurrying here and there and always fighting, brandishing their big claws in the air like a pigmy wielding a huge scoop-shovel.

It is then that the hawks are seen busily engaged in their pursuit of food, as these crabs form almost their sole diet in this particular locality. They always catch and kill more than they can eat at the time in order that they may not be wanting on the morrow when all the crabs have gone deep in their holes to escape the heat of the day. Occasionally I noticed a hawk flying to the nest with a large lizard or snake, but more frequently they were satisfied with the crabs obtained the night before. In not one instance did I see them in pursuit of any birds, nor do their nests with young show any signs that birds are ever taken as prey.

In flight they excel every one of the hawks, kites, or falcons except possibly the Swallow-tailed Kite. Their flight is really marvelous, excelling in some particulars even the far-famed frigate or Man-o-war Bird. The greater part of the year they are rather dull and sluggish but when nesting time comes they are ever on the wing until the young are able to take care of themselves.

It is very interesting to see them obtain material for the nest. They circle high in the air sending out their queer whistling cry, when suddenly one of them folds its wings very close to its side and plunges towards the ground with the speed of an arrow. One almost holds his breath expecting to see the great bird strike the earth with such force that he will be transformed into a lifeless mass of bone and feather. But suddenly just before he reaches the dead tree, thru whose branches you expect to see him crashing, he throws open his wings to their full extent, his tail spreads and flattens against the downward rush and the great talons hang loosely down. Then gliding swiftly over the topmost branch, the swinging and apparently useless feet suddenly stiffen, a faint crack is heard and he slowly fans his way over to the nearby nest, firmly grasping in his talons a twig from the tree on which he seemingly so nearly escaped destruction.   1936

GOLDEN EAGLE   *Aquila chrysaetos*

This magnificent eagle has long been named the King of Birds, and it well deserves the title. It is majestic in flight, regal in appearance, dignified in manner, and crowned with a shower of golden hackles about its royal head. When falconry flourished in Europe the golden eagle was flown only by kings. Its hunting is like that of the noble falcons, clean, spirited, and dashing.

[A] pair of eagles [near Tombstone, Arizona] had two nests, which they used in alternate years. One was in an easily accessible place on a low pinnacle of rock, but it was not is use. The alternate nest was on the farther side of a steep little mountain, which we reached by climbing up a steep slope to the rocky summit; here the ridge dropped off suddenly in rocky cliffs and steep slopes. At the brink of the cliff we could see no nest, but by rolling rocks over the edge we started the old eagle off her nest only about twelve feet below us. It was a difficult nest to reach from above on account of the overhanging cliff, but I found a place where I could climb to a ledge below it and come up to the nest on the ropes. It was located on an outlying spur of a high rocky cliff, about one hundred twenty-five up from the base. It was a large, old nest, four by five feet in diameter, made of large sticks, stems, and roots of yucca and other coarse materials; it was lined with grasses, weeds, strips of inner bark, and other soft fiber. Its contents were rather interesting, a small downy young, only a few days old, a very rotten egg, which burst in my hand, and the remains, mostly the hindquarters, of twelve rabbits.

The flight of the golden eagle is the embodiment of grace and power. Mr. Gordon (1915) writes:

Then one day the north wind crossed the sea, and arrived at the eagle's home. And the eagle felt the cool arctic breeze and sailed out from his giant rocks which by now were burning hot in the fierce rays of the sun. With his pinions wide outstretched he leaned on the refreshing wind, which bore him strongly upward, without a single stroke of his wings to help him on his way. So he mounted higher and higher till he had risen far above his native hill-top, and was outlined, a mere speck, against the dark blue of the sky. Still upwards he sailed, and for sometime longer the watching stalker kept him in view, in the field of his glass. But at length he reached a point at which he was invisible, even by the aid of a telescope. From that point what a gorgeous panorama must have been laid out before his sight in the light of the summer sun. Even the highest tops were now far, far below him, and the river in its windings down the great glen must have appeared as a thin silvery streak.   1936

GRAY SEA EAGLE   *Haliaeetus albicilla*   (Jourdain)

The gray sea eagle is included in the American list on the ground that it is resident on the west coast of Greenland, breeding up to latitude 70° N.

The difference in nesting sites is extraordinary and varies according to the locality. In Greenland the nest is always on a ledge of rock not far from the water, generally in one of the numerous fiords and within reach of a salmon river. Some nests are placed in situations difficult of access, others are comparatively easy to reach. The nest is an untidy heap of sticks and branches picked up from the shore, together with grass and seaweed, as well as bones and other remains of prey.

At rest the sea eagle is a heavy, lumpish bird. On the low-lying shores of the Black Sea where trees are scarce, it may be seen sitting humped up on the mud flats, with the head sunk among the shoulder feathers, looking more like a stump or accumulation of rubbish around a stake than a bird.

The decrepit-looking hermit invites the attention of the hooded crows, which slyly approach, one bird distracting attention in front while the other from behind tweaks a tail feather of the great bird and hastily flaps out of reach as a huge wing is outspread and used to aim a blow at the aggressor. Once on the wing the whole appearance of the bird is at once altered. The broad wings, with each primary standing out by itself, and the wedge-shaped tail, pure white and transparent-looking in the adult, form an impressive picture as with slow flaps the great bird rises and soars in circles overhead. From time to time it may utter its cry, *gak-gak-gak-gak*, four times repeated with outstretched neck and widely opened beak, but for such a large bird, the notes are not striking, and there is another distress call, a high-pitched querulous chatter. 1936

BALD EAGLE *Haliaeetus leucocephalus*

H.l. leucocephalus (Southern Bald Eagle)

The flight of the bald eagle is powerful and impressive, but not so graceful or inspiring as that of the golden eagle. Its ordinary traveling flight appears heavy and labored, as it moves steadily along with slow beats of its great wings, but it is really much swifter than it seems, as is often the case with large birds. But in pursuit of its prey it develops marvelous speed, which the swiftest wildfowl can seldom escape. It often sails along on a level course on widespread wings for a considerable distance; again it soars in great circles to an immense height, from which it sometimes makes a thrilling dive at terrific speed on half-closed wings.

About its nest the bald eagle is an arrant coward, leaving the nest

as the intruder approaches, flying about at a safe distance and squealing, or perching on a distant tree to watch proceedings. I have never
had one even come within gunshot range when I was near the nest.

H.l. alascanus (Northern Bald Eagle)

When I visited Alaska in 1911, bald eagles were very common and
conspicuous all along the coasts of southern Alaska and on some of
the Aleutian Islands. While navigating the beautiful inside passages, from British Columbia northward, we noted that these fine
birds were prominent features in the landscape; where the mountainous shores were heavily forested almost down to the water's edge,
their snow-white heads were conspicuous at a long distance in sharp
contrast against the dark-green background; and some of them were
almost constantly in sight. About Unalaska they were especially
abundant and not at all shy, frequently flying within easy gunshot
range. They were especially bold about their nesting places, or near
their favorite lookout points on the hilltops, where feathers and droppings indicated that they habitually used the same spot for a perch.

The very elaborate studies conducted by Dr. Francis H. Herrick
on the home life of the American eagle, and his numerous papers on
the subject, have given us a very complete picture of the nesting activities of these great birds.

The "great nest" at Vermilion, Ohio, one of several on which his
observations were made, has a history covering thirty-five years; and
for more than eighty years eagles have nested in that vicinity, during
which time six nests are known to have been occupied. The "great
nest" was built not later than 1890 and was added to and occupied
every year thereafter until it was blown down in a March storm in
1925. This nest, when measured in 1922, was twelve feet high and
eight and one-half feet across its top; the upper rim was eighty-one
feet from the ground in the dead top of a shellbark hickory.   1936

MARSH HAWK   *Circus cyaneus*

The above name recalls to mind those delightful days, now long
past, when we sat for hours in a flimsy blind on the Cape Cod
marshes, listening for the startling whistle of the yellowlegs or the
mellow notes of the plover. There is always something moving; and,
whether the yellowlegs and plover come to our decoys or not, we are
sure to see, sooner or later, a dark speck in the distance that soon
develops into a large, long-tailed, long-winged bird. On it comes
with an easy gliding flight, its long wings slanting upward; as it
turns we see its brownish breast and then its white rump, a young

marsh hawk. A lazy, loafing, desultory flight it seems, but really it is full of purpose, as it quarters low over the ground in a systematic search for its prey.

Many accounts of the spectacular nuptial flight have appeared in print, but I prefer to use the following description of it, one of the best, in some notes sent to me by Mr. Broley:

This is a vigorous and pleasing series of nose dives, mostly done by the male, although the female frequently takes part in them. This takes place sometimes at an altitude of 500 feet, but the usual flight averages 60 feet up, swooping down to 10 feet from the ground. It might be illustrated by placing a number of capital U's together as UUUUUUUUUUUUUUU-UUU, as the turn at the bottom is well rounded out, but at the apex the bird almost stalls, tipping downward again to continue the movement. Some observers claim it makes a somersault as it turns, but only on one occasion have I seen any indication of this. The wings are kept fully extended during the whole period, and they appear to be working easily all the time. I have seen a male make 71 of these dips in succession, fly on for a short distance and commence anew. The average number of dips would be perhaps 25. The flight is frequently made while the female is flying along near the ground hunting for mice, below the male, or again he may swoop continually in one location while she is standing on the ground. The movement is extremely graceful and is a welcome sight each spring.   1936

OSPREYS   Family Pandionidae

OSPREY   *Pandion haliaetus*

Gardiners Island [New York] now holds the largest breeding colony of which we have any record. The size of this colony has been variously estimated, but I doubt if any accurate census has ever been taken. Good descriptions of this colony have been written by Dr. Frank M. Chapman (1908), who estimated the number of nests as one hundred fifty to two hundred; by Clinton G. Abbott (1911), who estimated two hundred nests; and by Capt. C. W. R. Knight (1932), who thought the number exceeded three hundred. Gardiners Island is about seven miles long and three miles wide and contains about three thousand acres.

Of [this] famous colony Mr. Abbott (1911) writes:

Ospreys' nests on Gardiner's Island are placed in almost every conceivable situation. They are on trees by scores, both high up and low down; on rocks and boulders, whether on land or in the water; on sheds and buildings; on fences and walls; on piles of debris; on old stumps; on a floating wooden platform intended for the fishermen's use; on a channel buoy; on sand-bluffs; on pieces of wreckage, driftwood, and fish-boxes. The birds even attempted to build on the slender stakes supporting the fish-nets! In all of these varied nesting-sites, however, it will be noted that at least the suggestion of an eminence has probably first attracted the Osprey to the spot. Similarly, many of the ground nests are found to be very close to some prominent object—itself incapable of supporting the nest—such as a post, a notice-sign, a telegraph pole, or a pointed stone. The high, shelving beach, with its tempting piles of seawood, probably appealed to some of the first ground-nesters as an "eminence," and their offspring have come back and chosen a similar nesting-site. At all events, in 1910 there was a succession of no less than twenty-two nests at intervals varying from eleven yards to three hundred yards along the beach, on the south-westerly side of Gardiner's Island.

The eggs of the osprey are the handsomest of all the hawks' eggs; they show considerable variation, and the coloring is very rich; a selected series of them is a great addition to an egg collector's cabinet. I shall never forget my envious enthusiasm when a rival boy collector showed me the first fish hawk's eggs I had ever seen. Nor could I ever forget the peculiar pungent odor that clings to these eggs after many years in the cabinet, a fragrant reminder of many hard climbs.   1936

CARACARAS AND FALCONS
Family Falconidae

CARACARA   *Caracara cheriway*

In Texas its haunts according to George Finlay Simmons (1925) are

open pasturelands and prairies, generally where dotted by oak mottes or crossed by creeks and arroyos narrowly skirted with trees. Mesquite forests typical of the Rio Grande Coastal Plain from Austin southward. Open divides in the wooded mountainous country. Prefers prairies to wooded country, never breeding in tall trees in wooded bottoms. Wanders along streams into the wooded hills.

Herbert W. Brandt says in his notes:

Judging from past accounts, the caracara is on the rapid decline in southern Texas. On four trips from San Antonio to the coast we saw only one bird, where formerly, the ranchers told us, they were plentiful. We found a few breeding on the King ranch, making their abode about the various windmills. These birds always have the male lookout stationed conspicuously near the nest, and he flushes when the intruder is still some distance away. Every nest we examined was composed entirely of broomweed, and was usually deep, resembling an inverted Mexican hat. The nests are often very bulky and show successive layers. Two-thirds of the sets observed consisted of three eggs, while the remainder numbered two. An interesting nest was found in a huisache tree standing alone in the center of a large, wet, grassy meadow. In the tree was a caracara's nest and 50 nests of the great-tailed grackle,[1] seven of which were crowded under that of the caracara.

The caracara shares with the vultures the habit of feeding on carrion, which probably constitutes a large portion of its food. These birds often gather about the slaughterhouses in large numbers with the vultures, to feed on the offal that is thrown out. They also feed on any dead mammal, large or small, bird, or reptile that they can find. They are worthy of protection as good scavengers, as well as destroyers of many harmful rodents and insects, as they hunt and kill many small animals.

Mr. [S. A.] Grimes sent me a photograph showing the shells of forty-three mud turtles and a box tortoise, the head of a large snapping turtle, a small garfish, and the remains of a bass that he picked up in a few minutes around a caracara's nest that held large young. Twelve heads of small turtles were found in the nest. I wrote to him that I was curious to know how the birds carried the turtles and how they extracted the meat. He responded by spending two hours in a blind near a nest and watching how it was done; he writes to me that he—

saw the old birds make five trips to the nest with food for the young. Each of these times, and on three other occasions that I have seen food brought to the nest, the object was brought in the bill. Only one turtle was brought to the nest while I was watching. It was a 5-inch mud turtle, and was held by the edge of the shell, as the bird sailed in with it. The old caracara did not merely leave the turtle at the nest for the young (which were as large as the parent bird) to help themselves; but stayed there 35 minutes, removing the animal from its shell bit by bit and feeding the pieces to her offspring. At a distance of 100 feet I could plainly hear the bird's mandibles clack against the turtle's shell, as she held it down with her feet and strained and pulled at what it contained. After 35 minutes the old caracara turned the remains of the turtle over to the young birds.　　　　　　　　　　　　　　　　　　　　　　　1937

GYRFALCON　　*Falco rusticolus*

F. r. obsoletus　(Black Gyrfalcon)

This, the darkest of all the gyrfalcons, was formerly supposed to be confined to Labrador in the breeding season; but now it is generally conceded to be the dominant American form, breeding all across the northern part of the continent from Labrador to northern Alaska.

---

[1] As the subspecies *mexicanus* of the Boat-tailed Grackle was formerly called.

Mr. [L. M.] Turner's notes contain the following account of a nest he examined near Fort Chimo, Ungava, on May 22, 1883:

The "Chapel" is an immense rock some 300 feet above the surrounding rocks, and gradually slopes upward to the north end, which is almost precipitous and absolutely inaccessible. The eastern side is more abrupt, being in places over 200 feet almost perpendicular. Here are several ledges on which these hawks have built their nests for many years. On April 7, 1883, I observed beneath the nest site first selected a number of sticks and other refuse lying on the snow below, as if the situation had been subjected to a rearrangement or cleansing process; such material as appeared unnecessary was rejected and cast over the side of the ledge. The site of this nest was a narrow ledge of rock, which projected from the main wall and embraced an area of not over three superficial feet. Here was an accumulation of spruce and larch twigs and branches of various sizes imbedded in what appeared to be the accumulated debris of many generations. Among this a few grass seeds had found enough soil to enable them to send forth a rank growth which was now appearing. The mass or accumulation was about 10 inches deep and covered nearly the entire surface of the ledge, heaped up immediately under the new nest, forming an irregularly truncated cone of matter on which the nest was placed. In front of it huge icicles stood and joined with the slightly projecting roof above the ledge. Some of these ice columns were 2 or 3 inches thick and 4 inches wide. They formed an icy palisade around the edge of the nest and permitted approach to the interior only by a narrow space, or doorway, next to the main wall of rock. I was compelled to detach the ice before I could reach the four eggs which I saw within the nest. The nest was composed of a few twigs and branches of larch and spruce, irregularly disposed on only the outer side of the rim of the nest to prevent the eggs from rolling out, forming only a semicircular protection, while the rear portion was a part of the bare rock of the ledge. Below the twigs were the remains of former nests. Some of the sticks were so rotten that they would not support their weight when held by one end. The eggs were placed nearly touching each other.   1937

PRAIRIE FALCON   *Falco mexicanus*   (Skinner)

To use the wording of the hawking brotherhood, this is a noble bird, met with far out over the wild, lonely foothills, over the unsettled plains and prairies, and even over the deserts of the Southwest. It is strong, bold, and a fearless fighter, but wary, shy, and secretive where it has been subjected to molestation.

Dawson (1923) says:

The assaults of an angry Falcon are really dangerous. Even when the earliest efforts are discouraged by a show of sticks or stones, it is decidedly disconcerting to feel the rush of air from a passing falcon-wing upon your hatless pate, or to mark the instant change in pitch from the shrill uproar of impending doom to the guttural notes of baffled retreat. The Falcon has a nasty temper at best, and if she dare not vent her spite on you, she will fall upon the first wight who crosses her path. Woe betide the luckless Barn Owl who flaps forth from his den to learn the cause of the disturbance. I have seen such bowled into the sage in a trice. . . . At such times also the Raven is put on trial for his life. In spite of their close association, there is evidently an ancient grudge between these birds. . . . The Raven is an adept at wing-play himself, and the Falcon's thunderbolt is met with a deft evasion. . . . But the Raven takes no pleasure in it. His eyes start with terror, and while he has no time for utterance himself, the distressed cries of his mate proclaim the danger he is in.

The close association of Falcon and Raven at nesting time is the strangest element in the lives of both of them. To be sure, their requirements of nesting sites are similar; but it is more than that which induces the birds to nest within a hundred yards of each other in the same canyon, when neighboring or distant canyons offering as excellent sites are empty. So constant indeed is this association that when one finds the Raven's nest, he says, "Well, now, where is the Falcon's?" Of the entire number of Ravens' nests which came under my observation in one year, seven were thus associated with nests of the Falcon in the same canyon, and the remaining three were within a quarter of a mile of Falcons' in neighboring canyons separated by a single ridge. And it is impossible to tell from the stage of incubation which bird is the follower. . . . The only guess we dare hazard is that both birds reap advantages of warning in case of hostile approach. Concurrent with this association is the annual, or at least occasional, shifting of sites on the part of both species.   1937

PEREGRINE FALCON   *Falco peregrinus*

Joseph A. Hagar, Massachusetts State ornithologist, has been very active for the past two years, 1935 and 1936, in protecting the duck hawk in this State.

He contributes the following interesting account of the spring and courtship activities:

Having fed, the hawks are likely to sit quietly for some little time, occasionally wailing to each other, preening their feathers, perhaps lazily stretching first one wing and then the other. At length the tercel[1] starts off his perch and begins to soar and swoop about the cliff, describing a series of figure-eights in the air, sometimes in a horizontal, sometimes a vertical, plane. At times he lights on little shelves and *wichews;* again he returns to his tree and wails, or perhaps he soars higher and higher in the air, farther and farther out across the valley, until at last he shuts his wings to his sides and plunges down in a mile-long swoop that brings him back to

[1] The male.

the cliff. Sometimes the falcon[1] accompanies him on these flights, but for the most part she is distinctly passive. The culmination of these flight displays depends much on the weather, but eventually the patient watcher will see an exhibition of flying that is literally breath-taking. I have seen it at many nests sites, but never to better advantage than one beautiful spring morning at Black Rock when a rising southerly gale was whipping along the flanks of Mount Everett. We were hidden in the woods below the south end of the cliff, and the peregrines were quite unconscious of our presence at the time; again and again the tercel started well to leeward and came along the cliff against the wind, diving, plunging, saw-toothing, rolling over and over, darting hither and yon like an autumn leaf until finally he would swoop up into the full current of air and be borne off on the gale to do it all over again. At length he tired of this, and soaring in narrow circles without any movement of his wings other than a constant small adjustment of their planes, he rose to a position 500 or 600 feet above the mountain and north of the cliff. Nosing over suddenly, he flicked his wings rapidly 15 or 20 times and fell like a thunderbolt. Wings half closed now, he shot down past the north end of the cliff, described three successive vertical loop-the-loops across its face, turning completely upside down at the top of each loop, and roared out over our heads with the wind rushing through his wings like ripping canvas. Against the background of the cliff his terrific speed was much more apparent than it would have been in the open sky. The sheer excitement of watching such a performance was tremendous; we felt a strong impulse to stand and cheer.   1937

APLOMADO FALCON   *Falco femoralis*

This handsome little falcon, with its two closely allied races, is widely distributed throughout nearly all of South and Central America. Our northern race[2] is found in Mexico, and probably in Yucatan and Guatemala; its range northward barely crosses our southwestern border in southern Texas, New Mexico, and Arizona. Its haunts are the open plains, with growths of mesquite, yucca, and cactus.

Colonel Grayson (Lawrence, 1874) writes:

This handsome little hawk may be recognized when at some distance off, while upon the wing, by its lengthened and fan-like tail. I found it not uncommon in the vicinity of Mazatlan[3] and San Blas[3] where I have shot and preserved specimens in the winter months, and with many opportunities of observing its habits. It seems to prefer a sparsely wooded country, where there are scattered trees and low bushes. In its habits I am reminded at times of the Sharp-shinned Hawk (*A. fuscus*)[4] in its stealthy

---

[1] The female.
[2] *septentrionalis;* the southern race is *fusco-caerulescens*.
[3] Sinaloa, Mexico.
[4] Now *A. striatus*.

manner of hunting for its prey beneath the thick foliage of the woods, flying near the ground, or perching in secluded places, from whence it watched, cat-like, for quails, ground doves, etc. It, however, may be seen at other times, falcon-like, boldly pursuing its prey in the open country, and the smaller species of ducks, as well as pigeons, plovers and sand-pipers, are attacked and captured on the wing by this swift flying little falcon. I am not aware that it breeds in this locality, not having seen one during the season of nidification. 1937

PIGEON HAWK   *Falco columbarius*

The flight of the pigeon hawk is swift and dashing, like that of the larger falcons. Its trim body is propelled at tremendous speed by the rapid motion of its long, pointed wings. Few, if any, birds can escape it in straightaway flight; even the black swift, one of our fastest-flying birds, has been captured by it. But the prowess of this and other falcons has been somewhat overestimated by admiring observers; it is not always successful, and it often fails to capture birds of much slower flight that are skillful at dodging. William Brewster (1925) tells of a pigeon hawk's attempt to capture a titlark [water pipit; at Lake Umbagog, Maine, October 9, 1888]:

Titlarks were particularly abundant. As I was watching not less than one hundred of them circling over the marshes, a Pigeon Hawk dashed re-peatedly into the midst of the crowded flock without capturing any of its members, although one was finally separated from the rest, and pursued for upwards of five hundred yards. The Hawk rose above and stooped down at it fully twenty times in quick succession, with lightning speed and faultless grace. More than once I thought it had it in its talons, but it always eluded them at the critical moment by an abrupt turn or twist. This he could not seem to follow, but invariably descended straight for several yards farther before checking his impetus, to mount and swoop again. All the while the Titlark was nearing, if by devious courses, a dense thicket of alders into which it plunged at length, to be seen no more.

On June 3, 1909, while we were walking along the rocky shore of Eskimo Island, Canadian Labrador, we heard the cries of a small hawk; on climbing up to the edge of the spruce woods, we saw a pigeon hawk flying about, or perching on the top of a tall spruce and flying down occasionally into the woods. I began a careful search through the dense thickets of spruces and firs, where I finally found, in a thicket of taller spruces, what looked like an old crow's nest, about fourteen feet up in a red spruce. The hawks were not in evidence, but I climbed up to the nest and was surprised to find three beautiful eggs. It had long been my hope to collect a set of pigeon hawk's eggs, and four days later I returned and gratified the wish by taking a handsome set of five eggs and photographing them in the nest. The nest was apparently a very old crow's nest that had since been used by red squirrels, as the deep cavity had been filled with rubbish, including numerous seed scales from the cones of the white spruce. It rested on horizontal branches close to the trunk of the tree and was made of rather large, dead sticks, interwoven with soft mosses; the center had been hollowed by scraping out the rubbish, which had become quite rotted; very little lining had been added, merely a few small pieces of fine twigs and lichens; a few bits of down were visible in and around the nest and on the surrounding branches. The nest measured sixteen by fourteen inches in outside and eight by eight inches in inside diameter; the outside height was nine inches and the inner cavity was two and a half inches deep.   1937

SPARROW HAWK   *Falco sparverius*   (Tyler)

What appeals to us most in this daring little falcon is its lightness and quickness—the speed of lightning compared to the crash of thunder. Whether dashing past with sweeping wing beats, each wing beat carrying it far away; whether cruising along—the tail folded thin and the sharp wings, like a three-pointed star—the wings barely trembling, like the tips of oars just touching the water; or whether soaring against the sky, with tail fanned out, the wings stretched wide, it is always ready to veer like a flash, to mount higher, to drop to the ground, or to come to rest on a little twig.

Often too—perhaps the most remarkable of its aerial accomplishments—the bird, arresting its flight through the air, hovers, facing the wind, its body tilted upward to a slight angle with the ground, its wings beating lightly and easily. Then, sometimes, with a precise adjustment to the force of the wind, it stops the beating of its wings and hangs as if suspended in complete repose and equilibrium, seeming to move not a hair's breadth from its position. It is hunting, scanning the ground for a grasshopper or a mouse.

As we pass by train through the South Atlantic States during the winter months, the sparrow hawk is one of the common birds we see from the car window. Perched on dead stumps by the side of the cottonfields, flying off from the wires along the track, hovering above the bare brown stubble, we see them again and again, nearly always alone. The traveler soon comes to associate the lone sparrow hawk, the lone red-headed woodpecker, and the flocks of mourning doves with the desolation that winter brings to the Carolinas.   1937

CHICKEN-LIKE BIRDS—ORDER GALLIFORMES

CHACHALACAS Family Cracidae

CHACHALACA *Ortalis vetula*

This curious and exceedingly interesting bird, the chachalaca, brings a touch of Central American bird life into extreme southern Texas in the lower valley of the Rio Grande.

On May 27, 1923, I spent a good long day, from before sunrise until after sunset, in the haunts of the chachalaca, with R. D. Camp, George F. Simmons, and E. W. Farmer, the last named a chachalaca hunter of many years' experience, who knows more about this curious bird than any man I have ever met. The locality to which he guided us was the famous Resaca de la Palma, where so many other observers have made the acquaintance of the chachalaca, only a few miles outside of the city of Brownsville, Texas. This and other resacas in the vicinity are the remains of old river beds of the Rio Grande, which from time to time in the past has overflowed its banks or changed its course, cutting these winding channels through the wild, open country, chaparral, or forest. Some of these channels were dry or nearly so, but most of them contained more or less water below their gently sloping grassy borders. Above the banks were dense forests of large trees, huisache, ebony, hackberry, and mesquite, with a thick undergrowth of thorny shrubbery, tangles of vines, and an occasional palmetto or palm tree. In other places almost impenetrable thickets of chaparral lined the banks, with its forbidding tangle of thorny shrubs of various kinds, numerous cactuses and yuccas. These forests and thickets were teeming with bird life.

As we entered the chaparral before sunrise we heard the warning cry of the chachalaca on all sides; the woods fairly resounded with its cries, some of which sounded like a watchman's rattle, more wooden than metallic in quality; the birds were very shy and seldom seen; occasionally we saw one, perched on some small tree top and giving its challenge or battle cry; but as soon as it realized that it was observed, it would sail down into the thicket and keep still.

According to Mr. Farmer, courtship begins about March 20 in ordinary seasons, with the *chachalac* challenge calls of the male, perched in the tops of the highest trees in the chaparral; other males answer from every direction in competition, each trying to "out-holler" the others. The females can make a similar call, but it is on a higher key and less in volume. The concert begins at about sunrise or a little before. The male's call to the female is like the challenge, but it is less harsh and ends with a soft note. The females may climb up into the tree beneath the male, but in a less conspicuous place, generally keeping under cover and answering the male in their own way chattering, talking, and scolding. After the male has "hollered himself out" in the tree, he comes down to the ground and devotes himself to the females, walking about and strutting with head erect and making a low call hardly to be heard a short distance away. If another male appears he is promptly chased off. In Mr. Farmer's experience with the birds there have always seemed to be two females to one male in this courtship. The male seems strictly impartial. 1931

GROUSE AND PTARMIGAN
Family Tetraonidae

BLUE GROUSE   *Dendragapus obscurus*

D. o. richardsoni   (Richardson's Grouse)

A. W. Anthony (1903) gives a very interesting account of the extensive spring migration of Richardson's grouse in eastern Oregon. The flight was mainly southward from the higher ridges, heavily timbered with pine and fir, to the sage-covered benches and ridges where they nest. He writes:

On the first of March 1902, when the first of the migrating grouse made their appearance along the edge of the timber north of Sparta, the snow was from 2 to 4 feet in depth, though the lower slopes near Powder River were bare and had begun to show the first signs of sprouting grass. Snow squalls and rough weather seemed to check the southward flight until about the 10th, although a few birds were passing over daily. The tracks on the snow bore ample testimony as to the manner in which the migration was made.

From the higher slopes north of Eagle Canon, the birds sailed until the rising ground brought them to the surface of the snow on the south side

of the creek, usually well above the canon. From this time until the highest
point of the ridge south was reached the journey was performed on foot.
Immediately north of Sparta lies a conical peak known as Baldy, some 700
feet above camp, the highest point in the ridge south of Eagle Creek. From
the top of Baldy, and in an area not to exceed 100 feet square, I think fully
85 percent of the grouse passing over Sparta take their departure. From
east, north and west up the steep, snowy slopes hundreds of trails led
toward the top and not one could be found leading downward. The flight
from the top of the peak was almost invariably undertaken at about sunrise
or sunset. It is only when birds are disturbed and driven from the peak that
they will attempt to cross to the southern ridge during the middle of the
day. Throughout the day grouse are arriving along the upper slopes of
Baldy, singly, in pairs, and small flocks that have perhaps formed since
the southward march began, as I think they do not winter in company, but
the flight from the peak is usually in flocks of from a dozen to a hundred
birds. Though the ridge south of Sparta is 400 feet or more lower than
the top of Baldy, it is fully a mile and a half distant in an air line, and the
flight is seldom sustained to carry the birds to the top. Usually they alight
on the snow half way up the slope, and after a few moments' rest, continue the journey on foot; those passing over in the evening spend the
night, I think, in the pines, the last of which are seen along this divide;
but those arriving in the morning soon pass on, walking down any of the
small ridges leading toward Powder River.

D. o. fuliginosus   (Sooty Grouse)

Early in March the grouse begin to migrate downward from their
winter resorts in the heavily forested mountains to their summer
homes in the more open foothills and valleys. From that time until
the last of May their haunts resound with the loud, deep-toned
hootings of the male, his challenge to his rivals, or his courtship
love notes. I once had a good opportunity to watch a fine old cock
grouse hooting and displaying under very favorable circumstances.
It was on Mercer Island in Lake Washington, within the city limits
of Seattle, where Samuel F. Rathbun had taken us to see some of
these grouse. After some difficulty in following up the ventriloquial
notes, we located the performer on a horizontal limb, close to the
trunk of an enormous Douglas fir, fully fifty feet up in the densest
part of the tree, but in plain sight; we watched him for some time
through powerful glasses and could plainly see every detail. He
turned about occasionally on the branch, facing first one way and
then the other, with drooping wings, lifting and spreading his tail.
When ready to hoot he stretched out his neck, on which two large,
white rosettes appeared, swelling open and showing the naked

sacks of dull yellow skin, which puffed out to semiglobular shape with each of the four or five hoots; the plumage of the whole neck and throat swelled out with each note and the bill opened slightly. The hooting notes were much like the soft, low notes of the great horned owl; when near at hand they seemed to be softer and less powerful, but they really have great carrying power and can be heard for a long distance. They have been likened to the noise made by blowing into the bunghole of an empty barrel or by swiftly swinging a rattan cane. They were given in groups of four to six notes each; I wrote down the full group as *hoooo, hoot, hoot, hoot, a-hoot, hoot,* or sometimes as four, five, or six straight *hoots,* or as different combinations of the above notes. I recorded the intervals between the hootings as varying from twelve to thirty-six seconds.

During the intervals of silence the bird assumed a normal pose, or strutted about. Dawson (1909) says:

> The hooting, or grunting notes, of this Grouse are among the lowest tones of Nature's thorobase, being usually about C of the First Octave, but ranging from E Flat down to B Flat of the Contra Octave.   1931

SPRUCE GROUSE   *Canachites canadensis* (Townsend)

C. c. canadensis   (Hudsonian Spruce Grouse)

The Hudsonian spruce grouse thrives best in regions where man is absent. In fact it remains so woefully ignorant of the destructive nature of the human animal that, unlike its cousin, the ruffed grouse, it rarely learns to run or fly away, but allows itself to be shot, clubbed, or noosed, and, in consequence, has earned for itself the proud title of "fool hen." As a result, wherever man appears, the spruce grouse rapidly diminishes in numbers, and, in the vicinity of villages or outlying posts, is not to be found. It is a bird of the northern wilderness, of thick and tangled swamps, and of spruce forests, where the ground is deep in moss and where the delicate vines of the snowberry and twinflower clamber over moss-covered stubs and fallen, long-decayed tree trunks.

The chief characteristic of the Hudsonian spruce grouse is its unsuspicious character, which amounts, indeed, to stupidity. This is illustrated by an experience of Lucien M. Turner, who says:

> I once shot 11 and did not move a yard in distance to do so. The people of Labrador employ a method which they term "slipping," i. e., a slip noose on a long pole which enables the holder to slip the noose over the heads of the birds and jerk them down. One who is expert in this method rarely fails to obtain all the birds within reach.

D. G. Elliot (1897) says:

I have seen birds push this noose aside with their bills without changing their position, when through awkwardness, or unsteadiness of hand on account of a long reach, the noose had touched the bird's head but had not slipped over it.

I have known a botanist to kill an adult grouse by throwing his short-handled collecting pick at it.

The plumage of spruce grouse often makes them difficult to distinguish from their surroundings, and if their tameness depends on this protective coloration, they are overconfident, for, in a setting of reindeer lichen or snow, or an open branch of a spruce, they are very conspicuous. When flushed they generally fly only a few yards or even feet, and, alighting in trees, they continually thrust the head and neck now this way, now that, and appear to be blindly trying to discover what has disturbed them. As a rule the flight is noiseless, or a slight sound only is heard, but at times they rise with a loud whir of wing beats.   1931

RUFFED GROUSE   *Bonasa umbellus*

During the first warm days of early spring the wanderer in our New England woods is gladdened and thrilled by one of the sweetest sounds of that delightful season, the throbbing heart, as it were, of awakening spring. On the soft, warm, still air there comes to his eager ears the sound of distant, muffled drumming, slow and deliberate at first, but accelerating gradually until it ends in a prolonged, rolling hum. The sun is shining with all its genial warmth through the leafless woods, thawing out the woodland pools, where the hylas are already peeping, and warming the carpet of fallen leaves, from which the mourning cloak butterflies are rising from their winter sleep. Other insects are awing, the early spring flowers are lifting up their heads, and all nature is awakening. The breast of the sturdy ruffed grouse swells with the springtime urge, as he seeks some moss-covered log, a fallen monarch of the forest, or perhaps a rock on which to mount and drum out his challenge to all rivals and his love call to his prospective mate. If we are fortunate enough to find his throne, on which he has left many a sign of previous occupancy, we may see the monarch of all he surveys in all his proud glory.

Dr. Arthur A. Allen, who has made some careful studies of the display and drumming of the ruffed grouse and shown some wonderful photographs of them, has contributed, at my request, a very full account of the whole performance.

The first one or two wing beats are almost silent and are given while the bird is in a nearly normal horizontal position, the wings striking downward and inward. The bird's tail is being lowered against the log during this preliminary beat or beats. Then abruptly he stands erect with his tail against the log, wings drooping at his sides and appears to throw his 'shoulders' back. This might give the impression that the wings were struck behind the back, because the forward stroke of the wing follows so instantaneously that the eye scarcely perceives it, and it is given with such force and the wings come back to the normal position so quickly that the entire action registers on only one frame of the motion-picture film having an exposure of approximately one-fiftieth of a second. Between the 'thumps' the wings of the bird register on the film with scarcely a blur representing the intervals between thumps. The varying tempo of the intervals between thumps has been noticed by all observers and as registered on the film is as follows, each number being the number of pictures or the number of sixteenths of a second between thumps:

5-6-8-8-6-5-5-4-4-3-3-3-2-2-1-2-1-1-1-1-1-1-000000000000000000000-1.

If one now examines the series of pictures he will see that not once is the back blurred, as it would be if the wings struck behind the back, and that wherever the wings have moved with sufficient rapidity to cause a compression of the air and resulting sound, they are registered forward and upward. This then is the effective sound-producing stroke of the wing—*forward and upward*—not outward and upward as stated by Sawyer—more like his inward and forward, which he says is silent or nearly so.

Moreover, if one watches the tail of the grouse during the drumming performance, he will see it become more and more flattened against the log, for 'action and reaction are equal and opposite in direction' and the forward-upward stroke of the wings tends to drive the bird backward and downward on its tail. The reaction that follows cessation of drumming is even more clear to the observer, for always, upon the completion of the drum, the bird pitches slightly forward and the tail lifts from the log as if it were a spring under compression; when the pressure is suddenly released by the cessation of drumming, the tail throws the bird forward and upward and is itself carried upward by the impetus given the bird.   1931

WILLOW PTARMIGAN   *Lagopus lagopus*

The willow ptarmigan, with its various so-called subspecies, is of circumpolar distribution, inhabiting the arctic or subarctic regions of both the North American and Eurasian Continents.

When the snow covers the tundra so deeply that no food or shelter can be found there, the ptarmigan are forced to migrate into the interior valleys, river bottoms, and creek beds, where they can find shelter among the willows, alders, or spruces and can feed on the bugs and twigs of these trees or such berries and fruit as still remain above the snow. They often congregate at that season, and, particularly when migrating, in enormous numbers. Mr. [H.] Brandt says that, where the railroad crosses the Continental Divide in Alaska, he saw large flocks arising "like snow drifts in motion, alongside the snorting engines, and whirling away over the great white hills."

In winter the ptarmigan's feet are thickly covered with long, hair-like feathers, resembling the foot of a hare, which serve as snowshoes and enable the bird to walk on soft snow. Sandys (1904) writes:

And Nature, as if realizing the perils of the ptarmigan asleep, has taught it to plunge beneath the cold drifts to escape the cold, and to *fly at*, not *walk to*, the chosen drift, so that there will be no telltale trail for some keen nose to follow to the sleeping-place. And this the bird invariably does, going at speed and butting its way into the snow, leaving never a print to betray its retreat, from which it *flies* in the morning. The game of life and death is interestingly played up North—where the weak white snow-shoers are ever hiding from the strong white snow-shoers forever searching over a field of baffling ice-bound white.   1931

ROCK PTARMIGAN *Lagopus mutus*

L. m. rupestris (Rock Ptarmigan)

[Lucien M.] Turner says [of the Rock Ptarmigan] in his notes:

Their flight is rapid, and when flying with a stiff wind they require the quickest shot to stop them. The beat of the wing is so rapid that it is scarcely discernible, and when the bird is sailing the somewhat decurved wings are held almost motionless as it rolls from side to side. The direction of flight is always in a straight line, rising only sufficiently to clear a patch of trees or intervening ridge, the latter at times passed over only by a few inches in height, to the plain or valley beyond. Sometimes they will fly more than a mile before alighting and at other times only a few rods, depending altogether on the character of the weather. If it is a cold, blustering day with much snow drifting or falling, these birds dislike to take flight, and by using a slight amount of discretion the birds of an entire flock may be all secured, but if it is calm and cold, or warm, they take flight and at this time are rarely approached within shooting distance. Warm, damp, weather with gusty wind is best suited for hunting this ptarmigan.

Turner describes the courtship of the rock ptarmigan in his notes as follows:

The mating season begins in May, and during this period the male acts in the strangest manner to gain the affection of his chosen mate. He does not launch high in air and croak like the willow ptarmigan, but runs around his prospective bride with tail spread, wings either dragging like those of the common turkey, or else his head and neck stretched out, and breast in contact with the ground, pushing himself in this manner by the feet, which are extended behind. The male at this time ruffles every feather of his body, twists his neck in various positions, and the supraorbital processes are swollen and erect. He utters a most peculiar sound, something like a growling *kurr-kurr;* as the passion of the display increases the bird performs the most astonishing antics, such as leaping in the air without effort of wings, rolling over and over, acting withal is if beside himself with ardor.

The males engage in most desperate battles; the engagement lasts for hours or until one is utterly exhausted, the feathers of head, neck, and breast strewing the ground. A maneuver is for the pursued bird to lead the other off a great distance and suddenly fly back to the female, who sits or feeds as unconcerned as it is possible for a bird to do. She acts thoroughly the most heartless coquette, while he is a most passionately devoted lover. He would rather die than forsake her side, and often places himself between the hunter and her, uttering notes of warning for her to escape, while attention is drawn to him who is the more conspicuous.

L. m. dixoni   (Dixon's Ptarmigan)

Dixon's ptarmigan is one of the many dark-colored races so characteristic of the humid coast belt of the northwest.

Alfred M. Bailey (1927) gives us two good pictures of Dixon's ptarmigan in its autumn habitat [near Juneau, Alaska]:

During October there appeared a wealth of small birds, and many Ptarmigan were seen and collected. The vegetation was in the height of its "autumn glory," and a peculiar "lily pad," which flourishes abundantly, colored the hills an intense yellow above timber line, while still higher, among the piled boulders, there was a small ever-green growth upon which the Ptarmigan were feeding. A few were found in such a site, and some of them were extremely wild. The Ptarmigan in Granite Creek [southeastern Alaska] were taken among the boulders and slide rock on the summit of the highest mountains surrounding the valley, at an altitude of over 4,000 feet. There was absolutely no vegetation. That they are well named "Rock Ptarmigan" there can be no doubt after noting their habit of sunning themselves upon the tops of large boulders; one rested upon a little overhanging ledge which left a sheer drop to the valley floor far below. Several small flocks were seen flying about like so many Doves. They raised from the mountain on which we were hunting and sailed across the valley to the foot of a hanging glacier. One band flew over me and I tried to drop a bird on our narrow ridge, but the tumbling Ptarmigan sailed on into space and dropped at least 1,500 feet to the valley floor.

L. m. sanfordi   (Sanford's Ptarmigan)

Although I described and named this race myself (1912), in honor of my friend Dr. Leonard C. Sanford, who cooperated with me in organizing our expedition to the Aleutian Islands, I must confess that it is only slightly differentiated from the Adak ptarmigan [*L. m. chamberlaini*]. We all noticed a difference when our birds were collected, and when we laid our series of about forty specimens of *sanfordi* beside nearly as many of *chamberlaini*, it was easy to see that the Tanaga birds were appreciably paler in color than the Adak birds. The Tanaga birds are therefore the lightest in color of any of the Aleutian ptarmigan and have the finest vermiculations.

We landed on Tanaga Island on June 25, 1911, and spent only half a day on shore; so far as I know, no one had ever collected birds on this interesting island before; we found it very rich in bird life, and it is a great pity that we were not able to spend more time there. Back of the sandy beach on which we landed was a series of sand hills or dunes, covered with long grass, and beyond these was a flat, alluvial plain or tundra, with one large and several small streams flowing through it from the mountains farther inland, and dotted with a number of small ponds and wet meadows. Northern phalaropes were breeding commonly among the ponds and meadows, and Aleutian sandpipers[1] were abundant, indulging in their flight songs and nesting on the little knolls and hummocks on the tundra, where a brood of downy young was found. At the base of a steep hillside a colony of fork-tailed petrels was beginning to breed. The ptarmigan were tamer and more abundant here than on any of the other islands that we visited; we shot more than forty in one afternoon. They were commonest on the rolling, grassy hillocks and grassy hills on the tundra. They flushed at short range, did not fly far, and were easily shot.   1931

WHITE-TAILED PTARMIGAN   *Lagopus leucurus*

The white-tailed ptarmigan is an alpine species, a permanent resident in the high mountains, above timber line during most of the year at least. In the southern portion of its habitat it ranges from ten thousand to fourteen thousand feet altitude and somewhat lower farther north.

[1] As the subspecies *couesi* of the Rock Sandpiper was formerly called.

Illustrating the perfectly concealing coloration of the bird on its open nest, Evan Lewis (1904) writes:

On reaching timber-line a Junco was seen building, and a search was made for a loose stone to mark the spot for a photograph when the set was complete. In the search I was just about to put my hand on a Ptarmigan when I saw what it was. I then made two exposures with the small camera and left the camera on top of a large rock to mark the spot, the nest being three steps and one foot due south from the mark. I went to the cabin at the lake and got the large camera and tripod. When I returned I took three rather shorter steps, as I supposed, and looked for the bird or its nest. For ten minutes I looked over the ground foot by foot. I could not believe my own eyes that the bird was not there, yet I could not see her. At last I was about to return to the mark and step the ground over again, when a reflection from the bird's eye showed her to me just one foot from where I was standing.

Mrs. Bailey's (1918) account of the behavior of mother and young is worth quoting, as follows:

Listening, I caught it again—the softest possible call of a mother ptarmigan! There she stood, only a few feet from me, hard to see except when in motion, so well was she disguised by her buffy ground color finely streaked with gray. A round-bodied little grouse with a small head, she was surrounded by a brood of downy chicks, evidently just hatched, as their bills still held the sharp projection for pipping the shell. Preoccupied with the task of looking after her little family, as I talked reassuringly to her, she ignored my presence. Nothing must hurry the unaccustomed little feet, nothing must interfere with their needed rest. Talking softly she gradually drew the brood in under her motherly wings and sat there only a few yards from me, half closing one eye in the sun and acting oblivious to all the world. Once the downy head of a chick appeared between the fluffed-out feathers of her breast, and once she preened her wing so she showed the white quills remaining from the white plumage of winter.

Her bill opened and her throat palpitated as if she were thirsty, as she sat brooding the young, and I imagined that the last hours of hatching high above water had been long and trying to the faithful mother. But though water—clear cold mountain brooks—were below, no need of her own could make her careless of her little ones. Keeping up a motherly rhythmic *cluck-uk-uk, cluck-uk-uk,* interlarded with a variety of tender mother notes, she led them down by almost imperceptible stages, slowly, gently, carefully, raising a furry foot and sliding it along a little at a time, creeping low over the ground with even tread, picking about as she went, while the little toddlers gradually learned the use of their feet. Like a brood of downy chickens, some were more yellowish, some browner than others, but they all had dark lines on head and body giving them a well-defined color pattern. Peeping like little chickens, while their mother waited patiently for them they toddled around, trying to hop over tiny stones and saving themselves from going on their bills by stretching out wee finny wings. As chickens just out of the shell instinctively pick up food from the ground, they gave little jabs at the fuzzy anthers of the dryas, little knowing that pollen was the best food they could find, a rich protein food from which the bees make bee bread to feed their larvae. 1931

GREATER PRAIRIE CHICKEN *Tympanuchus cupido* (Gross)

T. c. pinnatus (Greater Prairie Chicken)

The prairie chicken ranks first among the game birds of the prairies of our Middle West. It is to the prairie what the ruffed grouse is to the wooded sections of the country. As intensive agriculture pushed to all sections of the range of the prairie chicken and as interest in hunting increased, this fine game bird at one time seemed in grave danger of following the course taken by the heath hen, to extinction as a game bird. In fact, it is gone from much of its former range, and its original numbers have been greatly reduced in practically the entire area of its distribution.

Prairie chickens, in common with other grouse, go through definite cycles of numbers. The problem of fluctuations in numbers of various species of wild life is not yet definitely solved.

The weather condition during the nesting season, especially during the height of the hatching period, is so important that it is frequently the determining factor in the number of young birds available for the next hunting season. A series of torrential cloud-bursts followed by long, cold, rainy spells during the first two weeks of June will cause hundreds of broods to perish.

During severe winters, especially when deep snows cover the ground, the birds are severely pressed to obtain enough food.

One of the major problems involved in the conservation of the prairie chicken is the menacing fires that have swept the prairie regions during the nesting season of the birds. A fire at this time will destroy hundreds of nesting birds and their nests and eggs and in the course of a few hours undo the work of years of conservation work. Fires in fall destroy quantities of prairie-chicken food and the much-needed cover, without which the birds are left exposed to predators.

Intensive hunting has done much toward decimating the numbers of prairie chickens. The automobile and the fine modern roads have all been in favor of the hunter and against the birds.

Predators in their relation to game birds are important, but the value of vermin control is frequently overestimated. The wholesale killing of all hawks and owls, for example, should be rigidly avoided, for in the past this practice has actually acted as a boomerang to the objective of conservation of game birds.

Diseases and parasites of birds have not been well known in the past, but they are now becoming to be recognized as important factors in the life of our game birds. Under ordinary conditions, diseases and parasites may be of minor importance, but just as soon as the vitality and normal resistance of the birds are lowered by a series of adverse conditions, such as severe weather and scarcity of food, diseases and parasites manifest themselves and become of prime importance. It is the exceptional bird that is not parasitized, and hence this menace is ever present. There is also danger of infectious diseases, such as blackhead, which has been found to affect the prairie chicken and which figured in the decline of the heath hen. It is highly probable that the cycles in the grouse population are primarily dependent on some disease, either in itself or in combination with other factors. The evidence points to the conclusion that the vast majority of the parasites and diseases of our game birds have been introduced through poultry and exotic game birds.

T. c. cupido   (Heath Hen)

The heath hen is among the first of the American birds to be mentioned in the writings of the early colonists who came to our shores.

William Wood (1635) in his New England Prospect writes as follows: "Heathcockes and Partridges be common: he that is husband, and will be stirring betime, may kill halfe dozen in a morning."

Thomas Nuttall (1832) wrote as follows:

According to information I have received from Governor Winthrop, they were so common on the ancient brushy site of Boston, that laboring people or servants stipulated with their employers not to have Heath Hen brought to table oftener than a few times a week.

The birds served as a valuable source of food, and because they were easily tricked and killed they were exterminated at an early date in the more accessible areas, and soon after 1840 were entirely gone from the mainland of Massachusetts and the State of Connecticut. The birds persisted for a longer time on Long Island, and a few continued to battle for existence on the plains of New Jersey and favorable places among the pines and scrub oaks of the Pocono Mountains in Northampton County, Pa. Since 1870 the surviving members of this interesting race have been restricted to Martha's Vineyard Island, off the southeastern coast of Massachusetts.

In 1890 William Brewster (1890) made a careful census and at that time estimated that there were two hundred birds on the entire island. Kentwood (1896) stated that there were less than one hundred birds in 1896. By the beginning of the twentieth century the birds had reached a very low ebb in their existence. The year 1908 witnessed the establishment of a reservation in the midst of the breeding range where the birds could be protected from poachers and predators by competent wardens.

When the reservation was established in 1908 there were only about fifty heath hens, but as a direct result of the efficient protection the birds increased very rapidly and by 1915-16 they were to be found in all parts of Martha's Vineyard with the exception of Gay Head, the extreme western end of the island. It was then possible to flush a flock of three hundred or more birds almost any day from the corn and clover plots planted on the reservation for the birds. An estimate made by William Day, then superintendent of the reservation, indicates there were probably two thousand birds on the island. This was a great triumph for those who had encouraged and fostered the reservation, but unfortunately success was not long-lived.

In spite of the unusual precautions taken to prevent the spread of fire, a terrific conflagration broke out during a gale on May 12, 1916, which swept the greater part of the interior of the island, destroying brooding birds and their nests and eggs, as well as the food and cover of the birds on more than twenty square miles, right in the heart of the breeding area of the heath hen. This fire undid in a few hours the accomplishment of many years of work. A hard winter followed the fire, and in the midst of this came an unprecedented flight of goshawks, which further decimated the number of birds. The net result of this catastrophe was an amazing decrease in the number of heath hens, which according to official estimates was reduced to less than one hundred and fifty birds, most of which were males.

In 1920 many birds were found dead or in a weak and helpless condition, indicating that disease was then exacting its toll.

The heath hen continued to decrease in numbers, and by 1925 it was apparent that they had reached their lowest ebb in history.

The 1927 spring census revealed but thirteen birds, only two of which were females. During the fall of 1928 only two birds were seen and after December 8 but one was reported. This bird was photographed from a blind on April 2, 1929, at the farm of James Green located on the State highway between Edgartown and West Tisbury.

It was seen at irregular intervals during the winter, and after the first warm days of March it appeared daily at the traditional booming field at the Green farm. The bird was studied and photographs were taken again at the time of the annual census in March-April 1930. The lone bird continued to appear at the Green farm during April and May, where it was observed by many ornithologists and bird lovers who journeyed to the island to get a glimpse of the famous last bird. In October it resumed its daily visits to the open field on the Green farm and at the time of this writing (November 15, 1930) was still alive. It is the first time in the history of ornithology that a bird has been studied in its normal environment down to the very last individual.

(During the fall of 1931, this lone survivor disappeared.)   1931

LESSER PRAIRIE CHICKEN
Tympanuchus pallidicinctus

Judged from Mr. Colvin's published accounts (1914) these birds were wonderfully abundant in earlier days, as a few quotations from Mr. Colvin's writings will show.

Two miles farther along we came to Ed Ward's [southwestern Kansas]. He informed us that there were a "few" chickens in a cane and kaffir corn field a quarter of a mile east. We flushed several birds from the tall bunch grass just before we reached the field, which were promptly despatched; however, in the field things became more lively. Such a sight I have never seen before nor since. Chickens were flushing everywhere, and droves of fifty to a hundred would take down the corn rows, sounding like a moving avalanche as they touched the blades of corn. Still birds were quite wary, and the only good shots were to be had over the dog.

As we thrashed back and forth across the grain field, the chickens arose in flocks of fifty to five hundred, and generally sixty to eighty yards distant, making shooting difficult. The majority of the birds, after being flushed, would fly back into the field, while some would go to the bunch-grass covered hills half a mile away. Mr. Ward and I estimated that there were from thirty-five hundred to four thousand chickens in this one field, a sight never to be forgotten.

A few years later, hunting over the same ground, he found the chickens much diminished in numbers; his thoughts are expressed as follows:

Gathering our duds together, we started for our long journey home. A few clouds, fringed with gold, freckled the western sky, and over all a red mantle was cast while the sun slowly lowered to the horizon. My mind went back to the events of the day and to the time when the chickens were more plentiful, and I realized with a shudder that we were nearing the sunset life of the king of upland game birds. But the decrease in their numbers is not due so much to the gunners, as gunners are few per capita in those parts, but is due largely to the cutting up of this vast wilderness into small farms. The bunch-grass land can not be mowed for hay; therefore, in such land the chickens have found an ideal home in which to rear their young and harbor themselves during the winter. Such land is soon destroyed by cultivation and small pastures. With the advancement of civilization the flocks scatter and become depleted.   1931

SHARP-TAILED GROUSE   *Pedioecetes phasianellus*

The courtship performance of the sharp-tailed grouse is no less interesting than that of other grouse. It is quite similar to that of the prairie chicken and the heath hen; perhaps not quite so grotesque but more animated. These birds have favorite spots, generally small knolls, to which they resort for this purpose every spring; these are know as "dancing hills."

Dr. D. G. Elliot (1897) gives a very good account of the "dancing," as follows:

In the early spring, in the month of April, when perhaps in many parts of their habitat in the northern regions the snow still remains upon the ground, the birds, both males and females, assemble at some favorite place just as day is breaking, to go through a performance as curious as it is eccentric. The males, with ruffled feathers, spread tails, expanded air sacs on the neck, heads drawn toward the back, and drooping wings (in fact, the whole body puffed out as nearly as possible into the shape of a ball on two stunted supports), strut about in circles, not all going the same way, but passing and crossing each other in various angles. As the "dance" proceeds the excitement of the birds increases, they stoop toward the ground, twist and turn, make sudden rushes forward, stamping the ground with short quick beats of the feet, leaping over each other in their frenzy, then lowering their heads, exhaust the air in the sacs, producing a hollow sound that goes reverberating through the still air of the breaking day. Suddenly they become quiet, and walk about like creatures whose sanity is unquestioned, when some male again becomes possessed and starts off on a rampage, and the "attack" from which he suffers becomes infectious and all the other birds at once give evidences of having taken the same disease, which then proceeds with a regular development to the usual conclusion. As the sun gets well above the horizon, and night's shadows have all been hurried away, the antics of the birds cease, the booming no longer resounds over the prairie, and the Grouse scatter in search of food, and in pursuit of their daily avocation. While this performance is always to be seen in the spring, it is not unusually indulged in for a brief turn in the autumn, and while it may be considered as essentially a custom of the breeding season, yet like the drumming of the Ruffed Grouse, it may be regarded also as an exhibition of the birds' vigor and vitality, indulged in at periods of the year even when the breeding season has long passed.

1931

SAGE GROUSE   *Centrocercus urophasianus*

The range of the sage grouse is limited to the arid plains of the Northwestern States and the southwestern Provinces, where the sagebrush (*Artemisia tridentata* and other species) grows; hence it is well named sage grouse or cock of the plains. Its range stops where the sagebrush is replaced by greasewood in the more southern deserts. Like the prong-horned antelope, another child of the arid plains, it has disappeared from much of its former range, as the country became more thickly settled and these large birds were easily shot.

Much has been written about the courtship of the sage grouse, which is the most spectacular performance indulged in by any of the grouse. Frank Bond (1900) writes:

During the months of April and May the Sage Cocks are usually found in small flocks of a half dozen or more, stalking about with tails erect and spread after the manner of the strutting turkey cock, but I have never seen the Grouse dragging their wings upon the ground, turkey fashion. Nor have I ever found a wing of a Sage Cock in this or any other season, which exhibited the slightest wearing away of the primaries. Instead of dragging its wings upon the ground the Sage Cock will enormously inflate the air sacks of the neck until the whole neck and breast is balloon-like in appearance, then stooping forward, almost the entire weight of the body is thrown upon the distended portion and the bird slides along on the bare ground or short grass for some distance, the performance being concluded by the expulsion of the air from the sacks with a variety of chuckling, cackling or rumbling sounds. This performance is continued probably daily, during the pairing and nesting season, and of course the feathers are worn away by the constant friction.

Dr. Sylvester D. Judd (1905*a*) says:

The feeding habits of the sage grouse are peculiar, and its organs of digestion are unlike those of other grouse. The stomach is not differentiated into a powerful grinding gizzard, but is a thin, weak, membraneous bag, resembling the stomach of a raptorial bird. Such an organ is evidently designed for the digestion of soft food, and we find that the bulk of the sage grouse's diet consists of leaves and tender shoots.

In the days of their abundance they used to gather in immense packs in fall. Bendire (1892) quotes the following from notes sent to him by Dr. George Bird Grinnell:

In western Wyoming the Sage Grouse packs in September and October. In October, 1886, when camped just below a high bluff on the border of Bates Hole, in Wyoming, I saw great numbers of these birds, just after sunrise, flying over my camp to the little spring which oozed out of the bluff 200 yards away. Looking up from the tent at the edge of the bluff above us, we could see projecting over it the heads of hundreds of the birds, and, as those standing there took flight, others stepped forward to occupy their places. The number of Grouse which flew over the camp reminded me of the oldtime flights of Passenger Pigeons that I used to see when I was a boy. Before long the narrow valley where the water was, was a moving mass of gray. I have no means whatever of estimating the number of birds which I saw, but there must have been thousands of them.   1931

QUAILS AND PHEASANTS
Family Phasianidae

BOBWHITE   *Colinus virginianus*

The most characteristic and best-known note of the bobwhite is the spring call, or challenge note, of the male, from which its name is derived. It is heard all through the breeding season in summer. It is subject to considerable individual variation and has been variously interpreted as *bob-white, more-wet, no-more-wet, peas-most-ripe, buck-wheat-ripe, wha-whoi, sow-more-wheat,* and others. This call is subject to considerable variation; the number of the preliminary *bobs* varies from one to two or rarely three; sometimes these first syllables are entirely omitted and we hear only the loud *white,* which again may be shortened to *whit.* Aretas A. Saunders, who has made a study of the voice of the bobwhite, has sent me some elaborate notes on it. He says that the pitch in this call, counting all his records, varies from G″ to F‴′, one tone less than an octave. One three-note call covered this whole range but the two-note calls generally begin on A″, most commonly have the *white* note begin a tone higher, and slur up a single tone or a minor third. Sometimes the second note gives more accent and time to the first part of the slur, and sometimes the lower note of the slur is on the same pitch as the first note. The least range of pitch is shown in a two-note call beginning on C, starting the slur on C♯, and ending on D. What he calls the slur comes, of course, in the last, or *white,* note.

The *bobwhite* note is almost invariably given while the bird is standing on some favorite perch.

Although many writers refer to the "bobwhite" note as the call of the cock bird to his sitting mate, Stoddard (1931) says:

We respectfully express our belief, based upon all data we have been able to obtain personally, that the "bob white" call note is *largely* the call of the unmated cocks; ardent fellows eager to mate, but doomed to a summer of loneliness, from lack of physical prowess or an insufficient number of hens to go around.

The sweetest and loveliest call, entirely different from the foregoing or the following, is the four-syllable whistle of the female, used to answer the male in spring and to call the young later in the season. My father, who was an expert whistler as well as a keen sportsman, could imitate this note to perfection. He often amused himself, when bobwhites were whistling in spring, by concealing himself in some thick brush and answering the *bobwhite* call of the male with this enticing note. It was amusing to see the effect on the cock bird, as he came nearer at each repetition of the answer to his call, looking in vain for his expected mate, and sometimes coming within twenty feet before detecting the deception. Once two cocks came to look for the anticipated hen; then a lively fight ensued, all on account of an imaginary bride. This call consists of four notes, the first and third short, soft, and on a low key, and the second and fourth longer, louder, richer, and on a much higher key. I have seen it written *je-hoi-a-chin,* or *whoooeee-che,* but to me it sounds more like *a-loie-ahee.* It is a beautiful, soft, rich note, with a decided emphasis on the second syllable, of a liquid quality with no harsh sounds.

The third whistling note is the well-known gather call, so often heard during the fall when the flock has become scattered and the birds are trying to get together again, particularly toward night when they are gathering to go to roost. It has also been called the scatter call. It is a loud, emphatic whistle of two parts, slurred together, with an emphasis on the first. It has a human quality and to my mind is much like the whistle that I use to call my dog. It sounds to me like *quoi-hee.*   1931

SCALED QUAIL   *Callipepla squamata*

The Mexican plateau, with its elevated and arid, or semiarid, plains, extends northward into southern Arizona, New Mexico, and western Texas. Much of this region is dry and barren, except for a scattered growth of creosote bushes, dwarf sagebrush, stunted mesquite, catclaw, mimosa, various cactuses, and a few yuccas. In the mesas between the mountain ranges and at the mouths of canyons, where underground streams supply some scanty moisture, there are grassy plains, with a scattered row of sycamores or cottonwoods marking the course of an unseen stream. Such are the haunts of the scaled quail, blue quail, or white topknot, as it is appropriately called in Arizona. Here, as one drives along over the winding desert trails, dodging the thorny shrubs or still more forbidding clumps of cactus, he may surprise a pair or perhaps a little bevy of these birds, invisible at first in their somber gray dress, which matches their surroundings so well. They do not attempt to escape by flight, but scatter in different directions, running with remarkable speed, with their necks upstretched and their white crests erected, dodging in and out among the desert vegetation, like so many rabbits scurrying off to the nearest brier patch. They are soon lost to sight, for they can run faster than we can and will not flush.

Hunting the blue quail will never figure as one of the major sports, although it is a gamy bird and makes a delicious and plump morsel for the table. The birds are widely scattered over a vast expanse of rough country, on desert plains covered with thorny underbrush, or on stony or rocky foothills where walking is difficult and slow. The hunter must be prepared to do some long, hard tramping, for he is more likely to count the number of miles to a bird than the number of birds to a mile. A dog is useless, for these quail have not yet acquired the habit of lying to a dog. Eastern quail have learned to lie close, a good way to hide from human enemies but a very poor way to escape from the many predatory animals in the West. Scaled quail are shier than Gambel's quail and are generally first seen in the distance running rapidly and dodging around among the bushes. They run faster than a man can walk, and the hunter must make fast progress over the rough ground to catch up with them. By the time he gets within range he will be nearly out of breath and will have to take a quick snap shot at a fleeting glimpse of a small gray bird dodging between bushes. This is far more difficult, under the circumstances, than wing shooting and can not be considered pot shooting. Sometimes, when a large covey has been scattered and rattled, the hunter may surprise single birds and get an occasional wing shot; but they are apt to jump from most unexpected places, ahead of or behind the hunter, and give him a difficult shot. Late in the season they are often found in large packs of one hundred or two hundred birds, when the chances for good sport are better. Even then the hunter may well feel proud of a hard-earned bag.   1931

CALIFORNIA QUAIL   *Lophortyx californicus*

L. c. californicus   (Valley Quail)

The valley quail in Pasadena and vicinity, southern California, is a common dooryard bird, coming regularly into the city to feed on the lawns and to roost in the trees and shrubbery. On Dr. Louis B. Bishop's lawn, in the thickly settled part of Pasadena, one might see from ten to twenty of the pretty birds almost any afternoon after four o'clock. Although rigidly protected and regularly fed, they seemed very nervous and shy; if they saw us moving, even at a window, they would run or fly into the shrubbery. J. Eugene Law has a flock of one hundred to two hundred birds, which he feeds every morning during winter on his driveway in Altadena.

John J. Williams (1903) made some very interesting observations on the use of sentinels by valley quail; his article is well worth reading in detail, but I prefer to quote Grinnell, Bryant, and Storer's (1918) summary of it, as follows:

A flock was heard calling and moving about on a brushy hillside[1] some distance from the observer, but before coming into view a single individual preceded the rest and took his station in the branches of an apple tree, whence he could survey the region round about. After carefully scrutinizing his surroundings for several minutes the *kayrk* note was uttered several times in a low guttural tone. Soon members of the flock were seen coming down the hill in the same direction as taken by the sentinel, but their manner of approach was entirely different; he had exercised great caution and carefully examined the surroundings for possible danger, while they came with their plumed heads held low, searching among the clover roots for seeds and other articles of food. Some preened and fluffed out their feathers; others took dust baths. While so occupied they all kept up a succession of low conversational notes. Meanwhile the sentinel remained on his perch and continued on the alert even after the flock had moved some distance beyond him. Then a second bird mounted a vantage point and took up the sentinel duty and after a few minutes the first relinquished his post. While the flock was still in view, yet a third bird relieved the second. It would seem that by this practice, of establishing sentinels on a basis of divided labor, the flock had increased its individual efficiency in foraging. The same observer also states that he had seen sentinels used when a flock

[1] Placer County, California, 1901.

was crossing a road, or when "bathing" in the roadside dust, and that the practice is made general use of in open areas; but he had never observed the habit when the birds were in tree-covered localities. During the breeding season it is known that the male mounts guard while the female is searching for a nesting site, and again when she is incubating the eggs. Sometimes he also performs this guard function after the chicks are out but not fully grown.   1931

GAMBEL'S QUAIL   *Lophortyx gambelii*

Springtime in Arizona is most charming as the desert plants burst into bloom with their profusion of many colors. The new fern-like foliage of the mesquite mingles with dangling yellow tassels. The long slender stems of the ocotillo are tipped with vermilion spikes. Even the lowly creosote bush is clouded with yellow haze. The various chollas and the pricklypears are studded with pink, yellow, or crimson flowers, and the little rainbow cactus blooms by the roadside with a wealth of large magenta and yellow blossoms. Even the giant cactus supports a crown of white, and the paloverde is the showiest of all, a great bouquet of brilliant yellow. Then we may look for the trim figure of the cock quail, perched on some low tree, bush, or stump, and listen to his challenging love call.

Major Bendire (1892) has described his courtship very well, as follows:

During the mating and breeding season, the former commencing usually in the latter part of February, the latter about the first week in April and occasionally later, according to the season, the male frequently utters a call like *yuk-kae-ja, yuk-kae-ja,* each syllable distinctly articulated and the last two somewhat drawn out. A trim, handsome, and proud-looking cock, whose more somber-colored mate had a nest close by, used an old mesquite stump, about 4 feet high, and not more than 20 feet from my tent,[1] as his favorite perch, and I had many excellent opportunities to watch him closely. Standing perfectly erect, with his beak straight up in the air, his tail slightly spread and wings somewhat drooping, he uttered this call in a clear strong voice every few minutes for half an hour or so, or until disturbed by something, and this he repeated several times a day. I consider it a call of challenge or of exultation, and it was taken up usually by any other male in the vicinity at the time. During the mating season the males fight each other persistently, and the victor defends his chosen home against intrusion with much valor. It is a pleasing and interesting sight to watch the male courting his mate, uttering at the time some low cooing notes, and strutting around the coy female in the most stately manner possible, bow-

---

[1] On Rillitto Creek, Fort Lowell, Arizona.

ing his head and making his obeisance to her. While a handsome bird at all times, he certainly looks his best during this love-making period.

In past years these quail were an important item in the market hunter's game bag. Herbert Brown (1900) was informed by an express agent that three thousand dozen quail were shipped out of Salt River Valley [Arizona] in 1889 and 1890. He says further:

The Mohawk valley, in Yuma county [Arizona], is probably the most prolific breeding spot in the territory. It was, at one time, a favorite place for trappers and pot-hunters, and it was not until the game law had been amended that their nefarious practices were broken up. In six weeks, in the fall of 1894, no less than 1,300 dozens were shipped to San Francisco and other California markets. The price at first realized, so I was told by the shippers, was $1.12½ per dozen, but later 60 cents only were realized. The Quail were trapped, their throats cut, then sacked and shipped by express. I was told by one of the parties so engaged that he and his partner caught 77 dozens in one day. They used eight traps and baited with barley. Their largest catch in one trap, at one time, was 11 dozens. At the meeting of the next legislature the game law was again amended, and it was made a misdemeanor to trap, snare, or ship Quail or Partridges from the Territory. This effectually stopped the merciless slaughter of the gamiest bird in Arizona—Gambel's Partridge.[1]   1931

MOUNTAIN QUAIL   *Oreortyx pictus*

O. p. pictus   (Plumed Quail)

[This], the largest and handsomest of the North American quail, is a shy, retiring species, more often heard than see. I have hunted for it, where it was common and where it could frequently be heard calling, and been favored with only an occasional glimpse of one walking stealthily away among the underbrush. It prefers to steal away quietly rather than show itself by flying. All the earlier writers speak of it as uncommon or comparatively rare; it was doubtless often overlooked because of its secretive habits. It is even more of a mountain bird than the preceding, ranging up to ten thousand feet in summer.

Bendire (1892) says that incubation lasts about twenty-one days and that "in the higher mountains but a single brood is raised; but in the lower foothills they rear two broods occasionally, the male caring for the first one while the female is busy hatching the second." Probably both sexes share the duties of incubation. Mrs. Irene G. Wheelock (1904) gives the following account of the hatching

[1] As this species was sometimes called.

process [in a nest along the Lake Tahoe stage road between Fyffe and Slippery Ford, California]:

I stole back alone for a last peep at them, and two had pipped the shells while a third was cuddled down in the split halves of his erstwhile covering. The distress of the mother was pitiful, and I had not the heart to torture the beautiful creature needlessly; so going off a little way, I lay down flat along the "misery," regardless of the discomfort, and awaited developments. Before I could focus my glasses she was on the nest, her anxious little eyes still regarding me suspiciously. In less time than it takes to tell it, the two were out and the mother cuddled them in her fluffed-out feathers. This was too interesting to be left. Even at the risk of being too late to reach my destination, I must see the outcome. Two hours later every egg had hatched and a row of tiny heads poked out from beneath the mother's breast. I started toward her and she flew almost into my face, so closely did she pass me. Then by many wiles she tried in vain to coax me to go another way. I was curious and therefore merciless. Moreover, I had come all the way from the East for just such hours as this. But once more a surprise awaited me. There was the nest, there were the broken shells; but where were the young partridges? Only one of all that ten could I find. For so closely did they blend in coloring with the shadows on the pine needles under the leaves of the "misery" that although I knew they were there, and dared not step for fear of crushing them, I was not sharp enough to discover them. 1931

HARLEQUIN QUAIL   *Cyrtonyx montezumae*

One of the handsomest and certainly the most oddly marked of the North American quails presents a bizarre appearance when closely examined; one look at its conspicuously marked face would brand it as a clown among birds; its dark-colored breast is contrary to the laws of protective coloration and would make it very conspicuous on open ground. But when one tries to find it in its native haunts, squatting close to the ground among thick underbrush, weeds, and grass, one realizes that its dark belly and spotted flanks are completely concealed, that the grotesquely painted face becomes obliterated among the sharp lights and shadows, and that the prettily marked back matches its surroundings so well that the bird is nearly invisible.

[H. W.] Henshaw witnessed a remarkable exhibition of the confidence that this bird shows in its protective coloration, for he says in some notes sent to Mrs. Bailey (1928):

Of the several quail known to me the "fool quail" of New Mexico and Arizona seems to depend for his safety upon his protective coloration more than any other. As an example I recall one that squatted on a log near the trail our pack train was following, and so closely did the colors of his back and sides harmonize with his surroundings that 12 or 15 pack mules and horsemen passed by him without seeing him or disturbing his equanimity in the least. He seemed so completely petrified by astonishment at the novel sight as to be incapable of motion, and he was so close to us that one might have touched him with a riding whip. While the bird was no doubt actuated to some extent by curiosity, he depended for his safety, I am sure, upon the nice way in which his plumage matched his surroundings and upon his absolute immobility. No one saw the bird but myself, and when the train had passed I had to almost poke him off his perch before he consented to fly. Whoso calls this the "Fool Quail" writes himself down a bigger fool than the bird, who has been taught his lesson of concealment by Mother Nature herself.   1931

RING-NECKED PHEASANT   *Phasianus colchicus*
(Townsend)

[In] 1881, Judge O. N. Denny, then American consul general at Shanghai, China, sent thirty ring-necked pheasants to Oregon. Of these twenty-six survived and were liberated in the Willamette Valley. Two years later more were sent (Shaw, 1908). The first successful introduction of pheasants into the East was in 1887 by Rutherford Stuyvesant, who brought over a number of birds from England and liberated them on his estate at Allamuchy, N. J. In the nineties, pheasants were brought from England and liberated in various places in Massachusetts and elsewhere.

The bird proved to be remarkably hardy and prolific and spread rapidly, partly by natural increase and partly by artificial breeding in private and State farms, and by this shipment of eggs and birds to new sections of the country. The bird thrives in the North, but south of Baltimore and Washington, according to Dr. J. C. Phillips (1928), although there have been many attempts at introduction, "the stock does not hold out long if thrown on its own resources."

W. L. McAtee (1929) says of this bird that it

now has an almost continuous distribution over the Northern States from coast to coast. It has proved hardy as to climatic conditions, wary as to enemies, and without doubt is more numerous than any native game bird in the area occupied. The success of the introduction of pheasants in the Northwestern States is well known, but how amazingly the birds have thrived in certain other sections is not generally appreciated. In South Dakota, according to the Director of the State Department of Game and Fish, pheasants increased steadily from the first, a fact justifying almost steady lengthening of the open season and increase in the daily bag limit. The total bag in 1926 was estimated at a million birds, and in 1927 from one and a half to two millions, a record that has scarcely been approached in all our history by a single species of game bird in a single State.

The cock pheasant is a prize well calculated to delight the heart of the sportsman. Splendid in plumage—a magnificent trophy—large and heavy, and delicious eating, it tests his skill to the utmost. In game preserves in England, numerous beaters drive the pheasants to the quiescent sportsmen and force the birds to fly high and at great speed over them. In this country, the sportsman seeks the bird, going on foot over the fields and shooting the pheasant as it flushes and makes off. Dogs are generally used, and although the pheasant often lies close to the pointing dogs and allows himself to be flushed by the sportsman, he may sometimes hide, or, worse still from the point of view of the owner of a well-trained dog, he may run long distances and entice the dog to follow. Only by continuous replacement with birds raised on private or State farms can the drain on pheasants by hunters be checked, for in these days of automobiles hunters may visit numerous favorable localities many miles apart in the course of one day.

A very important asset of the ring-necked pheasant, both from the sportsman's and the bird lover's point of view, is that it diverts gunfire from our fast-diminishing grouse and other game birds.

Under complete protection, where shooting is not permitted, as in public parks, pheasants become very tame, but when persecuted they quickly develop great wariness, and they seem to be able to distinguish the harmless farm laborer from the man with a gun. Any unusual noise, such as blasting, makes pheasants crow, and they are usually sensitive to any shock, whether from an explosion or an earthquake, and respond by crowing. This response to earthquakes or distant explosions is apparently due to the sense of feeling rather than of hearing. In Japan pheasants are believed to give warnings of earthquakes. It is found that they respond to earthquake shocks so slight that they are unnoticed by human beings, and the birds may in this way foretell a more severe earthquake shock that follows. Hartley (1922) states that "during the World War the pheasants in England developed into fairly responsible sentinels against Zeppelin attacks. The birds seemed particularly sensitive to far-off explosions and a raid generally was heralded by a concerted crowing of cocks." 1931

GRAY PARTRIDGE   *Perdix perdix*

Attempts to introduce the European gray partridge into North America have met with marked success in certain favorable localities and with many dismal failures in other places less congenial to it. Dr. John C. Phillips (1928) has summarized the whole history of these attempts. Of the earlier unsuccessful importations he says:

The earliest attempt at introduction, which so far as known was made by Richard Bache, son-in-law of Benjamin Franklin, who stocked his plantation on the Delaware River near what is now the town of Beverly, N. J., with Hungarian partridges,[1] dates back to the latter part of the eighteenth century. There were subsequent attempts in Virginia and New Jersey, most important of which was Pierre Lorillard's effort in 1879 at Jobstown, N. J. Later attempts commenced in a small way in 1899, but the real fever of importation along the Atlantic coast began about 1905 and has lasted up to the present, although the period 1907 and 1914 saw the height of the industry. In Eastern States importations of these hardy little birds have been put down all the way from Portland, Me., and northern New York to South Carolina, Georgia, Florida, and Mississippi. In Connecticut, Pennsylvania, and New Jersey, the work was done on a large scale and, at first, with encouraging results. In a few places the birds undoubtedly bred the first season, and in other places as in the Connecticut Valley, they persisted for 8 or 10 years in considerable numbers; eventually they vanished, however, between 1915 and 1920.

The results on the western plains and prairies have been quite successful, of which he writes:

The results in the far Western States and in western and central Canada may be briefly summarized. The most remarkable success followed immediately upon the first introductions into Alberta, near Calgary, in 1908-9.

The spread from this initial plant has carried the Hungarian partridge into Saskatchewan and all over its western part as far north as township 60 and south to the international boundary. All this happened within only five years from the time the bird was first recorded in the Province.

Provided that the Hungarian partridge does not seriously interfere with the welfare of our native species, it seems to be a wise and valuable addition to our list of game birds. I have never hunted it, but those who have speak very highly of it. It is a strong, swift flier, smart and sagacious, well fitted to test the skill of the best sportsmen. It is a fine bird for the table. Unfortunately it will survive and flourish only in certain favorable sections, mainly the northwestern grainfields and grassy plains. There it can probably survive much more intensive hunting than either the prairie chicken or the sharp-tailed grouse.

1931

[1] As this species is sometimes called.

TURKEYS   Family Meleagrididae

TURKEY   *Meleagris gallopavo*

When the noble red man roamed and hunted unrestrained throughout the virgin forests of eastern North America, this magnificent bird, the wild turkey, another noble native of America, clad in a feathered armor of glistening bronze, also enjoyed the freedom of the forests from Maine and Ontario, southward and westward. But the coming of the white man to our shores spelled the beginning of the end for both of these picturesque Americans. The forests disappeared before the white man's ax, his crude firearms waged warfare on the native game, and the red man was gradually eliminated before advancing civilization. In the days of the Pilgrims and Puritans the Thanksgiving turkey was easily obtained almost anywhere in the surrounding forest; the delicious meat of the wild turkey was an important and an abundant food supply for both Indians and settlers; and the feathers of the turkey held a prominent place in the red man's adornment.

Edward H. Forbush (1912) says:

In Massachusetts Turkeys were most numerous in the oak and chestnut woods, for there they found most food. They were so plentiful in the hills bordering the Connecticut valley that in 1711 they were sold in Hartford at one shilling four pence each.

Wild turkeys made their last stand in Massachusetts in the Holyoke range, where the last one was killed in 1851.

The last turkey in Connecticut was seen in 1813, a few remained hidden in the Vermont Hills until 1842, and they were said to be numerous along the southern border of Ontario as late as 1856.

Wild turkeys are essentially woodland birds. When the Eastern States were largely covered with virgin forests, they ranged widely over the whole of these districts. As the land became cleared they often resorted to clearings, open fields, savannas, or meadows in search of grasshoppers, other insects, berries, and other foods. As their numbers were reduced by persistent hunting, they became very shy and were forced to retire to the wooded hills and mountains, where in many places they made their last stand. There are many hills and creeks named for this bird because turkeys were once common there. Turkeys are now found, in the Northern and Eastern States, only in the more remote and heavily wooded mountains, the wildest and least frequented forests, or the most inaccessible swamps, far from the haunts of man. In the Southern States they are much more abundant and more widely distributed.   1931

CRANES, RAILS, AND ALLIES — ORDER GRUIFORMES

CRANES   Family Gruidae

WHOOPING CRANE   *Grus americana*

This magnificent species, one of the grandest and most striking of North American birds, is supposed to be on the verge of extinction. In its former abundance, its great migration flights, its curious conventions, in which it indulged in grotesque dances, and its interesting aerial evolutions must have formed some of the most spectacular performances in American ornithology.

Col. N. S. Goss (1891) says:

These birds are very wary and ever upon the lookout, rising over every suspicious spot when on the wing, and when on the ground spring into the air at the first sight or appearance of danger, with a warning note to others. In flight, their long necks and stiltlike legs are stretched out in line with the body to their full extent, moving strongly, with slowly beating wings, but not swiftly; I say strongly because then they are able to face a strong wind, and to sustain themselves for a long time in the air, often circling spirallike to a great height. They occasionally bunch up, and I have seen them in a triangular form, but, as a rule, they travel in single file, following their leader in a wavy line, croaking as they go, like hounds upon a cold trail.

Dwight W. Huntington (1903) refers to this interesting flight performance as follows:

I was once shooting mallard on the margin of a western lake, with an Army officer. The day was warm and bright, and, after a short morning flight, the ducks ceased to move about, and we retired to a slight elevation, ate our luncheon, and reclined in the grass to smoke our pipes and tell tales of shooting game of all sorts. A large flock of white cranes arose from the marsh and flew directly toward us, ascending, however, as they came, far beyond our range. When quite overhead, in the azure sky, their white feathers gleaming in the sunlight, they proceeded to go through many graceful evolutions, flying about in a circle, forming sides and crossing over and back and dancing in midair to their own loud music. We were much entertained by their performance, and observed them until the exhibition was ended and they continued their flight until quite out of sight. 1925

SANDHILL CRANE   *Grus canadensis*

The advances of civilization, the drainage of swamps, and the cultivation of prairies have doubtless driven this wary, old prairie scout away from all the central portions of the United States; and they are still driving it farther west and north into the unsettled wilderness; the wilderness is fast disappearing and with it will go the cranes and many other interesting forms of wild life.

Stephen S. Visher (1910) writes:

The sandhill crane is one of the most conspicuous birds of the prairie region. Every farmer boy knows its call, and on fair days has seen large flocks soaring at great heights, slowly passing northward. Constantly their unsurpassed calls drift down to earth. When only a slight wind is blowing, these rich, buglelike notes can be heard farther than the bird can be seen. Several times I have examined, for some moments in vain, the horizon before the authors sailed in view. On windy or rainy days, the flocks fly low and swiftly in a direct line, and each individual croaks in turn. Thus slowly the music moves along the undulating, curving line.

The mating habits of this bird are very interesting. In Sanborn County, South Dakota, I have often watched the mating dance; each time with increasing interest. In the early spring, just after the break of dawn, the groups that were separated widely, for safety, during the night, begin flying toward the chosen dancing ground. These flocks of six or eight fly low and give constantly their famous, rolling call. The dancing ground that I knew best was situated on a large, low hill in the middle of a pasture of a section in extent. From this hill the surface of the ground for half a mile or more in every direction could be seen. As soon as two or three groups had reached this hill a curious dance commenced. Several raise their heads high in the air and walk around and around slowly. Suddenly the heads are lowered to the ground and the birds become great bouncing balls. Hopping high in the air, part of the time with raised wings, and part with dropping, they cross and recross each other's paths. Slowly the speed and wildness increases, and the hopping over each other, until it becomes a blur. The croaking, which commenced only after the dancing became violent, has become a noise. The performance continues, increasing in speed for a few minutes, and then rapidly dies completely out, only to start again upon the arrival of more recruits. By 7 o'clock all have arrived, and then for an hour or so a number are constantly dancing. Occasionally the whole flock of 200 or so break into a short spell of crazy skipping and hopping. By 9 o'clock all are tired and the flock begins to break up into groups of from four to eight and these groups slowly feed to the windward, diverging slowly, or fly to some distance.   1925

LIMPKINS   Family Aramidae

LIMPKIN   *Aramus guarauna*

"The voice of one crying in the wilderness" is the first impression one gets of this curious bird in the great inland swamps of Florida. While exploring the intricate channels, half-choked with aquatic vegetation, that wound their way among the willow islands in the extensive marshes of the upper St. Johns, we frequently heard and occasionally caught a glimpse of this big, brown, rail-like bird; it peered and nodded at us from the shore of some little island, or went flying off with deliberate wing beats over the tops of the bushes; once one perched on the top of a small willow and looked at us.

William Brewster (1881) writes attractively about it, as follows:

But if our presence was a matter of indifference to the birds just mentioned we certainly were not ignored by the vigilant courlans[1], for any sudden noise, like the splash of a paddle in the water or the rapping of its handle against the boat, was sure to be instantly followed by a piercing *"kur-r-ee-ow, kurr-r-ee-ow, kurr-r-ee-ow, kr-ow, kr-ow,"* from the nearest thicket; or perhaps several would cry out at once as rails will do on similar occasions. For the most part the birds kept closely hidden but at length we discovered one feeding on the shore. His motions were precisely similar to those of a rail, as he skirted the oozy brink, lifting and putting down his feet with careful deliberation. Occasionally he detected and seized a snail, which was quickly swallowed, the motion being invariably accompanied by a comical side shake of the bill, apparently expressive of satisfaction, though it was perhaps designed to remove any particles of mud that may have adhered to his unique food. Finally he spied us and walked up the inclined trunk of a fallen tree to its shattered end where he stood for a moment tilting his body and jerking up his tail. Then he uttered a hoarse rattling cry like the gasp of a person being strangled, at the same time shaking his head so violently that his neck seemed in imminent danger of dislocation. Just as we were nearly within gun range he took wing, with a shriek that might have been heard for half a mile. His flight was nearly like a heron's, the wings being moved slowly and occasionally held motionless during intervals of sailing. Shortly afterwards

[1] As these birds were then called.

another, his mate probably, was detected under a palmetto leaf near at hand. In the shadow her form was dimly outlined and she stood perfectly motionless, evidently relying upon concealment for protection, but her quick eye took in every suspicious movement and at length, conscious that she was seen, she ran rapidly for a few paces and launched into the air, following the course taken by the first. He is perfectly at home in the tops of the tallest trees where he walks among the twigs with all the ease of a heron or stands motionless on some horizontal branch with one leg drawn up and the curved bill resting on his breast. These elevated perches are generally resorted to at daybreak. The people told us that when the country was first settled the "Limpkins," as they are called from their peculiar halting gait, were so tame that they could frequently be caught on their nests, but incessant persecution has had the usual result and they are now at all times among the most wary of birds.   1925

RAILS, GALLINULES, AND COOTS
Family Rallidae

KING RAIL   *Rallus elegans*

This large, handsome rail is an inhabitant of the freshwater marshes of the interior. It is never seen in the salt marshes of the coast except on migrations or in winter and even then it prefers fresh water.

Arthur T. Wayne (1910) says:

This fine species, which is locally known as the fresh water marsh hen, is abundant on abandoned rice plantations and in ponds of fresh water where there is a dense growth of reeds and water plants. It is a permanent resident, but during protracted droughts is forced to migrate from the ponds in order to procure food and water. On the freshwater rivers it is most numerous, and breeds in numbers.

C. J. Pennock tells me that in Florida, near St. Marks and about Punta Gorda, the habitats of the two large rails come together, or even overlap, in the marshes of the tidal rivers and creeks. The clapper rails fairly swarm, where the marshes are in wide open areas, even well up the rivers; but, at the first appearance of wooded tracts along these waterways, the clapper rails disappear and are replaced by the king rails. He found the latter nesting regularly in a small pond, near one of these creeks, which was usually fresh, but at high tides it became salty.

The only nest of a king rail that I have ever seen was shown to me by Oscar E. Baynard, near Plant City, Florida, on March 30, 1925. He had found it while investigating a colony of eighty pairs of boat-tailed grackles in an extensive swamp overgrown mainly with pickerel weed (*Pontederia*), a scattered growth of small "ty-ty" bushes and a few flags (*Typhus*). The nest was in the midst of the colony of grackles, which had nests in the bushes, and was not far from a least bittern's nest. It was beautifully concealed in a thick growth of pickerel weed, which grew all around and over it. It was well made of the dead, dry stems of pickerel weed and flags, and was deeply hollowed; it measured eight inches in diameter and the rim was about eight inches above the water, which was about a foot deep. It contained nine practically fresh eggs. The rail was heard, but not seen.   1925

CLAPPER RAIL   *Rallus longirostris*

R. l. crepitans   (Northern Clapper Rail)

In the salt water marshes of the Atlantic and Gulf coasts, from southern New England to Texas, the clapper rail, in its various forms, has been a widely distributed, well-known, and conspicuous feature, though more often heard than seen; its loud clatter is still often heard in many places, but its popularity as a game bird and as an egg producer has greatly thinned its ranks; it no longer exists anywhere in anything like the astonishing abundance described by the earlier writers. Audubon (1840) boasted of having collected as many as seventy-two dozen eggs in one day.

R. l. scottii   (Florida Clapper Rail)

C. J. Pennock has sent me the following notes on the courtship of this rail:

Regarding the mating of Scott's rail,[1] I have found these birds at St. Marks [Florida] and also about Punta Gorda [Florida] quite silent throughout the winter season. Only when considerably alarmed, at that period will they utter more than a hasty alarm. As nesting time approaches or by early March, they may be heard even with little or no cause, so far as the observer can determine. When mating is at the flood, one and not rarely two birds may be seen making short flights above the tops of the reeds. Only once did I hear one of these flying birds call out, and then two birds were in close company. On April 16, 1923, as I stood in a much-traveled roadway bordered on either side by a tidal ditch and small marshes and but 75 yards from the bay shore, what proved to be two males and a female Scott's rail came in sight. One and then quickly a second bird crossed the roadway and disappeared into a small clump

[1] As this subspecies was then called.

of scrub palmettos. The smaller, the female, promptly came out onto the open sand near the ditch, walking slowly and frequently stopping, the characteristic jerking of body and tail much exaggerated; two other birds now appeared near the palmettos and for two or three minutes they were in full chase in and out of different small covers. When this encounter ceased, with the running off of one bird, the other came toward the yet visible female and approached her by short runs, with turns and gestures of body and wings, at times half open; the female meanwhile moved slowly toward a small patch of reeds, and finally dropped with body quite flat and head stretched well forward, but not quite to the ground, when the male came to her and the mating was complete. 1925

VIRGINIA RAIL   *Rallus limicola*   (Townsend)

The Virginia rail, like most of its family, is rarely seen except by those who know its ways, and, even when heard, its strange noises are often attributed to frogs or other creatures. One who has seen only the usual short and feeble flights of this bird would receive with astonishment, if not with incredulity, the statement that some individuals migrate annually many hundreds of miles.

Verdi Burtch's (1917) observations of the young and their parents are of much interest. He says:

On May 11, 1908, the eggs were just beginning to hatch in a nest that I had found some few days before, and, as I approached, the female slipped from the nest and away through the cat-tails. She was quickly followed by the two little ones, although they were but a few hours old. The nest was surrounded by water so that the birds had to swim, but even then they managed to elude me. Hoping to get a picture of the nest and eggs I set up my camera, and, while focusing, the mother appeared, carrying one of the little ones in her bill, dropped it into the nest, went on, and settled down to brood.

In another nest on—

June 17 the eggs were beginning to hatch, and there were six silky little ones in the nest. Three of them followed the mother when she left the nest and hid in the flags around its base. The three others were not yet dry and with their bright eyes shining lay kicking and struggling to get out of the nest. Soon the mother came back calling softly "*ka-ka-ka-ka-ka*," and the young ones left their hiding place and ran to her. One of them fell into one of my foot tracks, and the mother came quickly and taking it up, ran off into the flags, carrying it dangling from her bill as a cat carries her kittens. The male now showed himself for the first time.

The exact length of incubation has not been recorded, but it is known to be not less than fifteen days. The young come out of the

egg with their eyes open and are so active that they leave the nest
even before the coal-black down in which they are clad is dry. The
first chicks often leave the nest before the rest of the eggs are
hatched. In a few days, at the latest, the nest is deserted, in all cases
observed, although it is possible that when undisturbed by visitors,
human or other, the young may remain in the nest a little longer. As
the female begins incubation before all the eggs are laid, several
days may elapse between the hatching of the first and the last egg.
Bowdish (1891) says that the young are conducted away by one
parent as fast as hatched, while the other parent continues to incubate.

From the beginning, the downy young are good swimmers and
divers, and are well able to run over the ground and to climb about
in the reeds and grasses, making use of their large feet and claws and
of their little wings, each of which is provided with a tiny claw on
the outer digit.   1925

SORA   *Porzana carolina*

The sora or Carolina rail is unquestionably *the* rail of North America. It is the most widely distributed and the best known of its tribe.

It is the most popular of the rails among sportsmen and, when one
speaks of rail shooting, he generally refers to this species. Being a
prolific breeder, it is astonishingly abundant in favored localities
during the fall migration.

My experience with rail shooting has been limited to one day on the
marshes of Essex, Connecticut, as the guest of Dr. L. C. Sanford. It
was the opening day of the season and we each shot the legal limit,
thirty-five birds, in a very short time. His description of it is so much
better than anything I can write, that I prefer to quote from Doctor
Sanford (1903), as follows:

When the wild oats along the tidal rivers of our coast begin to turn
yellow with the first touch of fall, the time for rail has come, and the high
tides of September give the sportsman his first chance. The Connecticut
River, where it broadens into the Sound, is one of the favorite haunts of
these birds. Here Essex is the usual destination. Some 3 miles up the
river from Saybrook, the little town of Essex, with its one hotel and old-
fashioned houses, looks now pretty much as it did a hundred years ago.
Rail tides generally come toward the middle of the day, and the pusher
is waiting for you at the landing; you stand for a minute looking up and
down the broad expanse of river. Everywhere along the shore are wavy
patches of high grass reaching far out into the water. These are the wild
oats, and here live the rail. A strong tide is running in, and you step into
a flat-bottomed skiff, which is rigged with a high stool firmly tied to the

front seat. The only task now is to sit still on this stool and be shoved. A short row up the river and you are in the midst of thick wild oats, so high it is difficult in many places to see over the tops, even from your exalted position. A flutter just ahead, and a rail rises, shot almost before it cleared the grass; a few feathers alone are left to tell the fate of the first bird of the season. The next is given a chance to get in range, and the score is two; three or four more straight exalt a man's idea of his shooting ability—without reason, though, for no easier mark ever flew in front of a gun. Now a rail runs among some broken grass ahead of the boat, and a whack from the pusher's pole starts him; at the shot half a dozen teal jump within range, and the last one is feathered but not stopped. Presently several rail start in quick succession; you fire, and load, and fire again—not a miss yet, but all idea of definite direction is lost and the last bird is the only one marked. Here a clever pusher shows his skill, and after you have given up all thought of retrieving he picks them up in order. Under these circumstances painted blocks can be used and tossed out to mark the dead birds before the position of the boat is changed. The time of high tide is short, but sufficient; every few seconds a bird rises, its slow flight affording a sure mark; generally in front or to the side, occasionally behind, when you are startled by the pusher's yell "Hi, rail!" in time to try a long shot.

Rail keep fluttering from the grass, less often now, though, than an hour ago, but you have some time since reached the limit—as well, for a falling tide makes the pushing hard and the birds refuse to rise.   1925

YELLOW RAIL   *Coturnicops noveboracensis*

This beautiful little rail, perhaps the handsomest of all our rails, is a most elusive bird. Although it has a wide distribution at certain seasons, ranging from Nova Scotia to California, it is seldom seen and is one of the least-known of this elusive group. Most of its life history is shrouded in mystery and even its voice is not too well known.

Mr. Peabody (1922) has well described its familiar breeding grounds, in the "Big Coulee," in Benson County, North Dakota, as follows:

One must give reasons why this bed of an ancient river should have been chosen as a summer home by that rarest of inland water birds, the yellow rail. The winding coulee, deep-set among the hills, is reached by steep ravines. These are clothed with partridge berry, rose, willow, aspen, and the silver-leafed buffalo berry. Rarely on these ravine sides are found huge boulders of yellow sandstone, under the edges of which at times a turkey vulture may place her eggs; and often beside them are the nests of the ferruginous roughleg.[1] On top of the morainic buttes are scattered

[1] As the Ferruginous Hawk was then called.

granite boulders of varied colors, all enriched by wonderfully varied lichens. Amid all these boulders, blossomed vetches, coneflowers, and puccoons, in glowing tapestries. Here, in this most radiant setting, was the paradisic home of the yellow rails. The faunal conditions in the coulee itself were rarely fine for the yellow rails. Everywhere were wide areas of salt grass, alive with appetizing snails. There were great expanses of soft, fine grass, unburned and unmown year by year. Better still as will appear later, there were great expanses of soft, fine grass that were annually mown leaving in spots just the sort of matted flotsam that the yellow rail so dearly loves for its nesting.

One unusual condition has, I am sure, determined the fitness of the Big Coulee as a breeding place for the yellow rail. Far up on the top of a butte, rising out of a boggy spring pool, there flows a tiny stream of clear, sweet water.

No one element of that wonderful coulee is more delightsome than this little stream of clear, cool water, and right here, throughout many of the years of my observation, has been the focal point of the nesting domain of the yellow rail in that famous coulee. Nowhere else in all that region, during many years, was the yellow rail ever found.   1925

BLACK RAIL   *Laterallus jamaicensis*

L. j. jamaicensis   (Black Rail)

Although the little black rail was discovered in Jamaica in 1760 and received its scientific name in 1788, it was not discovered in the United States until 1836, when Audubon (1840) described and figured it from specimens given him by Titian R. Peale. Practically nothing was known about its distribution and habits in North America for one hundred years after its discovery in Jamaica.

The black rail is not fond of flying and is seldom seen in flight. Ludlow Griscom (1915), who had a good opportunity to observe one [on Jones Beach, Long Island, New York, on May 24, 1914], says that

the flight is much more feeble than that of any other rail with which I am familiar; the bird seemed barely to sustain its weight in the air, while its legs dangled down helplessly behind.

But when on the ground it runs swiftly and disappears under the nearest cover as quickly as a mouse.

T. E. McMullen writes to me that he has seen them fly out of the marsh and alight on horizontal limbs of bayberry bushes and remain there until he was within six feet of them, just like sparrows.

George H. Stuart, 3d, has sent me the following notes:

On July 4, 1919, Julian K. Potter and the writer flushed a small rail in a marsh an acre or two in extent beyond the sand dunes immediately back of the ocean beach on an island below Beach Haven, N. J. Searching for the nest in the belief that the bird was a little black rail, we were rewarded by finding it placed in the long grass, the tops of which were so drawn over as to almost completely hide the eggs from view. The nest, which was composed entirely of the same rather fine grass, was placed about one inch from the damp ground and contained eight eggs, very heavily incubated. On returning several times at intervals of 10 minutes we had opportunities of observing the female on the nest, her bright red eyes being the most prominent feature. On each occasion when leaving the eggs it darted from the nest into the surrounding grass never raising and with such celerity that it was impossible to observe her movement, the action resembling more that of a mouse than a bird.

L. j. coturniculus   (Farallon Rail)

Mr. Ingersoll (1909) observed a bird in flight [on the tidelands of San Diego Bay, Caliifornia] of which he writes:

While packing the eggs a tuft of cotton was blown from my fingers; on making a quick grab, my hand was thrust into a clump of weeds, causing one of the elusive birds to rise and fly feebly 30 to 40 feet, then with a sort of boomerang flight, hover and return to within 16 feet (actual measurement) of the starting point. The bird flew so slow it seemed to have difficulty in keeping in the air; this appeared to be a flight of observation. The bird turned its head and scrutinized me with one of its red eyes while flying off. The legs were hanging down until the turning point was reached. They were then drawn up to the body and dropped as she settled out of sight in a tangled mass of weeds.   1925

PURPLE GALLINULE   *Porphyrula martinica*

The extensive marshes which border the upper waters of the St. Johns River in Florida gave us, among other thrills, our first glimpse of the purple gallinule in its chosen haunts.

We were thrilled with the striking beauty of this handsome species, as we saw for the first time its brilliant colors in its native haunts. One can not mistake it as it flies feebly along just over the tops of the "bonnets" with its long yellow legs dangling. And how gracefully and lightly it walks over the lily pads, supported by its long toes, nodding and bowing with a dovelike motion, and flirting the white flag in its tail.

Arthur T. Wayne (1910) says of this species in South Carolina:

This beautiful and graceful summer resident is locally abundant during the breeding season on abandoned rice plantations, and also on fresh-water rivers where the wampee (*Pontederia cordata*) grows in profusion. This plant bears purplish blue flowers which act as a protective coloration to this species. Where the plant is growing in profusion the gallinules are always most abundant, but where it is absent scarcely more than one or two pairs can be found. The birds generally arrive between April 10 and 17, and are common by the 25th.

The purple gallinule is easily recognized in life by its brilliant colors and by its bright yellow legs, which hang down in flight. Its flight is weak and raillike, slow, and not long protracted; it hovers feebly along, just clearing the tops of the vegetation, and then suddenly drops down out of sight. It cackles almost constantly while flying, the notes sounding much like the cackling of a hen or the syllables "*Kek, Kek, Kek, Kek.*" Mr. Wayne (1910) says that it has "very peculiar call notes. One, which is very guttural, is to be heard incessantly."

P. H. Gosse (1847) has drawn a good word picture of this bird, which he calls the sultana, as he has seen it in Jamaica, as follows:

I was struck with the remarkable elegance of one that I saw by the roadside, about midway between Savanna le Mar and Bluefields. It was at one of those pieces of dark water called blueholes, reputed to be unfathomable. The surface was covered with the leaves and tangled stems of various water plants, and on these the sultana was walking, supported by its breadth of foot; so that the leaves on which it trod sank only an inch or two, notwithstanding that the bird, according to its usual manner, moved with great deliberation, frequently standing still, and looking leisurely on either side. As it walked over to where the water was less encumbered, it became more immersed, until it seemed to be swimming, yet even then, from the motion of its legs, it was evidently walking, either on the bottom, or on the yielding plants. At the margin of the pool, it stood some time in a dark nook overhung by bushes, where its green and purple hues were finely thrown out by the dark background. I could not help thinking what a beautiful addition it would make to an ornamental water in an English park; and the more so, because its confining tameness allows of approach sufficiently near to admire its brilliancy. Nor are its motions void of elegance; the constant jerking of its pied tail is perhaps rather singular than admirable, but the bridling of its curved and lengthened neck, and the lifting of its feet are certainly graceful.   1925

COMMON GALLINULE   *Gallinula chloropus*

On its migrations to and from its more northern breeding resorts the Florida gallinule shows greater powers of flight than are apparent at ordinary times; when making such a long flight, or when flying from one pond to another, it travels at a reasonable height with a direct and fairly swift flight, the head and feet being extended. But when seen on its breeding grounds, or in the ponds where it feeds, its flight seems weak, labored, and awkward; it flutters along, barely skimming the surface, half-flying and half-running on the water, as if unable to rise: or, with a feeble, raillike flight, it just clears the tops of the swamp vegetation, into which it suddenly drops again, as if exhausted.

It swims with ease, in spite of its lack of webbed feet, punctuating its foot strokes with a graceful dovelike motion of its head; while swimming the forward parts are depressed and the hind quarters are raised, the white under tail coverts serving as a conspicuous signal. It can dive to obtain its food or to escape its enemies, often hiding under water, with its head or bill concealed among the water plants.

It seems most at ease, however, and its movements are most graceful, when walking lightly about over the lily pads, picking up its food with quick, nervous strokes, much after the manner of a barnyard fowl. It is equally at home on land where most of its food is obtained. If disturbed it runs swiftly to cover and disappears in the reeds, where it can travel with all the skill of a rail and can even climb to the tops of the tall stalks.

C. J. Pennock has sent me the following notes on the courtship of this species, as observed by him in a marsh near Wilmington, Delaware, on June 6, 1925:

Our attention was attracted to a pair of Florida gallinules swimming in one of the larger open tracts and we tarried for an inspection. It quickly became evident that this pair of gallinules were amorously intent; at least while the one appeared to the spectators as supremely indifferent to all extraneous affairs and placidly bobbed about within a quite restricted area the other bird was most intent on creating a responsive thrill or in convincing his lady love that he alone was the gayest, handsomest, and most infatuating Lothario in that muddy pond! While his movements were never rapid he was ever alert and continually in motion, paddling to one side of the female and across in front of her, then back and forth, close by, or veering he might get 5 or 6 yards distant, rarely farther away; now he would serenely sail toward her with brilliant, flaring figurehead or frontispiece, the red of shield and scarlet bill making a vivid mark as viewed against the dark background of water and reeds; again with quite as much seeming aplomb he would reverse his course when within perhaps but a foot or two of the female, and now it became evident that he considered his greatest charm was centered in the white feather patches of the undertail coverts, border of wings, and upper flanks, for these were flashed in display for her benefit in short or longer intervals, but usually well shown, as he bobbed off from her or tacked, now right, now left, with tail apeak and wings one-third or one-half open. At such times the three tracts showed to the greatest advantage, not quite as a single white area continuously, but when we had a direct stern view there was quite as much, probably more, white to be seen than of the dull plumbeous tint of upper wings and body. When swimming toward his mate, the male swam quite erect, head well up, evidently to make the brilliant face and bill most conspicuous, while on the reverse course, usually, I am not sure it was always so, the head and neck were inclined well forward and at this time the erected tail was often opened and closed, fanlike, which brought the white in greater evidence.   1925

AMERICAN COOT   *Fulica americana*

There is much that is interesting in the behavior of the coot, characteristic of and peculiar to this curious bird. The name of "spatterer" has often been applied to it on account of its well-known habit of rising noisily from the water; running along the surface, it beats the water with wings and feet, splashing alternately with its heavy paddles and making the spray fly, until it gains sufficient momentum to fly; it has been suggested that this and other noisy splashing antics are of use to frighten its enemies or warn its companions. When well under way its flight is strong and direct, much more vigorous and swifter than the flight of gallinules; the neck is extended, with the conspicuous white bill pointing slightly downwards, and the feet are stretched out behind, with the toes pointing upwards, to serve as a rudder in place of the useless little tail. The white tips of the secondaries show up well in flight as a good field mark. It flies usually near the water, or ten or fifteen feet above it, and seldom makes long high flights except when migrating. It is much more likely to escape by swimming or by scurrying off over the surface than by rising and flying away as the ducks do. It is ordinarily not a shy bird, unless persistently hunted.

It is a strong rapid swimmer, floating higher in the water than the ducks or the gallinules, with the back more level, less submerged forward. When either swimming or walking it nods its head in step with its foot movements, like a dove or a hen. Its white bill, in contrast with its black head, fairly gleams in the sunlight, an excellent field mark.

On land the coot walks about actively, often in a hunched-back attitude suggestive of the guinea fowl; its lobed feet give it a firm footing on soft ground, but do not impede it on firmer soil.

I have often observed the peculiar antics of a coot when its nest is approached; with head lowered until the bill almost touches the water and with wings elevated behind like a swan's, it paddles about splashing loudly and grunting a loud guttural "*kruk, kruk, kruk*"; it often "backs water" vigorously with both feet, raising the body backwards out of the water. Sometimes it stands upright on its hind quarters, flapping its wing and splashing with both feet. Such noisy demonstrations may be due to nervous excitement or may be intended to scare us away.

Back Bay, Virginia, is a favorite winter resort for coots where they find an abundant food supply in the seeds and tops of the foxtail grass and other duck foods and where they steal the wild celery from the canvasbacks and redheads. I thought I had seen coots in Florida, but that was as nothing compared with the countless thousands that I saw here in November. There were acres and acres and acres of them spread out over the smooth waters of the bay in vast rafts. They were much tamer than any of the ducks and geese; even these big flocks allowed our power boat to approach almost within gunshot; and then they only pattered or flew away for a short distance and then settled down again, thus making a pathway for us through the vast flocks.

1925

SHOREBIRDS, GULLS, AUKS, AND ALLIES—ORDER CHARADRIIFORMES

JACANAS Family Jacanidae

JACANA *Jacana spinosa*

I have never seen this curious bird in life, but can imagine that it must be a beautiful sight to see it tripping lightly over the floating lily pads, supported on its long toes, where it seems to be actually walking on the water; and it must produce quite a surprising thrill as it spreads its wings to fly, displaying the conspicuous yellow-green patches in its wings, which flash in the sunlight like banners of golden yellow. It seems like a strange connecting link between the spur-winged plovers and the rails or gallinules.

It is a sedentary species of decidedly local distribution and seldom strays far from its favorite breeding haunts. Thomas S. Gillin, who has sent me some very good notes on this bird, describes its habitat as follows:

I learned of a lake a few miles from Tampico [Mexico] and on my first visit to this lake on April 3, 1923, I found over a dozen birds feeding and chasing one another over the floating vegetation. As the first sets of eggs were found on April 25 I apparently found them right in the midst of the mating season.

During courtship the birds raise their wings over their backs very much as the Bartramian sandpipers[1] do and flirt their wings at each other as if they were attempting to strike one another with the sharp spurs with which their wings are armed.

I sometimes surprised the birds on their nests, but as a usual thing they would leave the nest at the first alarm. The number of eggs was invariably four, though in one case I collected a set of three. The nests consisted of a few bits of green leaves of cat-tails and small pieces of the green leaves of the plants on which they nested, in all nests containing fresh eggs,

[1] As the Upland Plover was sometimes called.

though in cases where the eggs were incubated the nest material had sometimes turned brown. There was merely enough material to prevent the eggs from rolling apart or falling through into the water, though in most cases the bottom side of the eggs was laying in the water. One day while watching the lake from a blind I saw a jacana go to its eggs and stand over them apparently shading them from the hot sun; this position was maintained for five or six minutes; no attempt was made to warm the eggs by sitting on them; at the end of this shading of the eggs the birds went back to feeding near by.   1928

OYSTERCATCHERS   Family Haematopodidae

AMERICAN OYSTERCATCHER   *Haematopus palliatus*

The usual impression that one gets of this large and showy wader is a fleeting glimpse of a big, black and white bird disappearing in the distance over the hot, shimmering sands of our southern beaches. It is one of the shyest and wildest of our shore birds.

It was evidently about as shy even in the days of Audubon and Wilson, for both mentioned its wariness. It was much commoner in those days, of course, and enjoyed a much wider distribution. Audubon (1840) records it at Portland, Me.

The oyster catcher prefers the same broad, sandy beaches as the Wilson plover and the least tern select for their breeding grounds; and at other seasons it frequents similar resorts with all the little sand plovers and beach birds. The small plovers are protectively colored, but the oyster catcher is not only big, but is most conspicuously colored. Perhaps it needs no protection against the ordinary foes of the little fellows; and evidently its wits are sufficient protection against larger enemies. But in spite of the fact that it is well able to take care of itself, its range has been greatly restricted and its numbers very much reduced during the past fifty years. It formerly bred abundantly on Cobb Island, Virginia, but when we were there in 1907 we saw very few and found no nests or young.

H. H. Bailey (1913) says:

This large, showy bird fell an easy mark to the spring gunners, breeding as it did during the height of the spring migration of "beach birds," from May 10 to 25. Nesting among the sand dunes or flat beaches back from the ocean, over which the spring gunners tramped daily, these birds were right in the line of travel, so to speak, and were either killed or their nests broken up.

C. J. Maynard (1896) writes:

When the outgoing tide[1] left the tops of the oyster bars exposed, they

[1] At Smithville, North Carolina.

would come flying silently in, at first singly, then in pairs, while groups of a few would follow, until, at last, they would come in flocks of a dozen or more. They would alight among the oysters and when the bivalves gaped open, as is their habit when the water first leaves them, the birds would thrust in the point of their hard, flat bills, divide the ligament with which the shells are fastened together, then, having the helpless inhabitant at their mercy, would at once devour it. They were not long in making a meal, for specimens which I shot after they had been feeding a short time were so crammed that by simply holding a bird by the legs and shaking it gently the oysters would fall from its mouth.   1928

BLACK OYSTERCATCHER   *Haematopus bachmani*

At the northern end of their range, in the Aleutian Islands, I first became acquainted with these big black waders. Here we frequently saw them at various points, as we entered or left the rock-bound harbors, sitting in little groups or in pairs on the rocks or outlying ledges. They were surprisingly inconspicuous on the wet and dark colored rocks, which were often half-hidden in the prevailing fogs. They seemed to fit very well into their dark and gloomy surroundings. They were not particularly shy, as they stood on the slippery rocks and nodded to us with grotesque dignity, or as they flew out around us uttering their loud and penetrating cries.

The flight of the black oyster catcher is strong and direct, but it seemed to me to be rather slow and heavy. Lucien M. Turner (1886) says:

The flight consists of a few rapid strokes of the wing, followed by a sail for a few yards. It is sluggish when on the wing, and flies with difficulty, and rarely long continued. When alarmed it flies over the water within a few yards of the shore, and in going from one point of rocks to another it either makes the trip in easy stages from one large rock to another, or else follows the indentations of the shore line. The bird is always on the alert, and not at all shy. It generally sees the hunter long before he suspects the presence of the bird. The bird either squats in a depression of the rocks, or stealthily creeps to the top of some huge boulder, where it utters a piercing, whistling chatter like that of a policeman's rattle. It causes the intruder long search to discover the presence of the bird, for its color is so near that of the rocks it frequents that it is not easily detected. The note is then answered by another bird, so that in a few minutes a dozen may be chattering hideously, making the hunter wonder where all the birds came from so suddenly, as all the birds within hearing assemble on the first note of alarm.

My notes refer to the cries of this bird as loud, penetrating screams, sounding like *whee-up,* or *whee-ep.*

Doctor Dall (1873) says [in the Aleutians]:

They utter, when disturbed, a peculiar, low whistle; which once heard, is likely to be remembered; and they have a habit of standing on the beach or rocks a little way apart, and whistling to one another; one calling and the other answering; and keeping it up for half an hour at a time. It is one of the most peculiar birds of the region, in its motions, having a grave, solemn and stilted gait, and bobbing its head up and down with every step. 1928

PLOVERS, TURNSTONES, AND SURFBIRDS
Family Charadriidae

RINGED PLOVER   *Charadrius hiaticula*   (Jourdain)

Dr. W. Elmer Ekblaw says in his notes:

The ringed plover is one of the most noticeable birds of the shorelands of northwest Greenland. Few beaches are unoccupied by these noisy little birds, and rarely is one out of sound of their shrill piping. They are quite as common about the streams and pools of the interior and along the seepage swales of the ground moraines. They come to the land as early as May 29 and stay until the last week in July. Almost invariably they are mated when they arrive and only rarely does one see more than a pair together, except where they congregate about swales or shallow pools to feed. They are sociably inclined and do not hesitate to make their nests near the Eskimo villages, probably feeling more secure from Arctic foxes when near dogs and human habitation.

The courtship of this species has been well described by Farren, Selous, and Stanford. The former (1910) says:

Ringed plovers may be seen in pairs skimming low over the ground, circling to a far height and descending again like a flash, almost touching the ground as they do so. They do not follow each other, but each describes similar evolutions, overlapping and crossing the other's line of flight. Their long pointed wings, showing much white, give a fictitious impression of size and as they alight on the ground after skimming a short distance with curved drooping wings they seem suddenly to vanish from sight as they touch ground; in place of the long-winged graceful flyer is a little plump-shaped gray bird, very difficult to see as it runs with short quick steps over the sand. 1928

SEMIPALMATED PLOVER   *Charadrius semipalmatus*   (Townsend)

This charming little wader, familiarly known as ring-necked plover or ringneck, is, during migrations, an abundant frequenter of our seashores as well as the shores of lakes and rivers.

In flight the flocks are often compact, twisting and turning as if animated by a single thought, but they also fly in loose order. On alighting they at once spread out on the sand in true plover fashion, and do not, like sandpipers, keep together and move along close to the wave line. Another plover habit which at once distinguishes them from sanderlings or other sandpipers of a similar size, is that of running about with heads up and dabbing suddenly at the ground from time to time instead of moving along with heads down diligently probing the sand. With erect figures they run about in various directions, often pausing and standing still as if in thought, occasionally jerking or bobbing their heads and necks and ever and again swiftly dabbing at some morsel of food.

In the latter part of May and early in June on the southern Labrador coast I have seen this bird flying about in circles uttering its loud and rapidly repeated courtship song. The song, which is entirely unlike the call note, may be heard, and the courtship performance watched, not only in the spring but in the autumn migrations, for there is a recrudescence of the amatory instinct at this season in most birds. The song, if such it may be called, is then generally given from the ground and may be likened to a whinny or to the sound of a bouncing ball. The notes are at first slowly repeated, but the speed increases until the notes follow one another so rapidly that they nearly run together. The birds that utter this song crouch low with tails spread and slightly cocked, wings partly open, and feathers, particularly of the breast and flanks, puffed out. Sometimes one walks in this way around another, sometimes two face each other, crouched motionless and then spring at each other and up into the air like fighting cocks. Sometimes one runs after another which, on taking flight is followed by the first, but the most amusing form of this courtship is where two, thus flattened, spread, and puffed, walk slowly side by side as if they were doing a cakewalk, all the time uttering their clucking song.

At Seal Island, off the southern point of Nova Scotia, I found several breeding pairs of semipalmated plover, here, probably, at its most southern breeding place. On one occasion I came upon a bird that performed the usual wounded bird act, falling on its side and fluttering its wings as if badly injured. Presently it made off, fluttering and dragging its spread tail on the ground, keeping up this method of progression for over a hundred yards, although I had stood still. I then walked in the opposite direction and found a downy young running off in company with the other parent.   1928

PIPING PLOVER   *Charadrius melodus*   (Tyler)

The piping plover's home is blue and gray and white; on one side is the long line of the horizon over a large lake or the sea, on the other the long line of the sand hills. It is a land the same the world over, wherever the sea meets the white, shifting sand. The sea slides back and forth over the hard smooth wet shining beach; above the reach of the tide is the dry, pale gray, pebbly upper beach with here and there a few strands of beach grass growing in it, and higher up are the dunes which mark on the land side the boundary of the plover's home.

Walk along the water's edge and, although the sea may be pounding on the shore and a northerly gale howling about our ears, we shall hear the plover's voice; a soft musical moan, we can not tell from where, but clear and distinct above the sound of waves and wind. The note has a ventriloquial quality and it is often our first intimation that a piping plover is near, for the soft gray of the bird's plumage matches the sandy background, whereas the note is pervasive and attracts our attention by its strangeness.

After the eggs are hatched, the parents display the utmost concern for the safety of their young. E. H. Forbush describes graphically this behavior, and also shows that even in the early days of the young bird's life the parents do not feed them. Mr. Forbush says:

A colony of piping plovers on the same beach had been much reduced in numbers, but the behavior of one pair showed that they had young on the beach. We saw one plover and then another fluttering along the ground like young or crippled birds. Their actions might deceive a novice, but by watching them with a glass, we soon saw that they were adult birds. They threw themselves on the ground, breast downward, and, drooping the flight feathers or primaries, raised and agitated the shorter secondaries, until the motion resembled the fluttering pinions of young or wounded birds, meantime pushing themselves along over the sand with their feet. As the wings were not spread, the long primary quills were not noticeable, and so the imitation of the struggles of a helpless bird was almost perfect. Immediately we began a careful search for the nest, looking in all the usual hiding places in or under the tufts of beach grass, but no nest could we find. As the old birds continued their plaintive cries and circled about, we extended our search, expecting to find some half-grown young flattened out somewhere on the beach. Finally, by hunting over the sand we found on the open beach, a nest exactly like that of the least tern. A few little pebbles had been grouped in a slight hollow, and there, partly beside and partly on the pebbles, lay three lovely little downy chicks and one egg. We attempted to photograph the parents, but they would not come to the young; and, as the little ones had already begun to run about, we sunk an old barrel in the beach, and put them and the egg in it, that we might know where to find them on the morrow.

The day was foggy and cold, and during the night a thunderstorm drenched the earth; but the next morning the egg had disappeared, and four lively youngsters were running around in our barrel. They were now so active, that if one were liberated it would be rather difficult to catch it, while if hidden, it would be almost impossible to find it.

We kept them there two days, until we made sure that the parents never fed them. They brooded them quite constantly, but brought no food whatever, and we made certain that the young were able and willing to find their own food within 24 hours after they were out of the shell. It was seen that unless they were liberated from the barrel they would soon starve to death.   1928

SNOWY PLOVER   *Charadrius alexandrinus*

The charming little snowy plover of the Pacific coast is the counterpart of our familiar piping plover, found in similar haunts, perhaps even tamer and more confiding, but not equal to our eastern bird in melody of voice. It is a child of the sand, with which its colors blend so well that when crouched in some hollow or against some bleached piece of driftwood or half buried clam shell it seems to be just one more of the numerous, inconspicuous objects which one passes unnoticed on the beach. Its favorite haunts are the broad expanses of flat, dry sand above the ordinary wash of the tides on ocean beaches. Such places are usually strewn more or less thickly with shells, pebbles, and various bits of debris, among which the little plover, or its eggs and young, are surprisingly inconspicuous. Here it was born and has always lived; here it woos its mate and rears its little family; and hence it seldom strays except to feed along the water's edge on the ocean beach or on the bare flats along some near-by tidal creek. There are, however, a few places in the interior where the snowy plover has been found along the shores of salt or alkaline lakes. But it is mainly a bird of the ocean beaches.

We spent a delightful day, May 29, 1914, among these birds with Mr. Chambers at Del Rey, Los Angeles County [California]. This was once a typical nesting place of this species, a broad stretch of sand flats above an ocean beach, backed by sand dunes and bordered on the inner side by a sluggish stream meandering through a marsh and some brackish lagoons. But civilization was encroaching on the plover's paradise, for several cottages had been built on the beach and it was much frequented. Some four pairs of snowy plover still clung to their ancestral home; we found three nests with three eggs each and one empty nest, in open spaces among the houses. The nests were mostly on little mounds of sand and scattered pebbles or among low sand dunes covered with low weeds and vines. They were deep hollows in the sand, profusely lined with finely broken white and pink shells, among scattered small stones, bits of wood, or other rubbish. Amid such surroundings the eggs were not easily detected; but we could usually locate the nests by the multitude of little footprints in the sand converging toward the nest.   **1928**

WILSON'S PLOVER   *Charadrius wilsonia*

All along the Atlantic coast from New Jersey to Florida is a broken chain of sea-girt islands, with broad or steep, sandy or shelly beaches on the ocean side, backed in many places by shifting sand dunes and bordered on the inner or bay side by wide marshes of waving grass or extensive flats exposed at low tide. Here, on the broader, more open sand flats, among a scattered array of shells, pebbles, and other debris cast up by the sea, or in the flat hollows among the sand dunes, this little sand plover makes its home, within sound of the pounding surf and fanned by the ocean breezes that carve the dunes into fantastic shapes. Here, if we love to wander in these seaside solitudes, we may see this gentle bird running along the beach ahead of us, his feet twinkling so fast that we can hardly see them; he is unafraid, as he stops and turns to watch us; the black bands on his head and breast help to obliterate his form and he might be mistaken for an old seashell or bit of driftwood; but, as we draw near, he turns and runs on ahead of us, leading us thus on and on up the beach. There is an air of gentleness in his manner and an air of wildness in his note as he flies away.

The female is a past master in the art of decoying an intruder away from her young. Mr. Thurston (1913) has described this strategy very well, as follows:

As I approached this strip, seemingly from nowhere there appeared a female plover, calling plaintively. Now I knew that the season of nesting had begun. She was soon joined by a male and another female that chorused with her their wishes for my departure. How she coaxed me to follow her! This I did for a time, trailing behind as she struggled along on one leg, the other crumpled under her. Tediously she kept ahead, calling—sobbing, I should have said—one of the most pathetic yet beautiful notes I have heard. Surely if ever there was a picture of parental distress it was she. Finally, as though exhausted, she sank to the sand and lay on her side gasping. The other two flew back and forth overhead, whistling plaintively, but she heeded them not, nor my approach, and lay there panting. I was sure now that she was tired by her exertion and hurried to catch her, only to learn that she was "playing possum." She allowed me to almost touch her, and fluttered off again. Evidently she was not satisfied that her nest was safe and she tried new tactics this time. With seemingly broken wings that trailed as though helpless at her sides, she started down the beach and once more I followed after, but this time increased my speed. As I had about caught up with her she gave a joyous whistle, sprang into the air, and those wounded wings carried her like a bullet around a point of wooded land and out of sight. She had accomplished her purpose, as I had hopelessly lost the place from which she started. Search as I might, and did, I could not find it.   1928

KILLDEER   *Charadrius vociferus*   (Townsend)

The killdeer is probably the most widely distributed and best known of all our shore birds. Unlike most of the group, it is not confined to the borders of lakes and of the sea but is found in meadows, pastures, and dry uplands often many miles from water.

Both parents play the usual wounded-bird act to beguile the intruder from the eggs or young. The following detailed account [from northwest Iowa] by Ira N. Gabrielson (1922) is worth giving here:

It is impossible to approach the nest on foot without alarming one or other of the birds, as one was always on guard some distance away. At the appearance of a person walking, the one on guard would fly in a circle about the nest, giving the alarm, at the first note of which the one on the nest ran rapidly until some distance away and then took wing to join its mate in circling about the intruder. A man ploughing corn was viewed with absolute indifference by both birds, the team often passing down the row next to the nest without disturbing the sitting bird. At an alarm, however, both birds flew about the field unless the intruder persisted in approaching the nest. In such a case one of the birds dropped to the ground near the person, invariably on the side away from the nest, and fluttered about apparently in the greatest distress. The attitude most frequently assumed was as follows: one wing was held extended over the back, the other beat wildly in the dust, the tail feathers were spread and the bird lay flat on the ground, constantly giving a wild alarm note. This performance continued until the observer came very near when the bird would rise and run along the ground in a normal manner or at most with one wing dragging slightly as long as pursuit was continued. If the observer turned back toward the nest, however, these actions were immediately repeated. When the parents had succeeded in luring the intruder about 100 yards, they seemed satisfied as they then flew away.

While the broken wing tactics are used by the birds for man, dogs, and other predatory animals, in order to draw them away from the eggs or young, quite different tactics are used for browsing animals that might step on them. Thus Howard Lacey (1911) noticed that a flock of driven goats divided. "I walked up to the place[1] expecting to find a rattlesnake, and found instead a killdeer standing over her eggs with upspread wings and scolding vigorously."   1928

MOUNTAIN PLOVER   *Eupoda montana*

The above name is not especially appropriate for this species. The name, Rocky Mountain plover, would have been better, for its breeding range is mainly in the Rocky Mountain plateau. It frequents elevated ground but it is not a bird of the mountains but of the dry plains.

Coues (1874) writes [that near Los Angeles, California]:

They were not difficult of approach, and I had no difficulty in securing as many as I desired. On being disturbed by too near approach, they lower the head, run rapidly a few steps in a light, easy way, and then stop abruptly, drawing themselves up to their full height and looking around with timid yet unsuspicious glances. When forced to fly by persistent annoyance, they rise rapidly with quick wing beats and then proceed with alternate sailing and flapping, during the former action holding the wings decurved. They generally fly low over the ground and soon realight, taking a few mincing steps as they touch the ground; they then either squat low, in hopes of hiding, or stand on tip-toe, as it were, for a better view of what alarmed them.

Grinnell, Bryant, and Storer (1918) say:

This plover is a flocking species found in bands of from fifteen to several hundred individuals. Often upon alighting after they have been in flight, the birds will immediately run to some distance, so that it is not always possible to follow them up easily as with other shore birds. The flocks fly low over the ground and are difficult to see, except when they wheel. As they do this the under surfaces of their wings show momentarily as silvery white flashes.

W. C. Bradbury (1918) has given us a very good account of the nesting habits of the mountain plover in Colorado. Of the nesting site [20 miles east of Denver] he says:

The ground is an open, rolling prairie, above the line of irrigation, and is devoted to cattle range. It is several miles from natural surface water and streams, and is covered with short-cropped buffalo or gramma grass, 2 or 3 inches high, with frequent bunches of dwarfed prickly pear, and

[1] On his ranch near Kerrville, Texas, March 24, 1896.

an occasional cluster of stunted shrub or weed, rarely more than a foot in height. With the six sets secured, in no instance had the parent bird taken advantage of the slight protection offered from sight or the elements by the nearby cactus, shrubs or uneven spots of ground. In each case, she had avoided such shelter, locating in the open, generally between the small grass hummocks and not on or in them; there was no evidence of the parent birds having given more thought to nest preparation or concealment, than does any other plover. In two of the sets the eggs were all individually embedded in the baked earth to a depth of one-eighth to one-fourth of an inch, evidently having settled when the surface of the ground was reduced to soft mud by rain-water collecting in the slight depresions, As the ground dried up the eggs were fixed in a perfect mould or matrix, from which they could not roll. In fact they could hardly be disturbed at all by the sitting birds. The only nesting material was a small quantity of fine, dry rootlets and "crowns" of gramma grass, the eggs in some instances being slightly embedded in this lining. As it is also present in all other depressions on the prairie it is highly probable that here as elsewhere it was deposited about the eggs by the wind and not through the agency of the birds themselves. The protective coloration of the nest and eggs, as well as of the rear view of the birds themselves, even when in motion, is unsurpassed. In no instance except one was the bird seen to leave the nest, nor was any nest found except in the immediate vicinity of moving birds.   1928

EURASIAN GOLDEN PLOVER   *Pluvialis apricaria*

The claim of the golden plover of Europe to a place in the American list rests on its occurrence in [migration in southern] Greenland.

Seton Gordon (1915) writes [of this species in England]:

During the season of courtship and indeed up to June is heard the song of the golden plover and this song is one of the most striking things in the habits of moorland birds. Before commencing to sing the cock bird mounts into the air to a height of at least 100 feet and flies slowly, deliberately around the spot where his mate is listening to him below, uttering as he flies a musical whistling cry of two syllables sounding like *whee-wheeu*, the last being long drawn out. His flight during this time is quite distinctive, he no longer cleaves the air with sharp and rapid wing beats, but moves his wings with slow deliberate strokes, holding them V-shaped for an instant between the beats. Should he cease his song— even for a few moments—the normal flight is at once resumed. His cry on these occasions carries over a great stretch of moor, and I think can be heard at a greater distance even than the vibrating notes of the curlew. After some time, during which these long-drawn whistles are regularly continued, the singer shoots earthward, uttering, just as he is reaching the ground, a curious purring cry, repeated rapidly five or six times. On paper the sounds resemble *trooeu, trooeu, trooeu.* These descriptions apply strictly to the southern race,[1] but the habits of the two forms in the breeding season are identical and the Icelandic birds[2] perform their song flights in the same way as the Scotch birds. Hantzsch points out very justly that the golden plover is not at all quarrelsome in disposition, and though rival males may vie in song with one another they meet frequently quite amicably and the natives have long noted the toleration which the plover extends to the dunlin and which has earned for the latter the name Loa-thraoll, or, as our forefathers put it, Plover's-page.   1928

AMERICAN GOLDEN PLOVER   *Pluvialis dominica*

P.d. dominica   (American Golden Plover)

The golden plover is not only one of our most beautiful shore birds in its brilliant spring plumage, but its wonderful migration excites our admiration and the comparison of its former abundance with its present scarcity furnishes a striking picture of the ruthless slaughter that has squandered our previous wealth of wild life.

Writing of conditions in Argentina about the middle of the last century, W. H. Hudson (1922) writes:

The golden plover was then one of the abundant species. After its arrival in September, the plains in the neighborhood of my home[3] were peopled with immense flocks of this bird. Sometimes in hot summers the streams and marshes would mostly dry up, and the aquatic-bird population, the plover included, would shift their quarters to other districts. During one of these droughty seasons, when my age was 9, there was a marshy ground 2 miles from my home where a few small pools of water still remained, and to this spot the golden plover would resort every day at noon. They would appear in flocks from all quarters, flying to it like starlings in England coming in to some great roosting center on a winter evening. I would then mount my pony and gallop off joyfully to witness the spectacle. Long before coming in sight of them the noise of their voices would be audible, growing louder as I drew near. Coming to the ground, I would pull up my horse and sit gazing with astonishment and delight at the spectacle of that immense multitude of birds, covering an area of 2 or 3 acres, looking less like a vast flock than a floor of birds, in color a rich deep brown, in strong contrast to the pale gray of the dried-up ground all round them. A living, moving floor and a sounding one as well, and the sound, too, was amazing. It was like the sea, but unlike it in character since it was not deep; it was more like the wind blowing, let us say, on thousands of tight-drawn wires of varying thicknesses, vibrating them to shrill sound, a mass and tangle of 10,000 sounds. But it is indescribable and unimaginable.

[1] *P.a. apricaria.*
[2] *P.a. altifrons.*
[3] Hudson was born at Quilmes, 10 miles from Buenos Aires, in 1841.

The golden plover has been a famous game bird. It was a most desirable table bird, as it was usually very fat and its flesh had a delicious flavor on account of its clean, upland feeding habits. The uncertainty of its appearance and its enormous numbers at favorable times made its pursuit most interesting. During the years of its abundance it was slaughtered in almost incredible numbers.

John C. Cahoon (1888) describes a method of shooting golden plover employed by old gunners on Cape Cod, as follows:

Several weeks before the time for the flights to occur, they go to an old field or pasture that they know the birds usually come into and burn off the old grass and bushes for quite a space. Then a hole is dug large enough for one or two persons to sit in comfortably, with only the top of their heads above the surface. In a few weeks the grass springs up and the green patch is easily distinguished from its duller surroundings by the plover flying about, and they are sure to come to this place. The gunner, with his decoys out, sits in his pit with only the top of his head out, which is covered with a green cap. A flock, before alighting to the decoys, will usually circle about several times, often flying directly over the gunner's head only a few yards away. An experienced gunner will not shoot when they are so near and scattered, as he could kill but one or two, but will wait for them to bunch at the right distance, which they are sure to do while turning, and seize that opportunity to fire, killing many at one shot.

P.d. fulva (Pacific Golden Plover)

This plover makes even more wonderful migratory flights than its American relative, for between its winter[1] and its summer[2] homes it travels twice each year over thousands of miles of trackless ocean.

How fast the birds fly or how long it takes them to make the two thousand miles flight across the ocean to the Aleutian Islands, we do not know. If they fly at the rate of forty miles an hour without stopping, it would take over two days. They probably can not sustain such a prolonged effort without food. Practically all shore birds are known to alight on and arise from the water at will; so the chances are that they stop to rest on the way. They probably obtain some food from floating masses of seaweed, from the refuse left by whales, or from the numerous forms of minute animal life to be found on the surface.   1928

BLACK-BELLIED PLOVER   *Squatarola squatarola*

The black-bellied plover is an aristocrat among shore birds, the largest and strongest of the plovers, a leader of its tribe. It is a

---
[1] New Zealand, Oceania, and Hawaii.
[2] Alaska.

distinguished-looking bird in its handsome spring livery of black and white; and its attitude, as it stands like a sentinel on the crest of a sand dune or on some distant mud flat, is always dignified and imposing.

Herbert W. Brandt says in his Alaska notes:

During courtship the male spends considerable time on the wing, speeding about like a racer; and amid the constant din of wild-fowl notes his cheery whistle *to lee, to lee,* is one of the pleasant sounds that greet the ear. But once the female is incubating her lord becomes as serious and silent as his sober black waistcoat, so that by early June it seemed as if every plover had left the country. He carries on his courtship regardless of weather, now mounting high, the next moment skimming low, with beautiful and bewildering grace, his wild whistling call meanwhile rising above the din of the storm. The advance guard of migrants of this plover arrived from the south in a "nor'wester" on May 7, passing like phantom voyagers, and the next instant were lost in mid-air in the swirling snow.

Mr. Brandt has sent me the following notes on the nesting habits of the black-bellied plover in the Hooper Bay region of Alaska:

We found this jauntily attired plover the most common nesting species of the larger shore birds, frequenting the upland rolling tundra, where it preferred the ridges. It often chose for a nesting site the edge of one of the more prominent bluffs which formed the margin of the valleys, from which location the sitting bird could view the entire surrounding country. On these barren areas, where even the close-cropped moss struggles for existence, the vegetation is mottled with black and white, and as a consequence the eggs, in spite of their exposed situation, are very difficult to find. One must almost touch them to be sure that they are there, so completely do they harmonize with their background. This protective coloration is so perfect that in one case a bird deserted its nest and the eggs remained unprotected for three days, during which time jaegers, which were continuously hunting overhead and about, were, even with their sharp eyes, not able to distinguish them.   1928

SURFBIRD   *Aphriza virgata*

From its summer home in the mountains of central Alaska the surf bird migrates down the Pacific coasts of North and South America as far as the Straits of Magellan.

The breeding grounds and the nesting habits of the surf bird long remained unknown. The birds vanished from the coast of Alaska about the first of June and were not seen again for six weeks or more, when they appeared again with their young. Rumors suggested that they bred in the mountains in the interior. O. J. Murie (1924) gave us the first definite information, when he discovered the breeding ground of the species in the Mount McKinley Park region of central Alaska. On July 13, 1921, he was descending a slope above timber line, "when two surf birds were flushed and circled about making an outcry." He was "presently rewarded by seeing a downy young one striding away bravely over the rough ground." The young bird was secured and one of the parents, which proved to be the male, thus establishing the first breeding record for the species.

Five years later Joseph Dixon (1927) spent considerable time in this same region and succeeded in finding, on May 28, 1926, the first nest of the surf bird. He writes:

One of the most striking things about the surf bird is the remarkable difference between its winter and summer habitat. Near the end of their northward migration in the spring these birds abandon the seacoast and take up their summer residence far in the interior, from 300 to 500 miles from salt water. This involves a great altitudinal shift. Instead of living at sea level as they do at other seasons, during nesting time they are to be found on barren, rocky mountains high up above timber line. During the entire summer we never found these birds below 4,000 feet elevation.

The rocky character of the surf birds' surroundings appears to remain fairly constant throughout the year. In summer the birds are to be found most frequently near the summits of the rock slides where the broken rocks are much the same as the rugged reefs they inhabit during the winter. We found in the Mount McKinley district that the summer range of the surf bird was almost identical with that of the mountain sheep and that it was useless to look for surf birds outside of "sheep" country.

When standing on a barren wind-swept ridge late in the afternoon of May 28, searching a nearby hillside with binoculars, Mr. Wright's attention was attracted to a grayish bird that was sneaking hurriedly along over the rocky ground. As he watched, the bird apparently faded out of sight some 600 feet away. Marking the point of disappearance he hurried over to the spot where the bird was last seen and, failing to find the bird, began to think he was mistaken. But, upon his taking one more step, the bird flew up suddenly right into his face, startling him mightily. As the bird flew away, the large white rump patch, together with a white patch on either wing, brought realization that this was the long-sought-for surf bird. A hasty glance at his feet revealed the nest and contents of four eggs. Another step forward and he would have placed his foot directly in the nest! To George M. Wright belongs the honor of being the first white man, of which we have any record, to lay eyes on the nest and eggs of this rare bird.

The surf bird's nest was located 1,000 feet above timber line on a rocky ridge that faced southwest and lay fair to the sun and hence was relatively free from snow. The nest site was on dry rocky ground and not on the wet tundra which was plentiful nearby.

The nest, which was barely large enough to hold the four eggs, which were placed as close together as possible, with little ends down, measured 4 inches in diameter and an inch and a half in depth. The eggs in the nest blended so well with the reddish brown moss of the tundra that it became difficult to make them out at a distance of more than 8 or 10 feet.   1928

RUDDY TURNSTONE   *Arenaria interpres*

The above species is cosmopolitan; it has a circumpolar breeding range, and its migrations extend over nearly all of the Northern Hemisphere and a large part of the Southern.

[It] is mainly a maritime species and its favorite feeding grounds are the stony and sandy beaches along the seashore and the rocky promontories and islets on the coasts. But on its inland migrations it finds its food on the shores and beaches of the larger lakes and rivers. The turnstone derives its name from its well-known and conspicuous habit of turning over, with its short, stout bill and sturdy muscles, stones, shells, clods of earth, seaweed, and other objects in search for the dainty morsels of animal food that it finds beneath them. If the object is not too large the bird stoops down and overturns it with a quick jerk of the head and neck; but against a larger obstacle it places its breast and pushes with all its strength; it is surprising to see how large a stone or clod it can move. It also has a peculiar habit of rooting like a pig in piles of seaweed or in the open sand. Windrows of seaweed and other rubbish are generally full of sand fleas and various worms and insects and their larvae, where the turnstones and other waders find an abundant feast. Frank T. Noble (1904) has described this very well [on a Maine Island], as follows:

He would select a likely spot on the loosely packed moss and go at his work with a vim and rapidity entirely different from the other species. Underneath the bits of weed, moss, and fragments of shell his sharp upturned bill would swiftly go and a perfect shower of these would soon be falling in front and beside him. Finding a morsel to his taste he would devour it in much less time than it takes to relate it, and the rooting and tossing of the bits into the air would continue. At times quite sizeable fragments of shell and pieces of moss more than an inch in length would be thrown fully 7 or 8 inches above the bird's head, and this he would keep up, with scarcely an instant's pause, for a quarter of an hour and until he had excavated a pit large enough to almost conceal his plump, mottled body. Occasionally he would turn about in his tracks, but as a rule he worked in one direction.

I have seen a similar method employed on a sand flat laid bare at low tide, where four or five turnstones were feeding, accompanied by sanderlings and peeps. The turnstones were digging holes in the wet sand, throwing out the sand for a distance of several inches, until the holes were big enough to admit the whole of a man's fist and deep enough to conceal the bird's head and neck.   1928

BLACK TURNSTONE   *Arenaria melanocephala*

The black turnstone replaces to a large extent on the Pacific coast our well-known ruddy turnstone; both species are found there on migrations and in winter, but the black is the commoner on that coast, to which it is restricted. It is a characteristic bird of the barnacle-covered reefs and rocky shores, being more often seen on the outlying islands and ledges than on the mainland. There it lives at the water's edge, seeking its food within reach of the waves and often drenched with ocean spray. As it stands motionless it is almost invisible in its coat of dark brown and might easily be mistaken for a knob of rock or a bunch of seaweed; but when startled into flight its conspicuous pattern of black and white flashes out a distinctive mark of recognition.

Mr. Brandt says in his notes:

Among the shore birds breeding along the coast of Bering Sea there is none more interesting and fascinating than this black and white turnstone. When the mud about the edges of the ponds and tidal sloughs begins to soften, and the accumulated snow water starts to move, this bird appears enlivening the bleak, cheerless marshes with its loud-toned cries and butterfly-like appearance. In the lowland area it is the commonest shore bird, and its contrastive black and white figure is doubly conspicuous because it resents intrusion of its haunts and sallies forth to meet the approaching stranger; whereas the rest of the shore-bird tribe found there either skulk away or exhibit indifference. As the Pacific godwit[1] is the self-appointed guardian of the upland tundra, so the black turnstone patrols the lowlands, often to the dismay of the hunter or the irritation of the ornithologist. In spite of its chunky body and comparatively short wings, it is gifted with elegance and swiftness of flight. It does not, like the phalarope, afford an inviting target for the young native hunters, because not only does it scold on the wing, but it also moves so nervously while on the ground that it is not quiet there even for a fraction of a second. No doubt the hunting jaegers consider it the pest of the flats, for while passing through its domain, these freebooters are usually being annoyingly followed by one or more of these fiery and courageous defenders.

The black turnstones, like many of the other shore birds during the mating season, spend considerable time chasing each other about. The female seems to say to the male, "catch me if you can," and then dashes off

[1] As the subspecies *baueri* of the Bar-tailed Godwit was formerly called.

with such speed that the pursuer has difficulty in following her, and she usually returns to the same spot from which her zigzag flight began. Often the male will mount high into the air alone, until completely out of sight, and then will produce with his wing or tail feathers, which of the two I have not been able to determine, the same strange *zum-zum-zum* noise as made by the Wilson snipe[1]. Before the nesting season this feather music could be heard on the flats at any time, and it deceived me at first, as I mistook it for that of the snipe. Later, however, as soon as the nesting duties began, it seemed to cease; and in this respect, the black turnstone differs from the Wilson snipe, because the feather music of the latter is continued throughout the incubation period.   1928

WOODCOCK, SNIPE, AND SANDPIPERS
Family Scolopacidae

AMERICAN WOODCOCK   *Philohela minor*

This mysterious hermit of the alders, this recluse of the boggy thickets, this wood nymph of crepuscular habits is a common bird and well distributed in our eastern states, widely known, but not intimately known. Its quiet retiring habits do not lead to human intimacy. It may live almost in our midst unnoticed.

The woodcock may be found by those who seek him and know his haunts, but it is only for a short time during the breeding season, that he comes out into the open and makes himself conspicuous. His spectacular evening song-flight has been seen by many observers.

The time to look and listen for it is during the laying and incubation period—say the month of April in Massachusetts, earlier farther south, even December and January in the Gulf states. The performance usually begins soon after sunset, as twilight approaches. On dark nights it ceases about when the afterglow finally disappears in the western sky; and it begins again in the morning twilight, lasting from dawn to broad daylight. On moonlight nights it is often continued through much or all of the night. The woodcock's nest is usually in some swampy thicket or on the edge of the woods, near an open pasture, field, or clearing; and here in the nearest open space, preferably on some knoll or low hillside within hearing of his sitting mate, the male woodcock entertains her with his thrilling performance. Sometimes, but not always, he struts around on the ground, with tail erect and spread, and with bill pointing downwards and resting on his chest. More often he stands still, or walks about slowly

[1] As the Common Snipe was formerly called.

in a normal attitude, producing at intervals of a few seconds two very different notes—a loud, rasping, emphatic *zeeip*—which might be mistaken for the note of the nighthawk, and a soft guttural note, audible at only a short distance, like the croak of a frog or the cluck of a hen. Suddenly he rises, and flies off at a rising angle, circling higher and higher, in increasing spirals, until he looks like a mere speck in the sky, mounting to a height of two hundred or three hundred feet; during the upward flight he whistles continuously, twittering musical notes, like *twitter, itter, itter, itter,* repeated without a break. These notes may be caused by the whistling of his wings, but it seems to me that they are vocal. Then comes his true love song —a loud, musical, three-syllable note—sounding to me like *chicharee, chicharee, chicharee* uttered three times with only a slight interval between the outbursts; this song is given as the bird flutters downward, circling, zigzagging, and finally volplaning down to the ground at or near his starting point. He soon begins again on the *zeeip* notes and the whole act is repeated again and again.   1927

COMMON SNIPE   *Capella gallinago*

On the wings of the south wind comes the first wisp of snipe, the will-o-the-wisp of the marshes, here to-day and gone to-morrow, coming and going under the cover of darkness. All through the spring migration and all through the nesting season we may hear the weird winnowing sound of the snipe's courtship flight, a tremulous humming sound, loud and penetrating, audible at a long distance. One is both thrilled and puzzled when he hears it for the first time, for it seems like a disembodied sound, the sighing of some wandering spirit, until the author is discovered, a mere speck, sweeping across the sky. The sound resembles the noise made by a duck's wings in rapid flight, a rapidly pulsating series of notes, *who, who, who, who, who, who, who, who,* increasing and then decreasing again in intensity. It has been termed the "bleating" of the snipe, but this does not seem to describe it so well as "winnowing." J. R. Whitaker, with whom I hunted snipe in Newfoundland, told me that both sexes indulge in this performance and George M. Sutton (1923) suggested the possibility of it.

Dr. Joseph Grinnell (1900) gives the best account of this courtship flight [Kowak Valley, Alaska, May 22, 1899], as follows:

I was in a broad grassy swale, studded here and there with scrub spruces and bordered by taller timber, when my attention was attracted by a curious far-off song which puzzled me for some time. Finally I descried the producer, a Wilson's snipe[1], so far overhead as to be scarcely discernible against the clear sky. It was flying slowly in a broad circle with a diameter of perhaps 600 yards, so that the direction of the sound was ever shifting, thus confusing me until I caught sight of its author. This lofty flight was not continuously on the same level, but consisted of a series of lengthy undulations or swoops. At the end of each swoop the bird would mount up to its former level. The drop at the beginning of the downward dive was with partly closed, quivering wings, but the succeeding rise was accomplished by a succession of rapid wing beats. The peculiar resonant song was a rolling series of syllables uttered during the downward swoop, and just before this drop merged into the following rise a rumbling and whirring sound became audible, accompanying the latter part of the song and finishing it. This curious song flight was kept up for 15 minutes, ending with a downward dash. But before the bird reached the ground and was yet some 20 yards above it there was apparently a complete collapse. The bird dropped as if shot for several feet, but abruptly recovered itself to fly a short distance farther and repeat this new maneuver. By a succession of these collapses, falls, recoveries, and short flights the acrobatically inclined bird finally reached the ground, alighting in the grass near me.

1927

LONG-BILLED CURLEW   *Numenius americanus*

One can not see this magnificent bird for the first time without experiencing a thrill of enthusiasm for the largest, one of the most interesting and notable of our shore birds, one that seems to embody more than any other the wild, roving spirit of the vast open prairies. Its large size, its long, curving bill, the flash of cinnamon in its wings, and above all, its loud, clear, and prolonged whistling notes are bound to attract attention. In its former abundance this species must have been a most striking feature of the western plains, as it flew in large wedge-shaped flocks in full cry.

The long-billed curlew formerly bred over a large portion of central North America, including all of the prairie regions, at least as far east as Michigan and Illinois, and probably Ohio. But, with the settling of the country and the disappearance of the prairies, it has been gradually driven farther and farther west, and even there into a more and more restricted range.

The spring behavior of these curlews, or what might be called a nuptial flight [in central Montana] is thus described by P. M. Silloway (1900):

After their arrival, the curlews inhabit the high, dry prairies, flying restlessly from one portion to another, showing a tendency to associate in pairs,

[1] As the Common Snipe was formerly called.

though as couples, these birds are not inseparable. In the mating season, one of the pair is likely to follow the other in a few moments, when the first bird has flown far over the prairie to a more distant station. At any time the loud, prolonged whistling of these birds, either when on the ground or a-wing, will call attention to their movements, warning the disturber of their domain that his presence is known and that his actions will be watched with the closest interest.

One of the pleasing sights to the ornithologist in watching the behavior of these curlews is seen when a pair are sailing upward in company abreast of the wind, moving in perfect accord on widespread, motionless pinions curved gently downward, within several feet of each other, then fluttering downward side by side or one in advance of the other, again to sail upward, uttering the characteristic whistles.

Although long since removed from the game-bird list, the "sickle-bill" was a fine game bird. Its large size made it a tempting target. It decoyed readily and could be easily whistled down by imitating its notes. The cries of a wounded bird were sure to attract others, which would circle around again and again until many were killed.

1928

WHIMBREL   *Numenius phaeopus*

N.p. hudsonicus   (Hudsonian Curlew)

Although Hudsonian curlews may fly swiftly at times and probably make good speed when traveling they appear to me to fly rather slowly and heavily, with steady and rather moderate wing beats; they often set their wings and scale for a long distance. When migrating over land they usually fly high, in flocks, much after the manner of ducks and geese; but when migrating over water or flying to and from their roosting grounds they often fly in long lines close to the water.

Herbert K. Job (1905) saw them here [South Carolina] in "scores of thousands"; he spent a night at each of several little low islands— mere sand bars—lying off the coast, and says:

About half past 5 or 6 o'clock, when the sun was low in the horizon or had set behind a cloud bank, the first advancing line is seen, and a string of from a dozen to 50 Hudsonian curlews come scaling over the beach, to alight on the bar, down at the other end. After a few minutes another flock is seen approaching. By half past 6 they are arriving fast, and by 7 there are two or three flocks in sight all the time, some of them containing as many as 75 birds. Meantime I am shooting at them as they pass, with my reflex camera, despite the dull light. As may be imagined, the company on the sand has become immense, covering many acres. They keep up a sort of murmuring noise, and now and then all fly up, with a perfect storm and tumult of wings and voices, soon to alight again. Even after dark they are yet arriving, as one may hear. I hazard the guess that there are often 10,000 curlews at such a roost each night. At the first glimmer of day they are off again for the marshes.

John G. Tyler (1913) writes:

There are no birds with which I am acquainted that can compare with these splendid waders in the rich, musical quality of their voices. On the last day of one April I encountered a large flock of curlews in a grain field, part of which was being flooded at the time with irrigation water. The nervous lispings that at my approach threatened to break into the clamorous, screaming flight calls finally subsided, and the birds fed and waded about in the water or preened their feathers while standing storklike on one leg. Suddenly I was thrilled with a medley of subdued pipings so marvelously sweet and musical that I could hardly believe the sound came from my flock of curlews. The faintest whispering it seemed, yet the liquid melody was really far-reaching and was, as I afterwards learned, distinctly audible from a distance of a quarter of a mile when atmospheric conditions were favorable. A strange nervous unrest seemed to affect the entire group on the ground. The whistlings became louder, and the cause was suddenly revealed to me when a curlew call from overhead drew my attention to a flock of new arrivals, nine in number, that were circling preparatory to joining the company at the pond. My surprise and admiration knew no bounds when I realized the sublime heights at which these travelers through the sky had been flying. Mere specks they appeared, and yet their melodious call rang clear and distinct. 1928

BRISTLE-THIGHED CURLEW *Numenius tahitiensis*

The breeding grounds[1] and the nesting habits of the bristle-thighed curlew are entirely unknown, an interesting problem for some enterprising ornithologist to work out.

Dr. Alexander Wetmore has sent me the following notes:

That a bird of the shore-bird family should destroy eggs may seem almost unbelievable in view of the habits ordinary in this group, yet in work in the Hawaiian Bird Reservation in 1923 we found the bristle-thighed curlew, as well as the turnstone,[2] making regular practice of eating the eggs of the birds nesting on these distant islands. The sooty and gray-backed terns were the greatest sufferers, as the curlew drove their long bills through the eggs with ease, or seized them in their long mandibles to carry them away and eat them at their leisure. On close observation we found that curlews

[1] Now known to breed in western Alaska near the mouth of the Yukon River.
[2] Ruddy.

attacked the eggs of all birds indiscriminately, even pulling an egg from beneath a frigate bird when the incubating bird raised on the nest for a moment, the theft being committed so adroitly that the egg seemingly was not missed. Mr. Donald Dickey in his motion pictures succeeded in filming a spirited scene in which a bristle-thighed curlew after a number of attempts accomplished the seemingly impossible feat of carrying away a frigate bird's egg held firmly between its mandibles, while a group of apparently admiring turnstones, robbers themselves but incapable of such herculean acts of banditry, scurried about in the background. On another occasion a curlew flew up to a red-footed booby's nest in a bush several feet from the ground in the temporary absence of the owner, impaled the egg, and dragged it away to be devoured. The booby was still brooding disconsolately in her empty nest two days later. On another day a curlew deliberately opened an old albatross egg found in the sand and ate eagerly from the putrid interior. As this egg had been lying unprotected from the sun for at least four months previous, its condition may be imagined, yet the bird returned avidly again and again to continue its horrid repast though I approached within 10 feet.   1928

ESKIMO CURLEW   *Numenius borealis*

The story of the Eskimo curlew is just one more pitiful tale of the slaughter of the innocents. It is a sad fact that the countless swarms of this fine bird and the passenger pigeon, which once swept across our land on migrations, are gone forever, sacrificed to the insatiable greed of man. "The Eskimo Curlew and its Disappearance," by Prof. Myron H. Swenk (1915), tells the story.

The greatest killings were made on the western plains during the spring migration, which Professor Swenk (1915) describes as follows:

During such flights the slaughter of these poor birds was appalling and almost unbelievable. Hunters would drive out from Omaha and shoot the birds without mercy until they had literally slaughtered a wagonload of them, the wagons being actually filled, and often with the sideboards on at that. Sometimes when the flight was unusually heavy and the hunters were well supplied with ammunition their wagons were too quickly and easily filled, so whole loads of the birds would be dumped on the prairie, their bodies forming piles as large as a couple of tons of coal, where they would be allowed to rot while the hunters proceeded to refill their wagons with fresh victims, and thus further gratify their lust of killing. The compact flocks and tameness of the birds made this slaughter possible, and at each shot usually dozens of the birds would fall. In one specific instance a single shot from an old muzzle-loading shotgun into a flock of these curlews as they veered by the hunter brought down 28 birds at once, while for the next half mile every now and then a fatally wounded bird would drop to the ground dead.

In Texas the Eskimo curlew came in immense flocks on the prairies from 1856 to 1875, after which year the large flocks disappeared. Small flocks were seen in 1886 and 1890. The last records of the species for Texas were 1902 and 1905, one and three individuals, respectively. The species were first definitely recorded for Kansas from Russell County in 1874. In that State these curlews were abundant as late as 1878, but in 1879 their numbers were much reduced and the birds decreased rapidly. There were still a few in the Kansas markets in the early nineties. The last record is for 1902. Eastwardly in the interior the birds were always uncommon and disappeared early. The last Michigan record is in 1883. The last Ohio record is in 1878. The last Wisconsin records are April 27, 1899, and September 10, 1912, the latter specimen a male taken at Fox Lake, Dodge County, Wis. The last Indiana record is, with some doubt, April 19, 1890.

The last records of collected birds for Nebraska were made in the spring of 1911 and of 1915. On March 22, 1911, while Mr. Fred Geiger was shooting ducks near Waco, York County, two of these birds came flying by within gun range, and both were shot by him. The birds were identified by an oldtime hunter, and were then brought to Lincoln, and mounted by Mr. August Eiche, in whose collection they are at present. Although no Eskimo curlews were noted in 1914, a single bird was killed about 10 miles due south of Norfolk, Nebr., on the morning of April 17, 1915. The bird was alone when taken. It came into the possession of Mr. Hoagland, who had it mounted by Allabaugh, a taxidermist of Omaha, in whose shop I saw it in May.[1]

The gunner's name for the Eskimo curlew was "dough-bird" not "doe-bird," for it was so fat when it reached us in the fall that its breast would often burst open when it fell to the ground, and the thick layer of fat was so soft that it felt like a ball of dough. It is no wonder that it was so popular as a game bird, for it must have made a delicious morsel for the table.   1928

UPLAND PLOVER   *Bartramia longicauda*

The voice of the upland plover is one of its greatest charms; once heard in its perfection it will never be forgotten; and it often serves to identify the species when the bird can not be seen. W. H. Hudson (1922) has referred to it very attractively, as follows:

Lying awake in bed, I would listen by the hour to that sound coming to me from the sky, mellowed and made beautiful by distance and the profound silence of the moonlit world, until it acquired a fascination for me above all sounds on earth, so that it lived ever after in me; and the image of it is as vivid in my mind at this moment as that of any bird call or cry,

[1] Last published sight records two birds, Galveston Island, Texas, April 29, 1945, and one bird, Galveston Island, Texas, March 22 to April 26, 1959.

or any other striking sound heard yesterday or but an hour ago. It was the sense of mystery it conveyed which so attracted and impressed me—the mystery of that delicate, frail, beautiful being, traveling in the sky, alone, day and night, crying aloud at intervals as if moved by some powerful emotion, beating the air with its wings, its beak pointing like the needle of the compass to the north, flying, speeding on its 7,000-mile flight to its nesting home in another hemisphere.

The courtship flight song of the upland plover is well described in some notes sent to me by Fred J. Pierce, as follows:

On still wings, these large birds circle slowly about, usually so high as to be mere specks in the sky, and give their shrill, penetrating whistle, which will carry nearly a mile, depending upon the wind and the altitude of the whistler. First there are a few notes sounding like water gurgling from a large bottle, then comes the loud *whip-whee-ee-you*, long drawn out and weirdly thrilling. When I first heard this strange cry I at once thought of some species of hawk as being the author of it, and I have known others to think the same thing. It is too loud and penetrating a cry to be attributed to one of the sandpipers. I have heard the bird whistling in this manner as late as July, but I do not believe that this is a common practice. On more than one occasion I have seen the bird, after circling at such height as to be almost out of sight, close its wings and shoot to earth like a falling stone. This thrilling performance is similar to that of the prairie horned lark,[1] which takes a headfirst drop to earth when it has finished singing its contribution to the usual spring morning chorus.

The most beautiful and striking note heard on its breeding grounds is a sweet, mellow, rolling trill, uttered as the bird flies along at a low elevation or while perched on a fence post or even on the ground; it is evidently a love note. Prof. Lynds Jones (1903) has described it very well, as follows:

The rolling cry is not unlike the rolling call of a tree toad, but of a different quality and caliber, which makes it unmistakable. The whistle is partly double, the first part passing upward nearly half an octave, terminating abruptly there, the second part beginning where the first began and rapidly swelling through nearly or quite an octave, then gradually falling again and decreasing in volume to the close, several tones above the beginning. The first part of the whistle is usually rattling or trilled, and sometimes the trill is carried to the end, but oftener it becomes a clear whistle before the culmination and continues clear to the end. *Tre-e-e-e-e-e-e-e, tre-e-e-e-e-e-e-e-e-e-e-e-e-e-p;* or *tr-r-r-r-e-e-e-e-e-e-p.* Often the whistled part is never reached, but the call stops as if interrupted by some threatened danger.   1928

---

[1] As the subspecies *praticola* was formerly known.

SPOTTED SANDPIPER   *Actitis macularia*   (Tyler)

The spotted sandpiper moves northward earlier than the other sandpipers. It enters the Transitional Zone in late April and early May, its time of arrival coinciding very closely with the chewink, another ground feeder. It returns to its breeding ground inconspicuously, never passing by in the large flocks characteristic of many sandpipers, but appears on the first day of its arrival running about on the shore of its chosen bit of water, apparently settled for the season.

Brewster (1925) speaks of the bird as:

Especially given to breeding on small islands in Lake Umbagog [Maine], scarce one of which is left untenanted by them at the right season or resorted to by more than a single pair. Their eggs, almost invariably four in number, are usually laid during the last week of May, in saucer-shaped hollows scraped in surface soil, and thinly lined with dry grass. . . . If the island be treeless and ledgy, the nest is likely to be on or near the most elevated or central part, and more or less well concealed by grass or other lowly vegetation. But if all the ground, not subject to inundation, be densely wooded, the spot where the bird has hidden her treasures is seldom far back from the shore, and perhaps scarce above highwater mark, usually where driftwood has accumulated, or beneath the leafy branch of some outstanding alder or Cassandra bush. In such places as these, it is by no means easy to find the nest, even when the total area to be searched is only a few rods square. The task may well seem hopeless if undertaken in the open farming country about the southern end of the Lake, for, although spotted sandpipers breed here not uncommonly, they are so widely and sparsely distributed over hilly pastures and fields of considerable extent, that it is only by the merest chance that anybody ever stumbles on a nest. The only one that I have happened upon was well hidden in a tangle of withered grass and ferns, covering a steeply sloping bank by the roadside.   1928

SOLITARY SANDPIPER   *Tringa solitaria*

This dainty "woodland tattler" is associated in my mind with some secluded, shady woodland pool in early autumn, where the summer drought has exposed broad muddy shores and where the brightly tinted leaves of the swamp maple float lightly on the still water. Here the solitary wader may be seen, gracefully poised on some fallen log, nodding serenely, or walking gracefully over the mud or in the shallow water. Seldom disturbed by man, it hardly seems to heed his presence; it may raise its wings, displaying their pretty linings, or it may flit lightly away to the other side of the pool, with a few sharp notes of protest and a flash of white in its tail. I have often seen it in other places where one would not expect to find shore birds, such as the muddy banks of a sluggish stream, somewhat polluted with sewage, which flows back of my garden in the center of the city, or some barnyard mud puddle, reeking with the filth of cattle; perhaps it is attracted to such unsavory places by the swarms of flies that it finds there.

To Evan Thomson belongs the credit for making the interesting discovery of the tree-nesting habit. This historic incident is described by J. Fletcher Street (1923) as follows:

Mr. Thompson many years ago took up a quarter section of land [in Alberta] under the Canadian homestead act, built himself a log cabin at the edge of a muskeg, and commenced the arduous task of clearing the land. Living alone in this wilderness without neighbors and possessing a keen love for nature and a particular interest in the abundant wild life about him, he came to devote his spare moments to the study of birds, counting as his immediate associates such hermit species as the great-horned owl, long-eared owl, saw-whet owl, goshawk, and a large host of water fowl and waders. Seated one day before his cabin he noticed a bird fly to a low tamarack and enter a nest. It was ostensibly one of the waders, and great was his surprise upon examining the nest to find it the structure of a robin. It contained four beautiful eggs, greenish white in ground color and heavily spotted and blotched with reddish brown. Thus, on June 16, 1903, the first authentic eggs of the solitary sandpiper were taken but it was not until a year later that the identity of the bird was definitely established. It was indeed interesting, 20 years later, to be shown the cabin and to view the original tree from which the eggs were collected. Subsequent to the finding of this nest many others have been located, the bird evidencing no particular choice of nest in which to deposit its eggs, the list including those of the bronzed grackle,[1] Brewer's blackbird, cedar waxwing, kingbird, robin, and Canada jay. These have been found at an elevation as low as 4 feet and as high as 40 and in locations contiguous to water and as far away as 200 yards.   1928

WANDERING TATTLER   *Heteroscelus incanum*

Along the rocky and stony portions of the Pacific coast, and especially on the islands and outlying reefs, this ocean wanderer is a common and well-known bird. Here it is much at home among the surf-swept rocks, drenched in ocean spray, and often enveloped in fog; it has no fear of foaming breakers, which it nimbly dodges as it

---

[1] As the subspecies *versicolor* of the Common Grackle was formerly called.

seeks its bits of marine food among the kelp and barnacles on the rocks. It is, at most seasons, essentially a bird of the seashore, but is seldom seen on the sandy or muddy shores. The dark color of its upper plumage matches its surroundings and it is not easily seen among the gloomy rocks, unless its characteristic outline can be seen against the sky or water as it poses on the top of some prominent rock to watch the intruder. If we approach too near, it flies off a short distance with loud, piercing cries and alights on another rock, to bob and teeter, somewhat like our familiar spotted and solitary sandpipers. It is generally solitary and seems to be satisfied with its own society.

It is well named, as it is a famous wanderer. I am tempted to quote Dr. E. W. Nelson's (1887) well-chosen words on this subject, as follows:

Over the entire coast of the Pacific north of the equator its presence has been noted by the various naturalists whose Bohemian tastes have made their lives somewhat akin to that of this gentle wanderer. Across the broad ocean it ranges to those bits of paradise dotting the South Seas, tripping its way daintily on the beaches of the coral-enclosed islands, their feet laved by the warm waters of the tropics, and their eyes familiar with the luxuriant face of nature in its gentlest and most lovely state. The next season may find them thousands of miles to the north, under the shadow of the stupendous cliffs and grand but desolate and repellent scenes of the Aleutian Islands.   1928

WILLET   *Catoptrophorus semipalmatus*

C.s. semipalmatus   (Eastern Willet)

The northward migration of willets, which breed north of the winter range, is along the Atlantic coast, starting in March. The first migrants reach Virginia during the first or second week in April, but do not appear in Massachusetts until May, the main flight passing between the middle and last of that month. The probability of an off-shore migration route is suggested by the following interesting observation made by Dr. George B. Grinnell (1916) during the last days of May 1907:

It was in the middle of the morning of a gray, but not foggy, day, when we were off the Grand Banks of Newfoundland, that I noticed a considerable gathering of birds resting on the water in the immediate path of the ship. As we approached them I thought they looked like shore birds, and as the vessel drew quite close to them those immediately near it rose on wing and flew off to right and left, and again alighted on the water among their fellows. In the way in which they left the path of the vessel they reminded me of similar flights of waterfowl seen in Alaska. When the birds took wing they were at once recognized as willets, and there must have been somewhere near a thousand of them, not all packed together in a dense clump on the water, but more or less scattered out, in groups of forty, fifty, or a hundred, yet all fairly near one another, and suggesting a single flock. They seemed to leave the water reluctantly and gave me the impression that they were weary.

C.s. inornatus (Western Willet)

We found western willets very common about the lakes in the prairie regions of North Dakota and Saskatchewan; but owing to their habit of flying a long distance to meet the intruder and making a great fuss everywhere but near their nests, we succeeded in finding only one nest. This was on the higher portion of the open prairie, a long way from any water, near Big Stick Lake, Saskatchewan. The nest was a hollow in the ground, measuring seven by six inches in diameter and three inches deep, lined with grasses and dry weeds. It was in plain sight in short grass; a few scattered dead weeds were standing around it, but no long grass. It contained three fresh eggs on June 14, 1906. Ernest T. Seton (Thompson, 1890) found a nest in Manitoba "which was placed in a slight hollow, shaded on one side by the skull of a buffalo and on the other by a tuft of grass," on an alkali plain.   1928

GREATER YELLOWLEGS   *Totanus melanoleucus*

The names, telltale and tattler, have long been applied to both of the yellow-legs,[1] and deservedly so, for their noisy, talkative habits are their best known traits. They are always on the alert and ever vigilant to warn their less observant or more trusting companions by their loud, insistent cries of alarm that some danger is approaching.

Mr. Nichols (1920) has published the results of a detailed study of the vocabularies of the two yellow-legs, which are noted for the variety of their calls. He has recognized and described nine different calls of the greater yellow-legs, as follows:

(1) The yodle (a rolling *toowhee toowhee*, etc.) is commonest in a flock from birds remaining in one locality, not traveling. I think I have heard it from a single bird in the fog. It is characteristically given in the air, generally with set wings, by birds which seem to contemplate alighting. It advertises birds tarrying in one general locality, and has probably

---

[1] The name of this species was formerly spelled with a hyphen.

the function of *location* notice. It is doubtless homologous with the gather call of the spotted sandpiper with which it has little analogy.

(2) Loud ringing 3, *wheu wheu wheu*. The characteristic cry of the species, spring and fall. It is commonly given by passing or leaving birds. It advertises the species—and a change of policy in the individual according to its loudness. Analogous with notes of other species spoken of as *flight notes* or identification notes; occasionally heard from an alighted bird. This call is subject to considerable variation, when heard from a bird about to drop down and join others feeding it is comparatively low-pitched and even, leaving or about to leave a feeding ground, highly modulated.

(3) Four *wheus,* heard as follows, seem to have a rather definite significance; low, hurried, descending, heard from a bird leaving companion; short, clear, four, by a following bird; loud, four, bird without intention of alighting, trying to flush decoys. This may be called a *recruiting* call.

(4) Twos (*wheu wheu*) seem to be characteristic of a *recruit*. A "gentle" bird which comes nicely to decoys is apt to call in twos when approaching and coming in.

(5) Rarely, in taking wing in the presence of an intruder, a single bird utters a string of unmodulated *wheus* which breaks up into threes or fours as it goes off. This is likely a note of *protest*, which would be more common in the breeding season.

(6) Conversational murmuring, from a flock dropping in, expresses *companionship* and confidence.

(7) Conversational *chup* notes from birds about to alight, also heard from birds alighted, moving about at ease. The *alighting* note.

(8) Unloud *chups* identical with the preceding but more hurried, given by a small flock of birds as they take wing. The *flushing* note.

(9) *Kyow,* common in spring, only rarely heard in southward migration; probably associated with the breeding season; seems to express *suspicion.*

1927

LESSER YELLOWLEGS   *Totanus flavipes*

John T. Nichols has sent me some very elaborate notes on the varied calls of the yellow-legs,[1] from which I quote as follows:

When on the ground in flocks the lesser yellow-legs is usually silent. The same is true frequently of single birds coming in. In the air it is more or less noisy and has two common, distinct notes—*wheu* and *kip* or *keup,* which seem to be used rather indiscriminately on various occasions and which vary into one another. Wandering singles and small companies seem to use the *wheu* more, often double. The combination *wheu hip* is frequent. From large companies, especially in uncertainty, one may hear a chorus of *kips.*

(1) The yodle probably corresponds in significance with that of the

[1] The name of this species was formerly spelled with a hyphen.

greater yellow-legs—*location*. It is certainly its homolog and scarcely, if at all, distinguishable from it. When a flock of a half dozen lesser yellow-legs came to decoys, one bird alighted first, had a low-pitched, unfamiliar *too-dle-hoo-hoo, too-dle-hoo-hoo, too-dle-hoo-hoo*, before the others, still on the wing, came back and alighted with it. Though probably of similar derivation, this note was quite different from the yodle of the species, and is probably more of a gather call (Long Island, August).

(2) The *wheu* is a regular *flight note*, likely advertisement. Generally silent birds alighted, sometimes call an occasional single *wheu* (at such times particularly soft and mellow) before others drop in to join them, as if in welcome.

When double, this note of the lesser yellow-legs is at times clear and full, difficult to differentiate from that of the larger species, and apparently likewise characteristic of a "gentle" bird, which will join decoys or others alighted.

(5) Whereas the *wheu* note of the lesser yellow-legs is most frequently single and very seldom more than double, I have heard a variation of it in series from one of an alighted flock (Mastic,[1] July 13, 1919), *hyu-hyu-hyu-hyu-hyu*, etc. Presumably this was in protest at my presence, corresponding to the similar note of the larger species.

(6) Soft, unloud murmuring of a flock in chorus, *yu yu yu*, etc., characteristically heard, as on August 10, 1919, from a flock moving leisurely over the meadows, after having been flushed, to shortly alight again, expressive of *companionship* and confidence.

(7) When dropping down to alight, often hovering over decoys, a flock of lesser yellow-legs has soft short, *cup, cup, cup*, etc., notes.

(8) At the instant of flushing almost the identical notes as above given hurriedly with more emphasis. This for the lesser yellow-legs is a rough analog of the cheeping note of the pectoral sandpiper, but in view of the different habits of the two species, can not be said to be strictly analogous with same.

(10) An unloud chuckle or series of short notes suggesting a very distant jack curlew,[2] heard sometimes, not very frequently, when one or more birds take wing. Should probably be considered a flushing note or signal to take wing. Seems like the attempt of one individual to reproduce the preceding, which is often from several birds of a flock.

(11) The *kip* is likely one bird calling to another close-by. It is typically a *flocking* note, otherwise used almost exactly as is note No. 2. A variation, *keup*, with broader sound, approaching the *wheu*, expressing *attention*, is frequent. It has been heard from a flock of birds which had been resting and bathing, just before taking wing (Mastic, September 15, 1918).

(12) An infrequent note of quite different character from the lesser yellow-legs' ordinary calls is very high and clear, *queep*. It is subject to much

[1] Long Island, New York.
[2] Whimbrel.

variation, as *peep-quip, eep!* but is characterized by the high *ee* sound. It has been heard from birds alighted, more particularly when their companions, alarmed or for some other reason, move on, and is thought of as the *tarrying individual's* note. On August 17, 1919, I had picked up decoys preparatory to leaving a pool in the meadows when a single lesser yellow-legs came down to the pool calling a similar *kee-a* on the wing, though I was in full view. It went on without alighting with *wheu* notes characteristic of the species. Probably this was an individual which wanted to stay, from a small company which had left the meadow.

(13) Wounded birds, on being pursued and captured, have a harsh scream of fear, *cheerp*. I have noticed this from birds of the year in southward migration only, not from adults under the same circumstances.

The above numbers indicate notes analogous with those of the greater yellow-legs, similarly numbered. Where the lesser has no notes analogous with certain notes of the greater, these numbers are omitted.

KNOT   *Calidris canutus*

The knot, or redbreast, as it is called on Cape Cod, was a very abundant migrant all along the Atlantic coast of North America during the past century. George H. Mackay (1893) writes:

On the Dennis marshes and flats, at Chatham, Nauset, Wellfleet, and Billingsgate, Cape Cod, and on the flats around Tuckernuck and Muskeget Islands, Mass., they used to be more numerous than in all the rest of New England combined, and being very gregarious they would collect in those places in exceedingly large numbers, estimates of which were useless. This was previous to 1850 and when the Cape Cod Railroad was completed only to Sandwich. Often, when riding on the top of the stage coach on the cape beyond this point, immense numbers of these birds could be seen, as they rose up in clouds, during the period that they sojourned there. It was at this time that the vicious practice of "fire-lighting" them prevailed, and a very great number of them were thus killed on the flats at night in the vicinity of Billingsgate (near Wellfleet). The mode of procedure was for two men to start out after dark at half tide, one of them to carry a lighted lantern, the other to reach and seize the birds, bite their necks, and put them in a bag slung over the shoulder. When near a flock they would approach them on their hands and knees, the birds being almost invariably taken on the flats. This practice continued several years before it was finally prohibited by law. I have it directly from an excellent authority that he has seen in the spring, six barrels of these birds (all of which had been taken in this manner) at one time, on the deck of the Cape Cod packet for Boston. He has also seen barrels of them, which had spoiled during the voyage, thrown overboard in Boston Harbor on arrival of the packet. The price of these birds at that time was 10 cents per dozen; mixed with them would be turnstones and black-bellied plover. Not one of these birds had been shot, all having been taken with the aid of a "fire-light."

S. F. Rathbun has sent me the following notes:

Late on the afternoon of May 16, 1921, we were on the south side of Gray's Harbor, Washington, on a marsh meadow bordered by the tide flats. At this hour the tide was nearly at its full, and the many shore birds that had been feeding on the flats were forced to retreat before the incoming waters and in consequence were driven close to the edge of the meadow. Not far from where we lay concealed a very large number of these had assembled on a somewhat elevated stretch of ground near the meadows border, among them being several hundred of the knots, these in two or three compact flocks all the individuals of which were facing the wind. At this time the sun was low in the west and its almost horizontal rays fell full on the breasts of the knots, for in facing the wind they happened to be turned toward the sun, whose light intensified the pale cinnamon of their breasts, this making a beautiful sight.   1927

PURPLE SANDPIPER   *Erolia maritima*

This hardy northern bird has well been called "winter snipe" and "rock snipe," for it is known to us only as a winter visitor on rocky shores.

The flight of the purple sandpiper suggests at times that of the spotted sandpiper, for when disturbed singly along the shore it is apt to fly out over the water with rapid downward wing strokes and, describing a large semicircle, return to the shore some distance ahead. When flying in a flock the birds are often closely bunched, the whole flock wheeling and turning in unison, showing alternately their dark bodies and their white bellies, in true sandpiper fashion. As a rule they do not make very long flights or fly very high. Their migrations are short and deliberate. They are rather sedentary birds and can generally be found in certain favorite localities all winter and year after year. But, as they show a decided preference for the outer sides of surf-swept ledges, they are not often seen from the land. They can swim almost as well as phalaropes and in calm weather they will often alight on half submerged seaweed or on the surface of the water.

The purple sandpiper is the "winter snipe" of the New England coast, where flocks of from twenty-five to seventy-five or more may be found regularly on certain outlying rocky ledges. Here they seek shelter among the rocks from the flying spray and from the wintry blasts; and here they find their food washed up by the waves or hidden in the half floating beds of rockweed.   1927

ROCK SANDPIPER *Erolia ptilocnemis*

E.p. ptilocnemis (Pribilof Sandpiper)

We found Pribilof sandpipers very common in July on the low tundra at the south end of St. Matthew Island,[1] where they were evidently breeding just back of the beaches. They were also common in the interior at the north end of this island and on the highlands of Hall Island.[1] We collected a few specimens of the birds, but had no time to hunt for nests. We are indebted to Mr. Hanna (1921) for his excellent account of the nesting habits of this bird, from which I quote as follows:

On St. George Island[2] the high upland tundra has been chosen for breeding ground. Here, among the reindeer "mosses" and light gray, lichen-covered rocks the sandpipers reign supreme in the fog. Some speculating may be indulged in to find a reason for so unusual a choice of locality. Elevations up to 500 feet are sought. Perhaps they shun the seacoasts on account of the presence there of large numbers of foxes. During all history this has been a greater fox island than either St. Paul[2] or St. Matthew. On the latter island in June and July the birds may be found in large numbers around and back of the drift-wood piles. If it were not for this fact being known, we might suspect that on St. George the light gray tundra was selected for protective purposes, the birds themselves being distinguished chiefly by their light colors. St. Paul Island, for some unaccountable reason, is not chosen as a breeding ground except by a very few pairs. In 1919 not over a dozen were found during the entire nesting season, when almost all of the available areas were seen.

On the breeding grounds of St. George and St. Matthew the birds are very common, and from one to a dozen are in almost constant attendance upon the visitor. They sight him from afar and fly to meet him. Some bird will almost always try to lead him astray. If followed, it flies from knoll to knoll, often not more than 20 yards away. It remains in front of the visitor regardless of the direction he may take; whether toward or from the nest, makes no difference. After several minutes of this a sudden flight, with the familiar "song," is taken to some distant hill and the searcher for a nest is left confused and confounded.

E.p. couesi (Aleutian Sandpiper)

In many ways the Aleutian sandpiper reminds one of its near relative, the purple sandpiper, but it is even tamer, less suspicious, and quieter in its movements. We had plenty of chances to get acquainted with it in the Aleutian Islands. We met it, and collected the first

[1] Now part of the Bering Sea National Wildlife Refuge.
[2] One of the Pribilof Islands, Bering Sea.

specimen of it, on the first island that we landed on, Akun Island, and after that we saw it on every island we visited, though it was much more abundant on the more western islands. These bleak islands, with their forbidding, rocky shores and stony beaches, washed with cold spray or enveloped in chilly fog, are the summer home of this hardy little "beach snipe," as it is called by the natives. It moves about so quietly and deliberately, and its colors match its surroundings so well, that we were constantly coming upon it unexpectedly. It was usually so intent on feeding that it paid no attention to passers-by. It is the tamest and most unsuspicious shore bird I have ever seen.

We frequently observed the charming song flight of this sandpiper in the Aleutian Islands. The birds were especially abundant on Tanaga Island, where we found them nesting on the little knolls or hummocks on the tundra in a large alluvial plain back of the beach hillocks. The males were very active and noisy, indulging in their hovering song flights, rising thirty or forty feet in the air and fluttering down while pouring out a delightful twittering song. Also, while flying about or while standing on some prominent hummock, they gave their loud, musical melodious calls of the upland plover; these loud notes were not heard anywhere except on their breeding grounds and were probably notes of greeting or of warning to their mates.

1927

SHARP-TAILED SANDPIPER   *Erolia acuminata*

This is a bird which few of us have been privileged to see. From its summer home in northeastern Siberia it migrates south to Japan, the Malay Archipelago, Australia, and New Zealand. On the fall migration it visits the coast of northwestern Alaska frequently, perhaps regularly, and often commonly. It occurs regularly, sometimes abundantly, on the Pribilof Islands in the fall. In southern Alaska and farther south it occurs only as a rare straggler.

Dr. E. W. Nelson (1887) tells us a little about the habits of this rare species, as follows:

They were nearly always associated with *maculata*,[1] whose habits they shared to a great extent. When congregated about their feeding places they united into flocks of from ten into fifty, but single birds were frequently flushed from grassy spots. Their motions on the wing are very similar to those of the latter, and they were rarely shy. On October 1, 1880, they were found scattered singly over the marsh,[2] and arose 30 to 40 yards

[1] Former specific name of the Pectoral Sandpiper.
[2] At St. Michael, Alaska.

in advance, and made off with a twisting flight, uttering at the same time a short, soft, metallic *pleep, pleep,* and pursuing an erratic, circuitous flight for a time they generally returned and settled near the spot whence they started. On the shore of Siberia, near North Cape, we found these birds very common, scattered over damp grass flats near the coast, the 1st of August, 1881. The ground was covered with reindeer tracks, and among these the sharp-tailed snipe[1] were seen seeking their food. They were very unsuspicious and allowed us to pass close to them, or circled close about us. From their movements and other circumstances I judged that this district formed part of their breeding grounds, whence they reach the neighboring coast of Alaska in fall.   1927

PECTORAL SANDPIPER   *Erolia melanotos*

The wonderful and curious courtship of the pectoral sandpiper has been well described by several writers. Dr. E. W. Nelson's (1887) pleasing and graphic account of it is well worth quoting in full; he writes [from an island in the Yukon delta, in 1879]:

The night of May 24 I lay wrapped in my blanket, and from the raised flap of the tent looked out over as dreary a cloud-covered landscape as can be imagined. The silence was unbroken save by the tinkle and clinking of the disintegrating ice in the river, and at intervals by the wild notes of some restless loon, which arose in a hoarse reverberating cry and died away in a strange gurgling sound. As my eyelids began to droop and the scene to become indistinct, suddenly a low, hollow, booming note struck my ear and sent my thoughts back to a spring morning in northern Illinois, and to the loud vibrating tones of the prairie chickens. Again the sound arose nearer and more distinct, and with an effort I brought myself back to the reality of my position and, resting upon one elbow, listened. A few seconds passed and again arose the note; a moment later and, gun in hand, I stood outside the tent. The open flat extended away on all sides, with apparently not a living creature near. Once again the note was repeated close by, and a glance revealed its author. Standing in the thin grasses 10 or 15 yards from me, with its throat inflated until it was as large as the rest of the bird, was a male *A. maculata.*[2] The succeeding days afforded opportunity to observe the bird as it uttered its singular notes under a variety of situations and at various hours of the day or during the light Arctic night. The note is deep, hollow, and resonant, but at the same time liquid and musical, and may be represented by a repetition of the syllables *too-u, too-u, too-u, too-u, too-u, too-u, too-u, too-u.* Before the bird utters these notes it fills its esophagus with air to such an extent that the breast and throat is inflated to twice or more its natural size, and the great air sac thus formed gives the peculiar resonant quality to the note. The skin of the throat and breast

[1] As Nelson called this species.
[2] As this species was then named.

becomes very flabby and loose at this season, and its inner surface is covered with small globular masses of fat. When not inflated, the skin loaded with this extra weight and with a slightly serous suffusion which is present hangs down in a pendulous flap or fold exactly like a dewlap, about an inch and a half wide. The esophagus is very loose and becomes remarkably soft and distensible, but is easily ruptured in this state, as I found by dissection. In the plate accompanying this report the extent and character of this inflation, unique at least among American waders, is shown. The bird may frequently be seen running along the ground close to the female, its enormous sac inflated, and its head drawn back and the bill pointing directly forward, or, filled with spring-time vigor, the bird flits with slow but energetic wingstrokes close along the ground, its head raised high over the shoulders and the tail hanging almost directly down. As it thus flies it utters a succession of the hollow, booming notes, which have a strange ventriloquial quality. At times the male rises 20 or 30 yards in the air and inflating its throat glides down to the ground with its sac hanging below, as is shown in the accompanying plate. Again he crosses back and forth in front of the female, puffing his breast out and bowing from side to side, running here and there, as if intoxicated with passion. Whenever he pursues his love-making, his rather low but pervading note swells and dies in musical cadences, which form a striking part of the great bird chorus heard at this season in the north.   1927

WHITE-RUMPED SANDPIPER   *Erolia fuscicollis*

The white-rumped, or Bonaparte, sandpiper is a great traveler; it breeds in a limited area on the Arctic coast of North America and winters in extreme southern South America.

From its winter home in South America, this sandpiper makes an early start; Dr. Alexander Wetmore (1926) writes:

At Guamini, Buenos Aires[1] from March 3 to 8, white-rumped sandpipers were encountered in northward migration from a winter range in Patagonia.[2] The species was fairly common on March 3 and increased greatly in abundance on the two days that followed. The northward journey was apparently as concerted as the movement that carried the birds southward, as on March 6 there was a noticeable decrease in their numbers, and by March 8, though the birds were still common, the bulk of individuals had passed. They arrived in flocks from the southward, often of several hundred individuals, that whirled in and circled back and forth along the lake shore to decoy to birds feeding on the strand or to rise again and continue swiftly northward. Those that paused kept up a busy search for food along the muddy beaches in or near shallow water, or in company with little parties of buff-breasted sandpipers on the drier alkaline flats

[1] Argentina.
[2] Southern Argentina.

back of the shore line. In early morning they were especially active and were in continual movement. Occasionally they worked out into comparatively deep water where in feeding it is necessary to immerse the head over the eyes nearly to the ear openings. When disturbed, flocks rose with soft notes that resembled *tseet tseet* or *tseup* to circle to new feeding grounds on the lake shore.

[On its return trip] August finds the white-rumped sandpiper migrating along the coast of Brazil and it has been known to reach Cape Horn[1] as early as September 9. Doctor Wetmore (1926) writes:

The white-rumped sandpiper was the most abundant of the migrant shore birds in the regions visited in southern South America. The species was not recorded until September 6, 1920, when it appeared in abundance in southward migration on the lagoons at kilometer 80, west of Puerto Pinasco, Paraguay. The first flocks from which specimens were taken were adult females, and two taken on the date when they were first recorded had laid eggs a few weeks previous as was shown by the appearance of the ovaries. The southward migration came with a rush as the birds passed through the night as witnessed by their calls. The flight continued until September 21, when a dozen, the last seen here, were recorded.

Farther south along the Rio Ajo white-rumped sandpipers were encountered in flocks of hundreds that came upstream to search the mud flats at low tide or were concentrated on bars at the mouth when the water was high. In early morning there was a steady flight of them passing to suitable feeding grounds. The birds flew swiftly, with soft notes, from 3 to 15 feet from the earth. In feeding they scattered out in little groups that covered the bare mud systematically. It was not unusual to record as many as 2,000 in a day.   1927

BAIRD'S SANDPIPER   *Erolia bairdii*

This sandpiper belongs to that class of birds which Abel Chapman (1924) so aptly terms "globe spanners," for on its migrations it traverses the whole length of both American continents twice a year. From its wintering grounds in Patagonia [southern Argentina] it must start north even earlier than the preceding species or else it must travel faster. Dr. Alexander Wetmore (1926) observed it migrating past Buenos Aires on March 5 in company with white-rumped sandpipers, and it has been known to reach Texas early in March. From there its course seems to be northward between the Mississippi River and the Rocky Mountains.

J. A. Munro gives me, as his spring dates for southern British Columbia, April 30 to May 10. Joseph Dixon (1917) says:

[1] On island at southern tip of South America.

On May 31, 1914, at Griffin Point, Arctic Alaska, the first pair of Baird sandpipers for the season were noted feeding along the rim of a frozen tundra pond. The weather had turned bitterly cold during the previous night, and as a result the newly formed ice on the ponds was thick enough to support a man. Strictly speaking, there was no night at this date, for the two months of continuous daylight had already begun; so in a short time the sandpipers were bustling about picking up the mosquito and other pupae which were being washed out by a newly-born stream that gurgled under the snow and ice on its way down to the frozen lagoon.

Baird sandpipers leave their northern breeding grounds rather early. E. A. Preble (1908) saw several flocks on migration at Great Slave Lake [Northwest Territories, Canada] as early as July 10.

The main flight seems to be directly south through the Mackenzie Valley and between the Rocky Mountains and the Mississippi River to Mexico and South America, where it probably migrates down the west coast to its winter home. But the route is also extended both east and west in the fall.

According to Prof. Wells W. Cooke (1912) this sandpiper reaches its winter home in September. Chile seems to be its principal winter home, where it has been taken repeatedly in the high mountains at ten thousand to twelve thousand feet and once at over thirteen thousand.   1927

LEAST SANDPIPER   *Erolia minutilla*   (Townsend)

Who has not been gladdened by the sight of flocks of these gentle little birds scampering along the beach or diligently feeding in the tidal flats and in the salt marshes!

The most noticeable part of the courtship of the least sandpiper is the song. [It] has been described at great length and with much appreciation by Robert T. Moore (1912) from intimate studies made by him on five nesting birds in the Magdalen Islands [Gulf of St. Lawrence], and he has recorded these songs in musical notation. He ranks it high among bird songs and dwells on its tremulous and pathetic qualities. He observed one that rendered its entire song from the ground within a foot of his hand.

It consisted of a series of trills, which ascended just one octave on a minor chord. The tone quality was pure and sweet and rendered pathetic by the minor chord, which served as its medium.

Fortunately this bird has been removed from the list of game by the federal law, and we may be sure it will never be replaced. In the absence of larger birds—too frequently the case—the gunner used to shoot these tiny birds in large numbers, and it must be admitted they were delicious eating. At his blind near a slough or mud hole in the salt marshes he would arrange his flock of tin or wooden decoys, generally made to represent yellow-legs, within easy reach of his gun, and he would call down with his tin whistle any passing flock. A projecting spit of mud extending out into the little pool afforded a convenient alighting place for the "peep," and their death trap, for here they could conveniently be raked by gun fire from the blind. The terrified and bewildered survivors spring into the air, and circling about over their dead and dying companions afford several more effective shots, which shower the victims down into the mud and water. Only a remnant of the flock escapes, to fall victims, perhaps, to their easy credulity at a neighboring blind. Sometimes the gunner in his greed would wait for the birds to bunch together closely on the spit, but before this took place to his satisfaction the alarm calls of a tattler or yellow-legs might ring out over the marsh and every bird would spring into the air and be off, much to his chagrin. Fortunately this destruction has not been carried too far. The law has stepped in before it is too late, as alas! may be the case with some of the larger shore birds. The increase of this species since the federal law went into effect in 1913 is very striking. Mr. Philipp (1925) says there is

a large increase in this dainty shore bird. In 1907 an exhaustive search for breeding birds in the Magdalens resulted in finding 11 pairs. In 1923 in the same territory over 50 pairs were located with eggs or young.   1927

RUFOUS-NECKED SANDPIPER   *Erolia ruficollis*

[This] species was firmly established as a North American bird by Alfred M. Bailey (1926), who reported the capture of two specimens in Alaska, an adult female at Cape Prince of Wales on June 11, and a bird of the year at Wainwright on August 15, 1922. The birds were breeding in that vicinity, an offshoot from the main breeding range of the species in northeastern Siberia.

The main migration route is northward from southern Asia, the Philippine Islands, and even Australia, through the Kurile[1] and Commander Islands[2] and Kamchatka[2] to its breeding grounds. Mr. Bailey (1926) was fortunate enough to see a pair building their nest, along a stream bed on the high tundra at the base of Wales Mountain, Alaska; in his notes for June 14, 1922, he wrote:

[1] North of Japan.
[2] Soviet Far East.

With my glasses I watched a pair of little pink-necked sandpipers[1] as they worked around the grass at the foot of the hill. The male would give up his searching among the dried grass stalks to demonstrate his love for his little partner, upon which she would take to wing and circle about. Finally she entered a little tussock of grass, standing on her "nose" fluttering her tail and wings. Soon the male pushed his way inside, too, and after a few more rustlings about, they took to wing. I looked in the grass and found a little cavity which they were just lining with leaves. Upon examining their nesting clump, I found a small pit, exactly similar to the nest of the western sandpiper, in which they had deposited about 20 small willow leaves. I marked the spot carefully, but upon my return found the nest abandoned.

1927

CURLEW SANDPIPER   *Erolia ferruginea*   (Jourdain)

Although Middendorff undoubtedly met with birds about to breed, and indeed extracted a partly developed egg from the oviduct of a female which he had shot on the Boganida River[2] in latitude 74° N., no one had actually found the nest of this species till Mr. H. Leyborne Popham (1898) visited the lower reaches of the Yenesei[2] in 1897. Two years previously (August 1895), he had met with family parties on the delta and had shot young which must have been reared in the neighborhood. On July 3, 1897, finding the way below Golchika[2] blocked by the ice, he turned back to explore an island of soft tundra with a rocky shore. One of his men called out that he had seen a sandpiper and at once, according to his own words:

I sent the other two men away and lay down to watch the bird, which stood still for some time, then flew some distance away and I lost sight of it among some turnstones. We again saw the bird near the same spot, so Hansen and I lay down to watch while the mosquitoes did their worst. The bird stood for some time watching us and then began running about; it was very difficult to keep it in sight for it took advantage of every little hollow to run in and every little ridge to hide behind. It then flew to another place and did the same thing again, so I asked Hansen to get up and walk away. The bird remained quite motionless, watching him go, and then ran backwards and forwards and finally stopped still behind a small tuft of grass. After waiting for some minutes I raised my head slightly; the bird instantly flew off and stood watching, but, as it saw nothing moving, it began running about again and settled down in the same spot; then I felt sure I had a nest safe, but to make doubly sure I went through the same performance again, a shower of rain no doubt hastening matters, and this time I distinctly saw the bird shuffle the eggs under it. I jumped up, shot the

---

[1] As Bailey called this species.
[2] Siberia.

bird as it ran away, and soon had the pleasure of looking at the first authentic eggs of the curlew sandpiper. The bird, which proved to be the female, remained silent throughout; at one time I thought I heard it make a sound like a dunlin, but, as I afterwards saw dunlins close by, I was probably mistaken. 1927

DUNLIN   *Erolia alpina*

E.a. pacifica (Red-backed Sandpiper)

Dr. E. W. Nelson (1887) gives an attractive account of the court-ship of this species [near the mouth of the Yukon, Alaska] as follows:

Soon after they arrive in spring they are engaged in pairing, and the males may be seen upon quivering wings flying after the female and utter-ing a musical, trilling note, which falls upon the ear like the mellow tinkle of large water drops falling rapidly into a partly filled vessel. Imagine the sounds thus produced by the water run together into a steady and rapid trill some 5 to 10 seconds in length, and the note of this sandpiper is repre-sented. It is not loud but has a rich full tone, difficult to describe, but pleasant to hear among the discordant notes of the various waterfowl whose hoarse cries arise on all sides. As the lover's suit approaches its end the handsome suitor becomes exalted, and in his moments of excitement he rises 15 or 20 yards, and, hovering on tremulous wings over the object of his passion, pours forth a perfect gush of music, until he glides back to earth exhausted, but ready to repeat the effort a few minutes later. The female coyly retreats before the advances of the male, but after various mishaps each bird finds its partner for the summer and they start off house hunting in all the ardor of a rising honeymoon. 1927

SHORT-BILLED DOWITCHER   *Limnodromus griseus*

The favorite feeding grounds of the dowitchers are the mud flats and sand flats in sheltered bays and estuaries, or the borders of shallow ponds on the marshes, where they associate freely with small plovers and sandpipers. Although not inclined to move about actively, their feeding motions are very rapid, as they probe in the mud or sand with quick, perpendicular strokes of their long bills, driving them in their full length again and again in rapid succession; while feeding in shallow water the whole head is frequently immersed and some-times several strokes are made with the head under water.

Various observers have noted among the food items of the dow-itcher: grasshoppers, beetles, flies, maggots, marine worms, oyster worms, leeches, water bugs, fish eggs, small mollusks, seeds of aquatic plants, and the roots of eelgrass.

Dowitchers are the gentlest and most unsuspicious of shore birds, which has made them easy prey for the avaricious gunner. Their flight is swift and steady, often protracted and sometimes at a great elevation, when looking for feeding places. They usually fly in compact flocks by themselves, sometimes performing interesting evolutions high in the air. They often fly, however, in flocks with other small waders, but the dowitchers are generally bunched together in the flock; I once shot four dowitchers out of a mixed flock without hitting any of the smaller birds. When a flock of dowitchers alights the birds are closely bunched, but they soon scatter out and begin to feed. If a flock is shot into, the sympathetic and confiding birds return again and again to their fallen companions until only a pitiful remnant is left to finally escape. Such slaughter of the innocents well-nigh exterminated this gentle species; but, now that it is protected, it is beginning to increase again.   1927

LONG-BILLED DOWITCHER

Limnodromus scolopaceus

S. F. Rathbun has sent me the following notes on the habits of this bird on its migrations through the State of Washington:

The long-billed dowitcher will be found in the company of almost any of the shore birds, in flocks of varying numbers, and even as single individuals, but appears to show somewhat of a partiality for the company of the black-bellied plover and the red-backed sandpiper. On this coast both its spring and autumnal migrations seem to be somewhat prolonged, for in the case of the former we have records from April 11 until late in May; and for the latter from early August until into November. It will be found alike on the sandy beaches and the muddy flats, seemingly showing no particular preference for either. When the tide is at its ebb on the flats the birds ofttimes become widely scattered and single ones may be found in unexpected places. On one occasion as we were walking across a grassy marsh the head and neck of a long-billed dowitcher was seen exposed above the growth along the edge of one of the little channels running through the marsh. As we approached the bird it could be seen making attempts to rise, but this it was unable to do on account of being impeded by the length of the grass, and we drove the bird ahead until an open spot was reached when it then took wing, at this time being but a few feet away.

On various occasions while we were watching flocks of the small sandpipers about some bit of water, dowitchers would fly past and, being attracted by the calls of other birds, they then after circling for a moment or two would alight at the pool to feed. When thus engaged they gave the impression of being somewhat deliberate in their actions and as they moved about some would frequently wade up to their breasts into the shallow water, often so remaining until by some action they seemed to lose a footing and when this occurred a retreat would be made into a more shallow part. Oftentimes one or more birds would suddenly cease feeding and assume a posture of repose and when this took place it was a common occurrence to see some standing on but one leg, thus to remain motionless for a time.

Dowitchers do not appear to be very shy when found in the flocks of the smaller sandpipers, but are the first birds to retreat as one approaches the flock; and on such occasions it is generally the case that one or more of them will suddenly take wing and put the entire flock in motion. They are swift-flying birds and when on the wing have a somewhat harsh note that is given from time to time. In their spring dress they are attractive, as at this time their under parts are a rich buff color, and a flock of dowitchers seen at this season with the light striking full on their breasts is indeed a handsome sight.   1927

STILT SANDPIPER   *Micropalama himantopus*

Strangely enough I have never seen, or rather recognized, a stilt sandpiper in life. As it is often associated with the lesser yellow-legs and so easily mistaken for it, I may have overlooked it.

Dr. Arthur A. Allen (1913), after referring to the companionship and resemblance between stilt sandpipers and lesser yellow-legs, says [of birds observed at Ithaca, New York, in August, 1912]:

In their habits, however, the two species were quite different. The yellow-legs were always rangy birds and covered a great deal of ground while feeding. Even when resting they were conspicuous by the nervous jerking of the head and neck. In flight they usually formed fairly compact flocks but scattered upon alighting. The stilt sandpipers, on the other hand, were quiet birds and went about their search for food very systematically, gleaning everything in their way. They frequently fed in a space a few yards square for over an hour at a time. When at rest they showed none of the nervous traits of the yellowlegs, being much more sedate, neither jerking the head nor tilting the tail. In flight they were quite similar to the yellowlegs, but as soon as they alighted they bunched and frequently the whole flock fed with their bodies nearly touching. Like the yellowlegs, the stilt sandpipers were seldom seen upon the exposed mud but preferred wading where the water was from 1 to 3 inches in depth, so that the entire head and neck frequently disappeared beneath the surface of the water while feeding. The notes of the two birds, though similar in form, were wholly unlike in quality, that of the stilt sandpiper being mellower and lower in pitch.

Following are Mr. Nichols' notes on this subject:

The common flight note of the stilt sandpiper is very like the single whistled *whu* of the lesser yellowlegs, but recognizably lower pitched and hoarser, at times with a quiver, *whr-r-u*, and varying down to a shorter, less loud *whrug*. An unloud, reedy *sher* has been heard from two birds when flushing.

Though with different feeding habits, stilt sandpiper, dowitcher, and lesser yellowlegs frequent the same grounds, associate very freely on the wing, and all three have a very similar flight note, though sufficiently different for identification. Perhaps the very lack of close relationship in these birds has facilitated convergence of their habits and calls, and it is not unreasonable to suppose that close association, even imitation, has played some part in bringing about the likeness of their voices. The greater yellowlegs differs more from the lesser, both in flight note and flight habits, than do these other two unrelated species.

I quote again from Mr. Nichols' notes on field characters, as follows:

On the wing the stilt sandpiper resembles the lesser yellowlegs closely. Its smaller size is scarcely appreciable, even in a flock of yellowlegs, the members of which will usually be at slightly varying distances from the observer. Adults have appreciably darker (barred) lower parts, and young birds, particularly, are greyer above than yellowlegs at the same season in this latitude. The somewhat shorter legs do not project so far beyond the tail, but the proportionately longer bill (with slight apparent drop at its tip) is the stilt sandpiper's best field mark. Its bill is proportionately longer even than that of the greater yellowlegs, with which this species is unlikely to be confused, varying as it does away from the lesser yellowlegs in an opposite direction, both as regards size and in other subtle characters. The head and neck of a yellowlegs are more "shapely," differing in this respect somewhat as a black duck differs from sea ducks.   1927

SEMIPALMATED SANDPIPER   *Ereunetes pusillus*
                                                    (Townsend)

This sandpiper is more of a musician than the least, and his song is well worth hearing. I can but repeat what I have already published on the subject (1905):

Rising on quivering wings to about 30 feet from the ground, the bird advances with rapid wing beats, curving the pinions strongly downward, pouring forth a succession of musical notes—a continuous quavering trill— and ending with a few very sweet notes that recall those of a goldfinch. He then descends to the ground where one may be lucky enough, if near at hand, to hear a low musical *cluck* from the excited bird. This is, I suppose, the full love flight song, and is not often heard in its entirety, but the first quavering trill is not uncommon, a single bird or member of a flock singing this as he flies over.

The fact that so many of these birds could be easily killed at one shot, and the fact that they were so fat and palatable broiled or cooked in a pie, made them always much sought after by the pot hunter. As large shore birds grew scarcer and it became more and more difficult for the gunner to fill his bag with them, "peep" shooting, even by sportsmen, was in vogue. The federal law has now wisely removed this species from the list of game birds and prevented its extinction. The bird has responded to this protection in a marked degree, and flocks of five hundred or more are common and pleasing sights on our beaches where one-tenth of this number was once rare.

The shooting of semipalmated sandpipers occurred largely on the beaches. The gunner dug a hole in the sand, banked it up, and put brush and driftwood, often reinforced with seaweed, on the ramparts. At a convenient distance decoys of wood or tin were placed, arranged like a flock of birds with their heads pointing to the wind. Occasionally large clamshells were stuck in the sand, simulating very well a flock of peep. Much depended on the skill of the gunner in calling down the birds as they flew along, by cunningly imitating their notes and by his care in keeping concealed and motionless until the moment that he delivered his fire. To bring down a score of birds from a closely packed flock required but little skill, where, to pick off a single peep, flying erratically and swiftly by, called for well-seasoned judgment; but the chances for these birds were small indeed when the beaches were lined with inviting decoys and concealed whistling gunners.

The extraordinary abundance of this species at certain times on migration is well illustrated by what Stuart T. Danforth (1925) says of it in Porto Rico. He writes:

The semipalmated sandpiper is by far the most abundant shore bird at Cartagena Lagoon, though it occurs only as a fall migrant. I have records from August 13 to October 20, 1924. During the latter part of August they are present in almost unbelievable numbers. On August 26, when they were at the height of their abundance, I am sure that 100,000 would have been a low estimate.   1927

WESTERN SANDPIPER   *Ereunetes mauri*

Herbert W. Brandt, who has had extensive experience with the nesting habits of this species, says in his manuscript notes:

The gentle little western sandpiper is the most abundant and most widely distributed shore bird occurring in the Hooper Bay [Western Alaska] region. Throughout the area, wherever dry ground is found, it is plentiful, and it even occurs on the lower mountain slopes of the Askinuk Range.

Before the tundra had discarded its snowy mantle the first birds of this species had responded to the lure of early spring, for they arrived on May 14, and two days later they were common, while on May 20 they were abundant, carrying on everywhere their dainty aerial butterfly courtship. The western sandpiper is usually found in large scattering colonies especially on the upland tundra where for large areas they average one or two pairs to the acre. Isolated couples, however, are occasionally encountered.

The nest of the western sandpiper is well concealed from view by the surrounding curly bunch-grass that everywhere in the dryer areas forces its way up amid the moss. Under this protection a depression is made and scantily lined with grass, and usually in addition with considerable tiny leaves of the prostrate berry-bearing vines, of the dwarf birch, and of the reindeer moss stems. In consequence, the nest is very fragile and loosely made, but before it is disturbed it is neatly cup-shaped. The range of measurements of 32 nests is: inside diameter, 2 to 3 inches; depth of cavity, 1½ to 3 inches; and total depth, 2½ to 4 inches. Both male and female share in the tender duties of incubation and are often very loath to forsake their nest, so that when crossing their chosen haunts an incubating bird, by fluttering up before one's very feet, will occasionally unwittingly betray its well-concealed abode.

Four eggs always constitute a complete set with the western sandpiper, but occasionally late nests with three eggs in each were observed, which were probably second layings. They are pyriform to subpyriform in shape and are placed in the nest with the small ends together and pointed downward, snuggling amid the loose interior contents of the nest. The shell is smooth, has a slight luster, and is strongly constructed. The markings on the same set of eggs always follow the same type in color, and likewise the ground color is always the same shade. In the series of eggs the prevalent ground color is "cream color," but the shades vary from dull white, which is very rare, to equally rare "wood brown." The ground color is often almost obliterated by the profuseness of the markings, especially on the larger two-thirds of the egg. The color of the surface markings is usually "Kaiser brown," but they show considerable variation, dependent upon the amount of pigment deposited, ranging from "brick red" to "chestnut brown." The spots are somewhat elongated and vary from small pin points to large blotches that may completely cover the larger end of the egg. These have a decided tendency to spiral from left to right. The underlying markings are inconspicuous and are only visible on eggs having a pale background and then they are of small size and indistinct. The eggs are generally flecked with additional markings consisting of a few intense irregular spots or fine lines of slate black to black. These blackbirdlike markings are almost always on the larger end, although on many eggs they are entirely wanting. In series the eggs of the western sandpiper have a decidedly bright red appearance, and are thus distinct from any eggs occurring in the Hooper Bay region.   **1927**

BUFF-BREASTED SANDPIPER

Tryngites subruficollis

W. H. Hudson (1922) gives a striking account of the spring migration of this species in Argentina during its former abundance, from which I quote, as follows:

Now, one autumn, when most of the emigrants to the Arctic breeding grounds had already gone, I witnessed a great migration of this very species—this beautiful sandpiper with the habits of a plover. The birds appeared in flocks of about one to two or three hundred, flying low and very swiftly due north, flock succeeding flock at intervals of about 10 or 12 minutes; and this migration continued for three days, or at all events three days from the first day I saw them, at a spot about 2 miles from my home. I was amazed at their numbers, and it was a puzzle to me then, and has been one ever since, that a species thinly distributed over the immense area of the Argentine pampas and Patagonia[1] could keep to that one line of travel over that uniform green, sealike country. For outside of that line not one bird of the kind could anywhere be seen; yet they kept so strictly to it that I sat each day for hours on my horse watching them pass, each flock first appearing as a faint buff-colored blur or cloud just above the southern horizon, rapidly approaching then passing me, about on a level with my horse's head, to fade out of sight in a couple of minutes in the north; soon to be succeeded by another and yet other flocks in endless succession, each appearing at the same point as the one before, following the same line, as if a line invisible to all eyes except their own had been traced across the green world for their guidance. It gave one the idea that all the birds of this species, thinly distributed over tens of thousands of square miles of country, had formed the habit of assembling previous to migration at one starting point, from which they set out in successive flocks of a medium size in a disciplined order on that marvelous journey to their Arctic breeding grounds.

Prof. William Rowan (1927) writes:

This is a remarkable sandpiper from many viewpoints. Like the American golden plover and the Eskimo curlew it used to exist in millions and was slaughtered in uncountable numbers. To-day there are many widely traveled collectors who have never in their lives met with it. After extensive inquiries I can discover only one spot on the continent besides our point[2] on which migrating buff-breasted sandpipers may be relied upon to turn up in any numbers. We get it in hundreds every spring, and, roughly speaking, it frequents only one field. Odd birds or moving flocks may be noted elsewhere from time to time, but on the rough pasture that forms the main body of the point this species arrives with unfailing regularity

[1] Southern Argentina.
[2] On a lake 50 miles from Edmonton, Alberta.

within a day or two of the 18th of May. Like the golden plover, it seems to migrate by night, for at daybreak there may be hundreds in place of the few or none at all of the previous evening.   1927

MARBLED GODWIT   *Limosa fedoa*

In southwestern Saskatchewan, in 1905 and 1906, I became acquainted with the marbled godwit on its breeding grounds.

While driving across a low, wet meadow, toward a reedy lake, on June 8, 1905, and when about two hundred yards from the lake, we were surprised to see a marbled godwit flutter out from directly under the horse, which was trotting along at a leisurely pace. We stopped as soon as possible and found that we had driven directly over its nest, which barely escaped destruction, for it lay between the wheel ruts and the horses's footprints, one of which was within a few inches of it. The nest was in every way similar to the first one, the bird having beaten down the short grass to form a slight hollow in which the four handsome eggs had been laid in plain sight.

On June 9, 1906, we visited the locality where the first nest was found, and I enjoyed a most interesting experience with an unusually tame individual of this normally shy species. While walking across the flat meadow near the creek, I happened to see a marbled godwit crouching on her nest beside a pile of horse droppings. She was conspicuous enough in spite of her protective coloration, for the nest was entirely devoid of concealment in the short grass. Though we stood within ten feet of her, she showed no signs of flying away, which suggested the possibility of photographing her. My camera was a half a mile away in our wagon, but I soon returned with it and began operations at a distance of fifteen feet, setting up the camera on the tripod and focussing carefully. I moved up cautiously to within ten feet and took another picture, repeating the performance again within five feet. She still sat like a rock, and I made bold to move still closer, spreading the legs of the tripod on either side of her and placing the camera within three feet of her; I hardly dared to breathe, moving very slowly as I used the focussing cloth, and changed my plate holders most cautiously; but she never offered to move and showed not the slightest signs of fear, while I exposed all the plates I had with me, photographing her from both sides and placing the lens within two feet of her. She sat there patiently, panting in the hot sun, apparently distressed by the heat, perhaps partially dazed by it, and much annoyed by the ants which were constantly crawling into her eyes and half-open bill, causing her to wink or shake her head occasionally. I reached down carefully and stroked her on the back, but still she did not stir, and I was finally obliged to lift her off the nest in order to photograph the eggs. 1927

BAR-TAILED GODWIT   *Limosa lapponica*

The bar-tailed godwit of Europe is represented in eastern Siberia and western Alaska by this larger race,[1] with a more spotted rump. From the above breeding grounds it migrates to a winter range in Australia, New Zealand, and many oceanic islands. South of Alaska it is a mere straggler in North America.

Doctor Nelson (1887) writes:

They frequent open grassy parts of the country[1] and are quick to protest against an invasion of their territory. As a person approaches, one after the other of the birds arises and comes circling about, uttering a loud *ku-wow* with such energy as to make the ears fairly ring. If their nests are near, or they have young, they come closer and closer, some of the boldest swooping close by one's head and redoubling the din. This same note is heard upon all sides while the birds conduct their courtships, and it serves also to express their anger and alarm. At the mating season the males have a rolling whistle also like that of the ordinary field plover, but shorter. When the birds fly at this time they hold the wings decurved and stiffened and make a few rapid strokes, then glide for a short distance. On the ground it walks gracefully, its head well raised, and frequently pauses to raise its wings high over the back and then deliberately folds them. They may be decoyed when flying in flocks if their whistling note be imitated.

Mr. Brandt says in his notes:

The Pacific godwit has wonderful powers of flight, and, as it wheels about protesting against an intrusion, the slightest beat of its long, decurved wings seems, without perceptible effort, to drive it forward like an arrow from the bow. That its power of flight is extraordinary is shown by the fact that it spends the winter time of the north in southern Australia and New Zealand. It migrates along the eastern coast of Asia and is one of the interesting Old World birds that find their northeastern limit on the Alaskan shores of Bering Sea. During the love-making period, shortly after this godwit's arrival on May 15, it could be heard for an hour at a time high up in the air, as it circled about, uttering continuously its wild far-reaching cry, which was very distinctive among the medley of voices. The call of the male is often answered by the female with the syllables, *tut-tut*, not unlike a clucking chicken. The Pacific godwit differed from the other shore birds nesting at Hooper Bay [western Alaska] in that individuals in immature plumage were breeding. Sometimes a gray-breasted immature female would

[1] *L. l. baueri* (Pacific Godwit); the European form is *L. l. lapponica*.

be paired with a rich plumaged male, or again both mates would be in full color; but I encountered many pairs in which both parents showed the light grayish breast of adolescence. In fact, the immatures seemed to be in the majority. It is believed that this godwit does not assume its fully adult feathers until the beginning of the third year; but, like the bald eagle, it breeds during the second year. The earliest spring arrivals at Hooper Bay were immatures and they seemed to migrate in separate flocks.   1927

HUDSONIAN GODWIT   *Limosa haemastica*

I can count on the fingers of one hand the red-letter days when I have been privileged to see this rare and handsome wader. It has always been among the great desiderata of bird collectors. Its eggs are exceedingly rare in collections. Many ornithologists have never seen it in life. I can find no evidence that it was ever common. All the earlier writers reported it as uncommon or rare. Audubon (1840) referred to it as "of rare occurrence in any part of the United States." He never saw it in life and handled only a few market specimens in the flesh.

The winter home of the Hudsonian godwit is in extreme southern South America, from Argentina and Chile south to the Straits of Magellan and the Falkland Islands.

A. H. Holland (1892) says that, in Argentina, it "appears in flocks late in the winter after heavy rains from July to August. They were met with both in summer and winter plumage." Ernest Gibson (1920) reported it as formerly "very abundant, in numerous flocks, some of apparently over one thousand," in the Province of Buenos Aires. He says that—

On more than one of these occasions several birds have dropped to my gun. The flock would then again and again sweep round and hover over the individuals in the water, uttering loud cries of distress, quite regardless of my presence in the open and the renewed gunfire. Though the godwit is such an excellent table bird, I found myself unable to continue the slaughter under these circumstances. I might select my birds, but so closely were they packed together that the shots went practically "into the brown," and caused innumerable cripples.

Conditions have changed since then, for Doctor Wetmore (1926) writes:

Though reported 50 years ago as found in great bands and among the most abundant of shore birds in this region,[1] the small number that I have recorded here are all that were observed in continued field work throughout

[1] Guamini, Buenos Aires Province, Argentina.

the winter range of the species. I was fortunate in seeing these, as by chance I found a spot where they tarried in northward migration from some point to the south.

The passing of this fine bird must be a cause for regret among sportsmen and nature lovers alike, to be attributed to the greed of gunners and to the fact that its large size and gregarious habit made it desirable to secure and when opportunity offered easy to kill in large numbers. There is little hope even under the most rigorous protection that the species can regain its former numbers. It would appear that the small number that remain winter mainly in Patagonia [southern Argentina] as the species was encountered in any number only when in migration from that region.   1927

RUFF   *Philomachus pugnax*   (Jourdain)
[This species in casual along the Atlantic coast in fall.]

The breeding habits of the ruff are so remarkable that it is necessary to treat of them in considerable detail. When the males reach the breeding ground they are in full breeding plumage, the bare skin of the face being covered with bright yellow warts, while a disk of feathers protects the neck and two tufts project from each side of the head. The extraordinary variation in the coloring of these feather adornments renders it possible to identify individual birds, as it is rare to see two with even approximately similar coloring, and this enabled Mr. Selous (1906) to make the valuable observations which are referred to below.

Where ruffs are common, as in North Holland, one finds from time to time bare areas of ground where the grass has been worn away in patches. They are the playing grounds of the ruffs, and were known in England technically as "hills." During the daytime they are resorted to from time to time by the male birds, which may often be seen sparring with one another, but the significance of these meetings was little understood until Edmund Selous (1906) spent a fortnight in the spring of 1906 in Holland, during which he concealed himself in a hide which commanded a good view of the "hill" at close quarters, and was often on the watch before daylight.

Summarizing the results of Mr. Selous' observations, it becomes evident that the "hills" are the pairing grounds to which both males and females resort, but the period of the greatest activity is during the early morning from about 3:30 a. m. onward. Each male has a definite place and the choice of a mate rests entirely with the female, the males adopting an attitude of supplication, crouching low with partially spread wings, tail and beak pointing to the ground. The hen marks her preference by nibbling the back of the neck of the prostrate male with her bill, and soon afterwards coition takes place, the surrounding males remaining usually quiescent. One reeve[1] was seen to pair with two ruffs in succession and it is probable that she is polyandrous as the ruff is certainly polygamous. There seemed to be no connection between the fighting power of the males and the preference exercised so strikingly by the females, but, on the other hand, the favored ruffs were apparently always handsome and strikingly colored birds.

In England its extermination was primarily due to the reckless way in which the breeding stock was netted not only in autumn but also on arrival in spring on the "hilling" grounds, in order to be fattened for the table. As [T.] Pennant [1728-98] spoke of forty or fifty dozen birds being taken by a single fowler in a season it is not surprising that the stock was rapidly reduced to so low a level that in spite of belated efforts to protect the birds and their eggs, it has now practically disappeared.   1928

SANDERLING   *Crocethia alba*

Along the forearm of Cape Cod, from the elbow at Chatham to the wrist near Provincetown, extend about thirty miles of nearly continuous ocean beaches, to which we can add ten more if we include that long, narrow strip of beach and marsh called Monomoy. Facing the broad Atlantic and exposed to all its furious storms, these beaches are swept clean and pounded to a hard surface by the ceaseless waves. Even in calm weather the restless ocean swells and surges up and down over these sloping sands, and the winter storms may make or wash away a mile or so of beach in a single season. Here on the ocean side of the beach, the "back side of the beach," as it is called on the cape, is the favorite resort of the little sanderlings in fair weather or in foul. They are well named "beach birds," for here they are seldom found anywhere except on the ocean beaches, and I believe that the same is true of the Pacific coast. They are particularly active and happy during stormy weather, for then a bountiful supply of food is cast up by the heavy surf. But at all times the surf line attracts them, where they nimbly follow the receding waves to snatch their morsels of food or skillfuly dodge the advancing line of foam as it rolls up the beach.

To the ends of the earth and back again extend the migrations of the sanderling, the cosmopolitan globe trotter; few species, if any,

[1] The female.

equal it in world-wide wanderings. Nesting in the Arctic regions of both hemispheres, it migrates through all of the continents, and many of the islands, to the southernmost limits of South America and Africa, and even to Australia.

I have always loved to walk by the seashore alone with Nature, and especially to tramp for miles over the hard sands of our ocean beaches, where the heaving bosom of the restless sea sends its flood of foaming breakers rolling up the steep slopes, cut into hills and valleys by the action of the waves.

At our feet is one of the characteristic features of the ocean beach, a little flock of feeding sanderlings, confiding little fellows, apparently unmindful of our presence. They run along ahead of us as fast as we can walk, their little black legs fairly twinkling with rapid motion. They are intent only on picking up their little bits of food and most skillfuly avoid the incoming wave by running up the beach just ahead of it; occasionally a wave overtakes one when it flutters above it; then as the wave recedes they run rapidly down with it, quickly picking up what food they find. If we force them to fly, which they seem reluctant to do, they circle out over the waves and settle on the beach again a short distance ahead of us; by repeating this maneuver again and again they lead us on and on up the beach, until, tired of being disturbed, they finally make a wide circle out over the water around us and alight on the beach far behind us. Their flight is swift, direct, and generally low over the water, with less of the twistings and turnings so common among shore birds.   1927

AVOCETS AND STILTS
Family Recurvirostridae

AMERICAN AVOCET   *Recurvirostra americana*

Wherever this large, showy bird is found it is always much in evidence. Its large size and conspicuous colors could hardly be overlooked, even if it were shy and retiring; but its bold, aggressive manners force it upon our attention as soon as we approach its haunts. Localities and conditions best suited to its needs are still to be found in many places on the great plains and in the interior valleys of the far west. Its favorite resorts seem to be the shallow, muddy borders of alkaline lakes, wide open spaces of extensive marshes, where scanty vegetation gives but little concealment, or broad wet meadows splashed with shallow pools. If the muddy pools are covered with reeking scum, attracting myriads of flies, so much the better for feeding purposes. Dry, sun-baked mud flats or low, gravelly or sandy islands, with scanty vegetation, furnish the desired nesting conditions. In such open spaces they can be seen from afar and, long before we reach their haunts, the avocets are flying out to meet us, advertising the fact that we are approaching their home, making the air ring with their loud yelping notes of protest, circling about us and darting down at us in threatening plunges.

The flight of the avocet is strong, direct, and rather swift, much like that of the greater yellow-legs, with neck and legs fully extended, fore and aft. It can alight on or rise from the surface of the water with ease. On alighting its long, black and white wings are raised above its back, and slowly folded, as it settles itself with a nodding motion of the head, stands still and looks about it for a moment or two. No bird is better equipped for the amphibious existence that it leads; its long legs and webbed feet enable it to wade through soft, muddy shallows of varying depths; and if it suddenly steps beyond its depth it swims as naturally as a duck until it strikes bottom again; the thick plumage of its under parts protects it and marks it as an habitual swimmer. It often feeds while swimming by tipping up like a surface-feeding duck and reaching down into the water with its long neck and bill. It can even dive when necessary.   1927

BLACK-NECKED STILT   *Himantopus mexicanus*

The flight of the stilt is steady and direct, but not particularly swift; the bill is held straight out in front and the legs are extended backwards, giving the bird a long, slim appearance. Over their eggs or young, stilts sometimes hover on steadily beating wings with dangling legs. In their excitement they sometimes climb up into the air and make startling dives.

But stilts are essentially waders; for wading they are highly specialized, and here they show to best advantage. At times they seem a bit wabbly on their absurdly long and slender legs, notably when trembling with excitement over the invasion of their breeding grounds. But really they are expert in the use of these well-adapted limbs, and one can not help admiring the skillful and graceful way in which they wade about in water breast deep, as well as on dry land, in search of their insect prey. The legs are much bent at each step, the foot is carefully raised and gently but firmly planted again at each long stride. The legs are so long that when the bird is feeding on land it is necessary to bend the legs backward to enable the bill to reach the ground.

Stilts can swim and even dive if necessary, but they are very awkward at both, as might be expected with such long legs and the absence of webbed feet; they never indulge in either action except in cases of dire necessity. They are usually gentle and unsuspicious birds, much more easily approached than most large waders. On their breeding grounds they are especially fearless and demonstrative. Some of their amusing antics are well described by Mr. Dawson (1923) as follows:

While all are shouting lustily, the birds whose nests are more immediately threatened are doing decoy stunts of several fascinating sorts. The favorite line of effort is the broken-leg act, in which the bird collapses suddenly, as though one of its little pipestem legs had snapped in two. The act is performed with such sincerity, even when the bird is standing in only an inch or so of water, that it never ceases to be amusing. Moreover, the trick is repeated diligently every few feet, so that it begins to look as though the bird had taken some fakir vow to prostrate itself every third or fourth step. The avocet, now that one thinks of it, does the same thing; but it does it awkwardly or, as it were, cautiously, and so unconvincingly. It has manifestly copied from its more agile neighbor. The second line of effort, most faithfully pursued, is wing fluttering. In this, again, the stilt is rather the mistress. It has perfected a trick of putting up one wing at a time and letting the wind towsle it about, as though it were really broken. Of course it also flutters both wings, and goes through other nondescript flopping and fluttering performances, such as are common to the family of shore birds.

1927

PHALAROPES   Family Phalaropodidae

RED PHALAROPE   *Phalaropus fulicarius*

The well-known reversal of sexual characters in the phalaropes makes their courtship particularly interesting, as the large, handsome females press their ardent suits against the timid and dull-colored little males. A. L. V. Manniche (1910) has given us the best account of it, as follows:

June 19, 1907, early in the morning, I had the pleasure of watching for hours the actions of a loving couple of phalaropes on the beach of a pool[1] surrounded by large sedge tufts, covered with long, withered grass. This act I found very funny, peculiar, and charming. When the male had been eagerly searching for food for some 20 minutes, often standing on his head in the water, like a duck, to fish or pick up something from the bottom, he would lie down on a tuft, stretching out his one leg and his one wing as if he would fully enjoy the rest after his exertions. The female for

[1] In northeast Greenland.

some moments was lying quietly and mutely in the middle of the pool; suddenly she began with increasing rapidity to whirl around on the surface of the water, always in the same little circle, the diameter of which was some 10 centimeters. As the male seemed to pay no attention to her alluring movements, she flew rapidly up to him—producing as she left the water a peculiar whirling sound with her wings and uttering short angry cries— pushed him with her bill, and then she returned to the water and took up her swimming dance. Now the male came out to her, and the two birds whirled around for some moments equally eager and with increasing rapidity. Uttering a short call, the female again flew to a tuft surrounded by water and waited some seconds in vain for the male; again she flew to the water to induce him with eager pushes and thumps to accompany her. They again whirled violently around, whereafter she, uttering a strong, alluring sound, flew back to the tuft, this time accompanied by the male— and the pairing immediately took place. In the matrimony of the grey phalarope[1] the female only decides. She exceeds the male in size and brilliancy of plumage and has the decisive power in all family affairs. If she wants to shift her place of residence she flies up swift as an arrow with a commanding cry—which may be expressed as *"pittss"*—and if the male does not follow her at once she will immediately return and give him a severe punishment, which never fails to have the desired effect. It is a well-known fact that she completely ignores her eggs and young ones.

Ludwig Kumlien (1879) writes:

Whalemen always watch these birds while they are wheeling around high in the air in graceful and rapid circles, for they know that as soon as they sight a whale blowing they start for him, and from their elevated position they can, of course, discern one at a much greater distance than the men in the boat. I doubt if it be altogether the marine animals brought to the surface by the whale that they are after, for if the whale remains above the surface any length of time they always settle on his back and hunt parasites. One specimen was brought me by an Eskimo that he had killed on the back of an *Orca gladiator*[2]; the esophagus was fairly crammed with *Laernodipodian crustaceans*, still alive, although the bird had been killed some hours; they looked to me like *Caprella phasma*[3] and *Cyamus ceti.*[4] According to the Eskimo who killed it, the birds were picking something from the whale's back. I have often seen them dart down among a school of *Delphinapterus leucas*[5] and follow them as far as I could see. On one occasion a pair suddenly alighted astern of my boat and were not 3 feet from me at times; they followed directly in the wake of the boat, and seemed so intent on picking up food that they paid no attention whatever to us. They had probably mistaken the boat for a whale.   1927

[1] As this species is called in Britain.
[2] Atlantic Killer Whale.
[3] Skeleton Shrimp.
[4] Whale Louse.
[5] White Whale.

WILSON'S PHALAROPE   *Steganopus tricolor*

I shall never forget my first impressions of a prairie slough with its teeming bird life, an oasis of moisture in a sea of dry, grassy plain, where all the various water birds of the region were thickly congregated.

In marked contrast to the clownish coots and the noisy killdeers and blackbirds, the almost silent, gentle, dainty, little phalaropes stand out in memory as charming features in the picture, so characteristic of western bird life. The virgin prairies are nearly gone, but there are still left a few oases of moisture in our encroaching civilization, where these graceful birds may continue to delight the eye with their gentle manners.

Unlike the other two world-wide species, the Wilson phalarope is a strictly American bird, making its summer home in the interior of North America and wintering in southern South America. It differs from the other two also in being less pelagic and more terrestrial; it is seldom, if ever, seen on the oceans, being a bird of the inland marshes; and it prefers to spend more time walking about on land, or wading in shallow water, than swimming on the water. Hence its bill, neck, and legs are longer, and its feet less lobed. It is a more normal shore bird.

During my various seasons spent on the western plains I have frequently seen these phalaropes flying about in trios, consisting of one male and two females, the male always in the lead, as if pursued. Females apparently outnumber the males; and, as nest building and incubation are entirely performed by the male, many of the females must remain unattached and unable to breed. I have actually seen the male building the nest and have never been able to flush a female from a set of eggs or a brood of young.   1927

NORTHERN PHALAROPE   *Lobipes lobatus*

This is the smallest, the most abundant, and the most widely distributed of the phalaropes; consequently it is the best known. Its breeding range is circumpolar, but extends much farther south than that of the red phalarope; it might be called sub-Arctic rather than Arctic. There seems to be only one homogeneous species around the world. It resembles the red phalarope in its habits, but is more often seen on inland waters than is that species.

Countless thousands of these dainty little birds migrate northward off both coasts of North America in May, but very few ever come ashore except in bad weather. While cruising off the coast, ten or more miles from land, one is likely to see them flying about in flocks, after the manner of small sandpipers, flitting about and alighting on drifting masses of seaweed or other flotsam, or swimming lightly on the smooth surface of the sea, darting hither and thither in a most erratic way, each seemingly intent on gathering its tiny bits of food. They are gentle, graceful, and charming little birds and well worth watching.

In flight these phalaropes remind one of the smaller sandpipers; their flight is swift and often erratic; when flying in flocks they twist and turn and wheel back and forth like a flock of peeps, flashing white or dark gray, as breasts or backs are turned toward the observer. Mr. Brewster (1883) has seen them pitch "down from a considerable height with closed wings, much as snipe will do under similar circumstances." Again he (1925) speaks of seeing one "rise abruptly to a height of fifteen or twenty feet, and poise there for a moment, beating its wings and shaking its tail in a violent and peculiar manner."

It is while swimming on smooth water that the northern phalarope seems most at home, most graceful, charming, and confiding; it is usually very tame and easily approached, but sometimes, especially when in large flocks, it seems to be afraid of a boat and keeps beyond gun range. It swims lightly as a cork, its thick coat of breast feathers giving it great buoyancy, its head is held high and carried with a graceful nodding motion. When a flock alights on the water, the individuals soon scatter and swim about rapidly and independently in zigzag lines or circles, jabbing their bills into the water in a nervous and excited manner. I have never seen them dive and doubt if they can do so, as they seem to have great difficulty in getting under water, even to bathe. They frequently alight on floating masses of seaweed, where they run about and feed with all the nervous activity of small sandpipers on a mud flat.   1927

JAEGERS AND SKUAS   Family Stercorariidae

POMARINE JAEGER   *Stercorarius pomarinus*

The predatory feeding habits of the jaegers are familiar to everyone who has studied the habits of our sea birds during the latter part of summer and fall. They are the notorious pirates and freebooters among sea birds, the highwaymen that persecute their neighbors on the fishing grounds and make them "stand and deliver." It is no uncommon sight on the New England coast to see one or two of these dusky robbers darting through a flock of hovering terns or small gulls, or giving chase to the lucky one that has caught a fish, following every twist and turn in its hurrying flight as it tries to dodge or escape, close at its heels as if attached by an invisible string. At last, in desperation, the harassed tern drops its fish and the relentless pursuer seizes it before it strikes the water. Occasionally the indignant tern voids its excrement instead, which the jaeger immediately seizes, as if it were a dainty morsel.

Off Chatham, Massachusetts, we often saw this and the next species, which are called "jiddie-hawks" by the fishermen, mingling with the shearwaters and browbeating them as they do the gulls and terns. As soon as the shearwaters began to gather about our boat to pick up the pieces of cod liver that we threw overboard, the jaegers would appear and take a hand in the general scramble for food. They are quick to sense the idea that a gathering flock of sea birds means a feast to be obtained by force. The "haglets"[1] are greedy feeders, and soon gulp down what pieces of food they can find, but they have learned by many a painful squabble that they are no match for the active, fighting "jiddie-hawks," and they are soon forced to disgorge or to surrender the field.   1921

PARASITIC JAEGER   *Stercorarius parasiticus*
(Townsend)

As one watches a flock of terns whirling like driven snow, now here, now there, and ever and anon plunging for fish, one may sometimes see a dark, hawk-like bird suddenly appear on the scene and spread devastation in the ranks. With relentless energy he singles out and pursues some hapless individual until it drops its prey. This is a jaeger, a gull-like bird, with hawk-like characteristics. A more appropriate name for him would be robber rather than jaeger or hunter, for he obtains his food by robbing other birds. He has, however, all the grace and agility of the true hunting birds—the hawks—but his actions rarely end in bloodshed. After all robbery is a less serious crime than murder, but the term robber is opprobrious, while that of hunter is not, so it is perhaps well that the name remains as it is.

Anderson (1913), under the heading "Parasitic jaeger," says:

The jaegers are the terror of the smaller birds, spending their time ceaselessly hawking back and forth over the tundra looking for eggs and young birds. Large numbers of eggs of eiders and gulls are destroyed in the

[1] Shearwaters.

rookeries by the jaegers. Whenever the Arctic terns are nesting their neighbors are comparatively safe, as the belligerent little terns speedily cause any marauding jaeger to beat a hasty retreat. I have also seen ruddy turnstones drive a jaeger away from the nests. I once observed a pair of jaegers chasing a flock of sandpipers. One sandpiper flew out of the flock, the jaegers in pursuit. They seemed to work together, one darting in while the other turned. The sandpiper finally escaped by flying upward until almost out of sight, and the jaegers finally gave up the chase. * * * Some other birds will also attack the jaegers, which are really cowardly birds when heartily opposed. I have on two or three occasions seen a rock ptarmigan fly fiercely at a jaeger which came too near his nesting place and put the jaeger to ignominious flight.

Its calling makes it one of the most interesting sea birds to watch. The advent of a jaeger among a flock of terns occasions loud cries of anger among the latter as they scatter to the right and left, while the hunter, singling out one individual, chases it with great energy. No matter how skillfully and rapidly the victim twists and turns, now up, now down, now to one side, now the other, sooner or later, with a few exceptions, it acknowledges defeat by dropping the fish from its beak or by disgorging the contents of its gullet. These, the jaeger, with great skill and agility, catches in mid-air and swallows at once, or on other occasions carries hanging from the beak for a short distance before satisfying its appetite. Sometimes it alights on the water, the better to enjoy its meal.   1921

LONG-TAILED JAEGER   *Stercorarius longicaudus*

On the rolling Arctic plains or tundra back of Nome, Alaska, we found these handsome birds very common and a conspicuous feature in the landscape, where they had probably reared their young and were spending the summer in congenial surroundings. Some of them were almost constantly in sight, and it was a pleasure to watch their graceful evolutions on the wing, as they coursed about the grassy borders of the little tundra ponds in search of food or perched on the little mossy hummocks to rest or to watch for passing birds that they might rob, or for some small mammal on which they might pounce. Certain of these little mounds seemed to be favorite lookout points for certain individuals or pairs, as there were signs of continued occupancy, and we frequently saw the same mound occupied at various times; perhaps each pair of birds has a sort of feudal domain of its own, from which intruders are driven away.

To watch the long-tailed jaeger in flight is one of the delights of the

Arctic summer, for it is one of the swiftest and most graceful of birds on the wing; its light and slender form is propelled by its long, pointed wings with the speed of an arrow, its broad tail serving as an effective rudder, as it twists and turns in pursuit of its fellows or some luckless gull or tern, with its long central tail feathers streaming in the wind. Doctor Nelson (1887) says:

They appear to be much more playful than the other jaegers, and parties of six or eight may be seen pursuing one another back and forth over the marsh. The long, slender tail feathers and extreme grace on the wing of these birds render them very much like the swallow-tailed kite.

During the breeding season[1] these birds and the preceding species have a cunning habit of tolling one away from their nest by dragging themselves along the ground and feigning the greatest suffering. They roll about among the tussocks, beat their wings, stagger from side to side, and seem to be unable to fly, but they manage to increase the distance from their starting point at a very respectable rate, and ere long suddenly launch forth on the wing.   1921

SKUA   *Catharacta skua*

The following quotation from the graphic pen of Mr. F. St. Mars (1912) gives a better introduction to this bold and daring species than anything I could write, and his article, *The Eagle Guard,* from which I shall quote again, is well worth reading as a striking character study:

Then the scimitar wings shut with a crisp swish, and he became a statue in dull, unpolished bronze, impassively regarding the polecat, who lay with her back broken, feebly struggling to drag into cover. It is a shock to the human nerves to see the life blasted out of a beast almost 'twixt breath and breath; what one moment is a gliding, muscular form, instinct with life and energy, confident in power, and the next moment a crumpled heap of fur, twitching spasmodically. But it was a searchlight on the reputation of the eagle guard and the stories one had heard anent the superstitions of the natives.

The polecat, being hungry with the gnawing hunger of a mother and presuming on a swirl of mist, had tried to steal up the knoll to the two great eggs that lay in the hollow atop all unguarded. Had come then a thin, high, whirring shriek, exactly like the noise made by a sword cutting through the air, and a single thud that might have been the thud of a rifle bullet striking an animal. Then—well, then the scene described above.

Big, powerfully built, brown with the black brown of his own native peat bogs, armed to the teeth, long and slash-winged, whose flight feathers were like the cutting edge of a sword, insolent with the fine, swelling in-

[1] Near St. Michael, Alaska.

solence of power, and greatly daring, no wonder men had chosen him as the eagle guard, this mighty bird, this great skua of the naturalists, this Bonxie, mascot, and superstitious godling of the fishermen. Wah! he was a bird.

Mr. Walter H. Rich has sent me the following notes on the flight of this species:

When on the wing, which is the greater part of the time, the skua shows in the air hawk like, rather than like the gulls, with whom we rather expect to find its resemblances. Its appearance in the air is somewhat like the buteonine hawks, except that its wing action, in its seemingly restrained power and forceful stroke, suggests the unhurried flight of a falcon, or, perhaps, more accurately—since the wings are at all times fully opened, employing their full sweep in their action, their primaries slightly separated at the tips and slightly recurved—the majestic flight of an eagle. The wing spread is ample, the wing well balanced in its proportions of length and breadth, well combined to produce both power and speed. The figure is somewhat burly and chunky as compared with the lighter appearance of the gull and the more racy lines of the yager.[1] The impression of muscularity is heightened by the short, square-cut tail, carried somewhat uptilted, giving the fowl an appearance unmistakable in the eyes of one having once recognized it. This peculiarity of tail, which to me seemed slightly forked instead of having the central feathers lengthened, as in others of this group, together with the broad white patch across the bases of the primaries, furnishes a good field mark for the identification of the species.

1921

GULLS AND TERNS　　　Family Laridae

GLAUCOUS GULL　　　*Larus hyperboreus*

The name burgomaster is a fitting name for this chief magistrate of the feathered tribes of the Arctic seas, where it reigns supreme over all the lesser water fowl, levying its toll of food from their eggs and defenseless young. Well they know its strength and dread its power, as it sails majestically aloft over the somber, rocky cliffs of the Greenland coast, where, with myriads of sea fowl, it makes its summer home; and useless is it for them to resist the onslaught of its heavy beak when it swoops down to rob them of their callow young. Only the great skua, the fighting airship of the north, dares to give it battle and to drive the tyrant burgomaster from its chosen crag. Its only rival in size and power among the gulls is the great black-backed gull, and where these two meet on the Labrador coast they treat each other with dignified respect.

[1] Jaeger.

The Eskimos find the breasts of this and other gulls desirable as food, the young birds being considered a delicacy, and the eggs are very good to eat when fresh. Many an Arctic explorer also has found these birds a welcome addition to the food supply. Kumlien (1879) thus describes the primitive methods of the Eskimos in capturing these birds:

One of the most popular is to build a small snow hut on the ice in a locality frequented by the gulls. Some blubber or scraps of meat are exposed to view on the top and seldom fail to induce the bird to alight on the roof of the structure. This is so thin that the Eskimo on the inside can readily see the bird through the snow and, with a quick grab, will break through the snow and catch the bird by the legs. Some use a spear, thrusting it violently through the roof of the hut. Many are killed by exposing pieces of blubber among the hummocky ice and lying concealed within proper distance for bow and arrow practice.   1921

ICELAND GULL   *Larus glaucoides*   (Townsend)

The Iceland gull is a smaller edition of the glaucous gull, which it resembles closely in appearance and habits. Like its larger relative it breeds in the Arctic regions in Victoria Land,[1] Boothia Peninsula,[1] Greenland, Iceland, and east to Nova Zembla.[2]

The Iceland gull nests in communities by itself and with other species of gulls both on high, rocky cliffs and on low, sandy shores. Ross (1835) found it breeding on the faces of precipices on the shores of Prince Regent's Inlet[1] with the glaucous gull, "but at a much less height and in greater numbers." Hagerup (1891) at Ivigtut in Greenland says:

About a thousand pair nest on the "bird cliff," above the kittiwakes. The lowest nests are built at a height of about 200 feet; the highest at about 500 feet above sea level.

Like other gulls and terns the Iceland gull is sometimes of value to man in indicating the presence of fish. Baird, Brewer and Ridgway (1884) quote from Faber a statement that in 1821 "on the 1st of March the shore[3] was free of sea gulls; but early on the 2d the air was filled with numbers of this species which had arrived during the night. The Icelanders concluded from the sudden appearance of the birds that shoals of codfish must have arrived on the coast, and it was soon found that this conjecture was correct." He adds that these gulls "would indicate to the seal shooters in the fiord where the seals

[1] Canadian Arctic.
[2] Two large islands in the Soviet Arctic.
[3] At Debratte, south coast of Iceland.

were to be looked for, by following their track to the sea and hovering over them in flocks with incessant cries." In both cases it is probable that the larger creatures stirred up the water so that the smaller food of the gulls could be obtained. In the same way flocks of terns follow whales, not with any expectations of feeding on the whale, but on the smaller marine life stirred up by the whale and on which both feed.

1921

GLAUCOUS-WINGED GULL   *Larus glaucescens*

This, the most abundant, the most widely distributed, and the characteristic gull of the north Pacific coast, is an omnipresent and familiar sight to the travelers along the picturesque coast and through the numerous inside passages leading to Alaska.

Mr. Dawson (1909), who spent a week studying the vocal performances of this species and their significance, has thus classified its various notes:

1. *The beak-quaking notes.* Harsh, unmusical, and of moderate pitch, used to express distrust and continued disapproval. During the delivery the mandibles are brought together three or four times in moderate succession. This is the ordinary scolding or distress cry of characteristic and uniform pitch, save that it is raised to a higher key when the speaker becomes vehement. The phrase varies from three to five notes, and is uttered in the following cadences: *kak-ako; ka ka, ka ka; ka ka kaka; kaka; kaka, ka kakak; kak-a kak-a-ka.*

2. *Kawk.* A note of inquiry or mere communication; has many modifications and varies from a short trumpet note to the succeeding.

3. *Klook.* A sepulchral note of uniform interest but uncertain meaning.

4. The trumpet notes, long or short, single or in prolonged succession, high-pitched, musical, and far-sounding. During delivery the head is thrust forward, the neck arched, and the throat and mandibles opened to their fullest capacity. These are pleasure notes and are used especially on social occasions, when many birds are about, *keer, keer, keer, keer.*

5. *A(n)k, a(n)k, a(n)k, a(n)k, a(n)k, a(n)k.* Minor trumpet notes of regular length and succession, used in expostulation or social excitement; frequent and varied.

6. *Klook, klook, klook.* In quality a combination of *kawk* and the trumpet tones, uttered deliberately and without much show of energy. Used chiefly in domestic conversation of uncertain import.

7. *Oree-eh, oree-eh, oree-eh, an an an.* An expression of greeting as when uttered by a sitting bird welcoming one about to alight. The notes of the first series are trumpet tones, in which the second syllable of each member is raised to a higher pitch, while the voice is dropped again on the third. The second series is lower and more trivial, but still enthusiastic, as

though congratulatory to the guest arrived.

8. *Ko.* Shouted once, or thrice repeated, in quelling a clamor. "Hist! Hist! You're making too much noise; he's watching us."

9. *Arahh.* A slow and mournful trumpeting, usually uttered awing to express anxiety or grief, as at the loss of a chick.

10. *Oo anh, oo anh.* Repeated indefinitely. Notes of coaxing and endearment usually addressed to children, but occasionally to wedded mates. The cooing of doves does not express so much adulation or idolatrous devotion as the gull throws into these most domestic tones.   1921

GREAT BLACK-BACKED GULL   *Larus marinus*

While cruising along the bleak and barren coasts of southern Labrador I learned to know and admire this magnificent gull, as we saw it sailing on its powerful wings high above the desolate crags and rocky islets of that forbidding shore, its chosen summer home.[1] Its resemblance to the bald eagle was striking, as it soared aloft and wheeled in great circles, showing its broad black back and wings in sharp contrast with its snow-white head and tail, glistening in the sunlight. It surely seemed to be a king among the gulls, a merciless tyrant over its fellows, the largest and strongest of its tribe. No weaker gull dared to intrude upon its feudal domain; the islet it had chosen for its home was deserted and shunned by other less aggressive waterfowl, for no other nest was safe about the castle of this robber baron, only the eider duck being strong enough to defend its young.

When traveling its flight is slow and heavy, as might be expected in the largest of the gulls, but it is always strong, dignified, and protracted. Macgillivray (1852) writes:

Its flight is strong, ordinarily sedate, less wavering and buoyant than that of smaller species, but graceful, effective, and even majestic. There, running a few steps and flapping its long wings, it springs into the air, wheels to either side, ascends, and on outspread and beautifully curved pinions hies away to some distant place. In advancing against a strong breeze it sometimes proceeds straight forward, then shoots away in an oblique direction, now descends in a long curve so as almost to touch the water, then mounts on high. When it wheels about and sweeps down the wind its progress is extremely rapid. It walks with ease, using short steps, runs with considerable speed, and, like the other gulls, pats the sands or mud on the edge of the water with its feet. It generally rests standing on one foot, with its head drawn in; but in a dry place it often reposes by laying itself down.
     1921

---

[1] Now breeds "south to . . . New York"—1957 *A.O.U. Check-list.*

WESTERN GULL　　　*Larus occidentalis*

Along the numerous beaches of the California coast the dark-mantled western gull is the most conspicuous and the most universally abundant sea bird throughout the whole year, everywhere much in evidence and everywhere tame and familiar—a welcome visitor as a useful scavenger and a pretty feature in the seashore scenery. The immaculate purity of its snow-white plumage is kept spotlessly clean, in spite of its untidy feeding habits. As we see these beautiful black and white birds sailing along the ocean cliffs they seem to reflect the clear freshness of the beach and sea and sky; and as we see them walking daintily on their long legs over the clean sand it seems incongruous to associate them with the struggling screaming mob of hungry birds that we have just seen fighting for and gorging themselves on the refuse from the sewers or the garbage dumps.

The behavior of western gulls toward their neighbors is truly scandalous. They must be cordially hated and seriously dreaded by the various species among which they nest, for they are arrant thieves, ever on the alert to improve every opportunity to steal and devour any unprotected eggs or young which they can find. They usually select a breeding place among nesting colonies of cormorants, murres, or pelicans, chiefly because they can there find an abundant food supply in the nests of their peaceful neighbors. Cormorants, being rather shy, are easily driven from their nests by human intruders and do not readily return, so that the gulls often succeed in cleaning out a whole colony.

Mr. A. W. Anthony (1906) has graphically described this performance as follows:

The advent of man in the region of a cormorant rookery is hailed with delight by every gull on the island, but to the poor cormorant it is a calamity of the darkest hue. As the frightened birds leave the nests, which have so far never been for a moment left without the protection of at least one of the parents, the screaming gulls descend in swarms to break and eat the eggs or kill the young, as the case may be. Small cormorants are bolted entire, despite their somewhat half-hearted protest; larger birds are dismembered by two gulls assisting in the operation, after the well-known manner of barnyard chicks with a worm; and before the adult cormorants have recovered from their fright and returned to protect their homes a colony of several hundred nests will be almost destroyed. I have found young western gulls feasting on cormorant squabs half a mile or more from the nests from which they have been abducted.　　　　　　　　1921

HERRING GULL   *Larus argentatus*   (Townsend)

The most widely distributed sea gull of the Northern Hemisphere and the one that is best known because it frequents the haunts of man, visiting his most populous harbors, is the herring gull.

From the beach and among the rocks of the seashore the herring gull obtains a variety of food other than dead refuse—crabs and other crustaceans, mollusks of all sorts, such as clams, mussels, sea snails, etc., and echinoderms and worms. Many crabs and mollusks are broken with the bill, but if this cannot be accomplished the gull seizes the difficult morsel and flies up with it into the air, nearly vertically or in circles, drops it onto the hard sand or rocks, follows closely the descent, and alights to regale itself on the exposed contents. If unsuccessful the first time the gull tries a second and sometimes a third or fourth time. This habit, which is also a common one with crows, explains the fact that mollusk shells, crabs, and sea urchins are scattered so universally along our coast, sometimes half a mile from the sea.

At times these gulls are able to sail directly into the teeth of the wind without a single stroke of the wing. Mr. William Brewster (1912) has described the manner in which herring gulls keep pace with a vessel, gliding along on almost motionless wings into the teeth of the gale, sometimes within a few yards of the deck, but always on the windward side [of the SS *Arabic* off Eire, August 1911]:

As the gale increased they flapped their wings less and less often, until most, if not all of them, were gliding ceaselessly, minute after minute, over distances certainly exceeding a mile, without a single wing beat, but not without changes or readjustments in the bend or the inclination of the wings, which took place not infrequently and often were very obvious.

Several explanations of this mysterious means of propulsion have been offered, but the following by F. W. Headley (1912) seems to me the most satisfactory. He says:

There is a feat perhaps more striking than any of the others already described—a feat which, nevertheless, gulls often achieve. A steamer is advancing against a fairly strong wind, which, if not absolutely a head wind, strikes the vessel at an acute angle. There results a steady up current over the stern of the vessel, or slightly to one side or the other of the stern. Poised on this up current the gulls hang in mid-air, their wings held rigidly expanded. Only very slight wing movements, evidently for purposes of balance, can be detected. Standing on the deck and watching these gulls one is irresistibly reminded of the poising of the kestrel[1] high in air, with

[1] The European *Falco tinnunculus,* somewhat like our Sparrow Hawk.

wings held motionless, when he finds a wind that is all that he could wish. It is sometimes easy to forget that, unlike the kestrel, they do not remain in one spot, but that all the while they are moving forward and, in fact, keeping pace with the steamer. The gulls, like the kestrel, are poising on an up current of air; but they give their bodies a rather different incline, with the result that they keep traveling forward. ° ° ° The general incline of their body and wing surfaces is slightly downward. Hence the upward-streaming wind not only maintains them in the air or lifts them higher, but acting at right angle, also drives them forward.   1921

CALIFORNIA GULL   *Larus californicus*

The feeding habits of the California gull make it one of the most useful of birds to the agriculturist of the western plains, where it makes its summer home. Rev. S. H. Goodwin (1904) says of its habits in Utah:

I have watched them for hours as they circled about the newly plowed field, or followed close behind the plowman, as blackbirds do in some localities, or sunned themselves on the ridges of the furrows after a hearty meal of worms. I have studied them as they fared up and down the river in search of dead fish and other garbage, or assembled in countless numbers in some retired, quiet slough where they rent the air with their harsh, discordant cries and demoniac laughter, or sailed on graceful wing in rising circles till lost in the deep blue of heaven.

Mr. Dutcher (1905) publishes the following interesting letter from Mr. John E. Cox, of the Utah Board of Agriculture:

Gulls go all over the State for insects, the greatest number visiting the beet fields, where they keep down the crickets, grasshoppers, cutworms, etc. They took a new diet this summer. Some alfalfa fields were so badly honeycombed with mice holes and runs that it was impossible to irrigate them, and they were plowed up, mostly for beet culture. When the water was turned into the irrigation ditches the mice were forced out of their holes, and the gulls then caught them. They became so perfect in their work that they kept abreast of the head of the water and picked up every mouse that appeared. When gorged with victims they would vomit them up in piles on the ditch bank and recommence their feeding. Gulls are sacred in Utah,[1] and are so tame that oftentimes they may be caught by hand as they follow the plow so closely.

Mr. Dawson (1909) pays the following tribute to their prowess on the wing:

[1] A flight of California Gulls destroyed a plague of long-horned grasshoppers that threatened the crops of the early Mormon settlement at Salt Lake city in 1848.

Graceful, effortless, untiring, but above all mysterious, is that power of propulsion by which the bird moves forward into the teeth of the gale; indeed, is advanced all the more certainly and freely when the wind is strong. From the deck of a steamer making 15 miles an hour against a 15-knot breeze, I once stretched my hand toward a soaring gull. He lay suspended in mid-air without the flutter of a feather, while the air rushed past him at the rate of 30 miles an hour; and he maintained the same relative position to my hand, at 5 or 6 feet, for about a minute. When he tired of the game, he shot forward. And again, there was not in the motion the slightest perceptible effort of propulsion, but only a slightly sharper inclination of the body and wings downward. We see clearly how it must be, yet we can not understand it. The gull is a kite and gravity the string. The bird is a continually falling body, and the wind is continually preventing the catastrophe. Yes, we see it—but then, gravity isn't a string, you know; and so why doesn't the wind take the kite along with it? 1921

RING-BILLED GULL   *Larus delawarensis*

My first experience with the nesting habits of the ring-billed gull was on "the enchanted isles" of Stump Lake, North Dakota, three small islands in a western arm of the lake, now included in the Stump Lake Reservation.[1] On May 31, 1901, and again on June 15, 1901, I visited these interesting islands, with Mr. Herbert K. Job (1898) who had previously described and named them. Two of the islands contained breeding colonies of ring-billed gulls, consisting of about one hundred pairs each.

The gulls' nests were placed upon the ground along the upper edges of the beaches and among the rocks and bowlders which were scattered all over the islands. They were made of dried grasses and weeds, sometimes of small sticks; were lined with finer grasses and were often decorated with feathers. On May 31 all the nests contained eggs, many of which had been incubated a week or ten days; on June 15 not over one quarter of the eggs had hatched and many of them still held incomplete sets.

We found this and the foregoing species frequenting regularly the garbage dumps on the outskirts of the prairie towns and acting as scavengers along the shores of the lakes in Saskatchewan. On the seacoasts it does its part with other species in cleaning up the floating refuse in our harbors, and gathers in large numbers where garbage is regularly dumped, feasting on the miscellaneous diet it finds. It does considerable damage on its breeding grounds by destroying the eggs of other species associated with it. I have seen a party of ring-

[1] Now the Stump Lake National Wildlife Refuge.

billed gulls break and suck nearly every egg in a colony of double-crested cormorants when the latter had been kept off their nests for an hour or two; but I doubt if they would have dared to molest them if the cormorants had not been driven away by our presence. It occasionally robs the nests of the avocet, but it does not seem to molest the nests of the common tern, with which it is intimately associated; and I have never known of its disturbing any of the ducks which nest on its breeding grounds. Probably the terns are able to defend their eggs and the duck's nests are too well hidden.   1921

MEW GULL   *Larus canus*

L. c. brachyrhynchus   (Short-billed Gull)

The short-billed gull is a widely distributed and common species throughout the whole of the interior of Alaska and the northern portions of the northwest territories. It is a marsh-loving species and frequents all the flat marshy country of the coast and interior, as well as much of the wooded region in the vicinity of lakes, ponds, and streams.

Dr. Joseph Grinnell (1900) made some interesting observations on the nesting habits of this species on the Kowak delta, Alaska. He writes:

The lakes which the short-billed gulls mostly frequented were usually surrounded by spruce trees, which in the delta are more low and scrubby than farther in the interior. I had in vain searched for the gulls' nests on small bare islets in the lakes and on grassy points, such as the gulls with which I was previously familiar would be likely to select for nesting sites. Although I failed to find any sign of nests, still the birds, by their uneasy actions, intimated that there must be eggs or young somewhere. Finally on the 16th of June I determined to discover the secret, and, armed with patience, selected a secluded hiding place among some scrub spruces near a lake, yet where I had a good view of it. Two pairs of short-billed gulls kept flying about above me for a long time, occasionally alighting on the tops of the spruces surrounding the lake. I kept track of each of the four gulls as best I could, and finally saw one settle close down on the bushy top of a tree on the other side of the lake. Then it dawned on me that the nests might be in trees. I took my bearings on the tree, and started around the lake. Before I had nearly reached the vicinity I was met by the gulls, one of which began to dive at me again and again. It would fly high above me and then swoop down past my head with a shrill, startling scream. Just as the bird passed me it would void a limy mass of faeces, and with such disagreeable precision that I was soon streaked with white. On climbing the spruce, which was about 12 feet tall, I discovered the nest. It was almost completely hidden from below by the flat, bushy top of the spruce on which it was placed. The nest was a shapeless mass of slender twigs and hay, 9 inches across on top. There was scarcely any depression and I found the shells of two of the eggs broken on the ground beneath, probably pitched out by a severe wind of the day before. The single egg secured was considerably incubated.   1921

LAUGHING GULL   *Larus atricilla*

High above the gleaming sands of Muskeget Island [Massachusetts], amid the whirling maze of hovering terns that swarm up into the blue ether until the uppermost are nearly lost to vision, may be seen some larger birds, conspicuous by their size, by their black heads and black-tipped wings, soaring at ease among their lesser companions. In the ceaseless din of strident cries may be heard occasionally the hoarse notes of this larger bird—notes which, from their peculiar character, give the bird the fitting name of laughing gull.

The Muskeget Island colony is certainly the largest breeding colony of laughing gulls north of Virginia. These gulls formerly bred here abundantly, but constant persecution reduced their numbers until they became very scarce about 1880, and would have been extirpated except for the protection afforded them by the passage of suitable laws and by the personal efforts of Mr. George H. Mackay in seeing that the laws were enforced. They increased slowly during the next ten years, but after 1890 their increase was more encouraging. In 1894 the colony nearly doubled in numbers and it continued to flourish, increasing a little each year, until, at the time of my last visit (in 1919) it consisted of several thousand pairs.

Similar colonies formerly existed along the Long Island coast, where in Giraud's day[1] the laughing gull was a common summer resident. It occurs there now chiefly as a migrant, and I doubt if there are any breeding colonies left. According to Mr. William Dutcher's notes it bred at South Oyster Bay up to 1884, at Amityville until 1887, and at Cedar Island as late as 1888.

Dr. Witmer Stone [1909] says of its status in 1908 in New Jersey:

Formerly an abundant summer resident on the salt meadows along the coast, it is now restricted to two colonies—one at Brigantine and the other on Gull Island, Hereford Inlet—both under the protection of the National Association of Audubon Societies. The birds arrive April 4 to 20, and have mostly departed by October 1. The first sets of eggs are laid in May.

[1] *Circa* 1844.

On Cobb's Island, Virginia, and on the surrounding islands we found the laughing gulls still abundant in 1907, though considerably reduced in numbers by many years of persecution. Their eggs were persistently collected daily by the oystermen all through the breeding season up to July 4, after which date they were protected by law and the birds were allowed to raise their broods. [Protection has now greatly increased the numbers of this gull everywhere.]   1921

FRANKLIN'S GULL   *Larus pipixcan*

A breeding colony of Franklin's gulls is one of the most spectacular, most interesting, and most beautiful sights in the realm of North American ornithology. The man who has never seen one has something yet to live for—a sight which once seen is never to be forgotten. No written words can convey any adequate idea of the beautiful picture presented by countless thousands of exquisite birds, of such delicate hues and gentle habits, in all the activities of their closely populated communities.

On June 9, 1905, after driving for miles over the rolling plains of southwestern Saskatchewan and exploring many lakes and sloughs in vain we discovered a splendid colony of these elusive birds. As we drove over the crest of a billowy ridge among roving bands of grazing cattle we saw a broad, level, grassy plain spread out before us, and beyond it in the distance a lake fringed with marshes. With the aid of our glasses we could barely make out a cloud of white specks hovering over the marsh, and we knew at once that we had won the long-sought prize. Another mile of rapid driving brought us to the marshy shore, where scores, yes hundreds, of the dainty birds began flying out to meet us with a chorus of shrill screams and harsh cries of protest. We tethered our horse and waded out into the marsh, where the reeds or bulrushes (*Scirpus lacustris*) grew for a distance of two hundred or three hundred yards out from the shore and for half or three-quarters of a mile along that side of the lake. The water was not over knee-deep anywhere, except on the outer edge, and usually much less than that; perhaps a foot deep on the average. The reeds were three or four feet high and were not very thick except on the outer edge, where they grew in thick clusters, dense and tall. Most of the reeds were of last year's growth, dead and more or less flattened down, with scattering tall, straight, green reeds growing up through them.

As we waded out toward the colony, clouds of gulls began to rise and circle over us, cackling and screaming, but it was not until we were one hundred yards from the shore that we began to find nests. When we were fairly in the midst of the colony the excitement grew intense; clouds and clouds of the beautiful birds were rising all around us, and the din of their voices was terrific, as they hovered over, circled around, and darted down at us in bewildering multitudes. If we kept still they would gradually settle down all around us, but if we gave a shout the result would be startling as the whole surrounding marsh would seem to rise in a dense white cloud, and the roar of their wings mingled with the grand chorus of cries would be almost deafening. But they were very tame and we had plenty of opportunities to admire the exquisite beauty of their plumage, seldom surpassed in any bird; pearl gray mantles, delicate rosy breasts, black heads, and claret-colored bills and feet. We could form no very definite idea of their numbers, but there were certainly a mighty host of them; to say that there were thousands would be putting it mildly, for their nests were as thick as they could be over a large area. Assuming that there were from fifteen to twenty nests in an area ten yards square, or in one hundred square yards, which is certainly a conservative estimate, I figured that there were at least from fifteen thousand to twenty thousand nests in the colony, meaning a population of from thirty thousand to forty thousand birds.

1921

BONAPARTE'S GULL   *Larus philadelphia*

During the first warm weather in April, when the shad and herring are beginning to run up our rivers, we begin to see the migrating flocks of this pretty little gull moving northward along our coasts or up the valleys of our great rivers in the interior.

The flight of this species is very light and buoyant, as well as active and graceful. It is more tern-like than gull-like, and it might easily be overlooked in a flock of loitering terns. When moving about looking for food its flight seems listless and desultory; every stroke of its long wings lifts its light body perceptibly, as it drives it along much faster than it seems. Like snowflakes wafted by the wind the loose flock drifts along; one hardly realizes that it has come before it has swept away beyond our vision. Yet with all this apparent listlessness there is no lack of the power of control; it can breast the heaviest storms, it can rise and fall over the crests of the largest waves, and can go whither it will with the utmost ease and grace. It swims with equal buoyancy and grace, resting on the surface as lightly as an eggshell. I have sometimes seen it dive, though its food is often picked up while it is swimming on the surface; but more often it drops lightly down in the air, picking the morsel from the water with its bill, and perhaps touching the surface with its feet.   1921

LITTLE GULL   *Larus minutus*   (Townsend)

[This European species is casual along the Atlantic coast.]

In flight and general habits the little gull is said to closely resemble the black-headed gull. They are very tame and fearless of danger. Their flight is graceful and active, and it is said at times to be butter-fly-like or to resemble that of swallows. Professor Liljeborg, quoted by Dresser, says that their graceful and quick evolutions in pursuit of insects "almost surpass goatsuckers." In a word, these gulls resemble terns in flight rather than the larger gulls.

Gätke (1895), at Heligoland[1] says:

All the gulls leave their northern breeding stations before the approach of winter in order to betake themselves to more temperate latitudes. In the case of none, however, does this movement so much partake of the nature of a true migration as in that of the present species. Long-extending flights of these pretty little birds may be seen traveling over the sea past the island at the close of September and during the first half of October. Their movements, however, are quite different from what one is accustomed to see in the case of most migrants. Companies of from 100 to 200 in-dividuals travel in motley throng quite low over the sea, continuously dropping to the surface to pick up food. All the time, however, they rigidly maintain their western course of flight, and speeding along with great rapidity are very soon lost to sight. Moreover, considerable quantities of these gulls, intermingled with the larger species, are met with here all the winter months during violent westerly and northwesterly gales, when they seek a temporary shelter on the lee side of the island. While roving over the sea in all directions in search of food they execute many rapid beats with their wings.   1921

HEERMANN'S GULL   *Larus heermanni*

Although the food of Heermann's gull consists largely of fish and other sea food, which it obtains offshore, it also indulges freely in a great variety of other foods and does its part as a scavenger along the [West Coast] on the beaches with the other gulls, where it does not seem to be at all fastidious as to its diet.

Though not so much of an egg thief as some other gulls, it is somewhat of a pilferer of food and quite bold in attacking species

[1] Island in North Sea, off Germany.

larger than itself which are too stupid to resist its persecution. Mr. Anthony (1906) has given us the following interesting account of its method of robbing the [brown] pelicans:

Heermann's gull is by far the most active and successful in catching small fish from the surface; but as a rule will seldom attempt to catch his own dinner if there are any pelicans among the delegates to the convention. There are times when the herring are so thick and so driven from below by the large fish that the pelicans will sit on the surface and snap them up without plunging, as is their normal method, from a height of from 10 to 30 feet in the air. If the fish are swimming the deep plunge often carries the bird completely under the surface, and when a second later he bobs up like a cork he is sure of finding at least one, often two Heermann's gulls expectantly awaiting the result. If there are two they will usually take up stations on each side and but a foot in front of the pelican, which still holds its huge bill and pouch under the water. It may be that the pelican does not yet know the result of his efforts, for in plunging the pouch is used as a dip net and, if nothing else, it is full of water, which is allowed to escape past the loosely closed mandibles until, perhaps 5 or 10 seconds after the bird made his plunge, a flutter is seen in the pouch, announcing one or more struggling victims. It is still an open question, however, whether they will be eaten by the gull or the pelican, and the latter is seemingly well aware that a herring in the gullet is worth two in the pouch, for it will often wait several seconds for a favorable opportunity for disposing of the catch; the gulls meantime constantly uttering their nasal whining note and keeping well within reaching distance of the pouch. When the critical moment arrives the pelican throws the bill up and attempts to swallow the fish, but, with cat-like quickness, one or both gulls make a similar effort, and should the fish in its struggles have thrust its tail or head past the edges of the mandibles, as very often happens, it is an even chance that the gull gets the prize; in fact, I have often seen a Heermann gull reach well into the pouch and get away with a fish in the very act of slipping down the throat of the pelican.   1921

IVORY GULL   *Pagophila eburnea*

This beautiful, snow-white gull of the Arctic regions is decidedly boreal in summer and seldom wanders far south even in winter. It is circumpolar in its distribution and has been noted by nearly all Arctic explorers in both hemispheres.

A most interesting account of the home life of this species in Franz Josef Land[1] is published by Mr. W. Eagle Clarke (1898), in which he quotes from the journal of Mr. William S. Bruce, of the Jackson-Harmsworth Expedition, as follows:

[1] Now Fridtjof Nansen Land, Soviet archipelago in the Arctic Ocean.

August 7. To-day we landed at Cape Mary Harmsworth, and the first thing we noted was an immense number of ivory gulls, and from their demonstrations and shriekings it soon became evident that they were nesting. As we traveled across the low-lying spit we found this was so. Here there are 5 or 6 square miles or more of fairly level ground, more or less terraced, being evidently a series of raised beaches. This, if not the largest, is one of the largest areas of bare ground in Franz Josef Land. Beyond a few lichens and occasional patches of moss there is very little vegetation, only two flowering plants being found—a saxifrage and a grass, and these very sparingly, indeed. There is very little actual soil, and the surface is rough and rugged with large stones. Scattered all over it are numerous fresh-water ponds, the largest of them perhaps 200 yards across. The first signs of the ivory gulls' nests were patches of old moss every here and there, which at first we could not make out. As we advanced we saw more of these patches, and these seemed more compact. On approaching closer to these the birds made still more vehement demonstrations, swooping down upon us and giving vent to their feelings by uttering a perfectly deafening shriek close to our heads.

Once in the midst of their nests—for these patches of moss were their nests—we had many hundreds of birds around us, first one swooping down to within a foot of our heads, and immediately after another. In some cases they actually touched us, and in one instance knocked the hat off a man's head. Most of the nests were empty, owing to the late date; but here and there was a single egg, and in two nests I found two eggs. Going on through this gullery we found that near certain nests, which were apparently empty, the birds made even more violent demonstrations than before, and in looking carefully about we descried a young ivory gull in its greyish-white downy plumage, and hardly visible against the stones, which were of a very similar color. Even the older ones, which were more whitish, were difficult to see among the stones. These young birds would sit crouched in between two or three large stones, and one might at first sight take them for stones also. On picking up a young bird the parents became quite distracted and threatened us more vehemently than ever.   1921

BLACK-LEGGED KITTIWAKE   *Rissa tridactyla*

R. t. tridactyla   (Atlantic Kittiwake)

The hardy kittiwake has been well named, on the New England coast, the "frost gull" or the "winter gull," for its arrival seems to indicate the coming of hard frosts and the beginning of real winter. It seems to bring with it the first cold breath of ice and snow from the rugged Arctic coasts where it makes its summer home. This species is always associated in my mind with icebergs and the great

Greenland ice packs, which drift southward with the Arctic current, and in its summer home, with the dark, frowning cliffs of the frozen north, which tower for hundreds of feet above the stormy ice-bound seas until lost to sight in shrouds of mist and fog, where the "frost gulls" find a safe retreat in which to rear their hardy offspring.

Mr. Walter H. Rich has sent me the following notes on the behavior of the kittiwake or "winter bird," as it is called, on Georges Banks.[1]

As might be guessed from the name, it is during the coldest weather that this bird is most abundant, and at this season, so the writer was informed, not infrequently they became so tame as to perch in rows upon the main booms of the vessels on frosty mornings, awaiting their breakfasts. The first arrivals (five birds) appeared on the morning of October 12, 1913.

Every day following their arrival showed increasing numbers until in a fortnight there were always "hundreds," and at times "thousands" would make but a moderate estimate of their flocks. My records for November 16 says, "winter birds in millions"—perhaps an exaggeration, yet so it seemed. Scarcely a daylight hour after their arrival but was filled with their chattering squeal; scarcely a moment but saw them wheeling about the steamers, appearing just before sun up and standing by to give any needed assistance as long as the sun held above the western rim of the ocean.

The signal for hauling the net brought great activity among the flocks banked up on either side of the steamer's path in 2½-mile-long lines of white birds roosting upon the water. There were literally thousands of gulls that rose and drifted along over the swells, just keeping pace with the steamer's slow progress. Other gulls there were, both brown plumaged and full plumaged—ring-bill, herring gull, black-backed, and a few of the large white or pearly gulls, of species undetermined where they wheeled in a safe offing. But all these were at a disadvantage, both numerically and otherwise, with the kittiwakes, who stole from them and beat them to every piece of liver and waste thrown overside. If the prize sinks the big gull has lost it; not so the little "winter bird," who dives swiftly and gracefully from the wing and brings it up. This is the only gull which the writer has ever seen to dive. Naturally their success makes them unpopular with the losers, who pursue and harry the kittiwake, but to little effect, since the small gull is too active to suffer much in these attempts at reprisal.

R. t. pollicaris (Pacific Kittiwake)

Dr. W. H. Dall (1873) gives us the following good account of a breeding colony in the Shumagin Islands, south of the Alaska Peninsula:

[1] Fishing banks in the North Atlantic on east border of Gulf of Maine.

On entering Coal Harbor, Unga, we were at once struck with the peculiar white line which wound around the precipitous cliffs of Round Island, and was seen to be caused by the presence of birds; and as soon as an opportunity was afforded I took a boat and went to the locality to examine it. The nests, in their position, were unlike anything I had ever seen before. At first it appeared as if they were fastened to the perpendicular face of the rock, but on a close examination it appeared that two parallel strata of the metamorphic sandstone of the cliffs, being harder than the rest, had weathered out, standing out from the face of the cliff from 1 to 4 inches, more or less irregularly. The nests were built where these broken ledges afforded a partial support, though extending over more than half their width. The lines of nests exactly followed the winding projections of these ledges, everywhere giving a very singular appearance to the cliff, especially when the white birds were sitting on them. The nests were built with dry grass, agglutinated together and to the rock in some unexplained manner; perhaps by a mucus secreted by the bird for the purpose. The nests had a very shallow depression at the top in which lay two eggs.   1921

RED-LEGGED KITTIWAKE   *Rissa brevirostris*

Mr. William Palmer (1899) writes, concerning his impression of this species on the Pribilof Islands [Bering Sea]:

To my mind this is the most beautiful species on the islands. Always graceful, whether on the cliffs or flying, its beautiful form and delicate snow-white plumage, with its vermilion feet, adds much to the avifaunal wonders of these islands. Unlike its cousin, which carries its feet extended when flying, this species nearly always buries them in the feathers of its under body, as if fearful of showing their beauty except when absolutely necessary. When fog envelops these islands, both the land and sea, the sea birds away from home find their way by flying along the edges of the bluffs, where the stored heat in the rocks dissipates the rapidly drifting fog. The wily Aleut, knowing these characteristics, ensconces himself behind a rock in a suitable location and with a large dip net intercepts the birds on their way along the bluffs. Thus many a meal is obtained, and, unfortunately, our pretty red-legged kittiwake too often falls a victim.   1921

ROSS' GULL   *Rhodostethia rosea*

The rosy gull[1] is not only the most beautiful of the gulls but it is the most strictly Arctic, one of the rarest in collections and, to all but a favored few, the least known. Owing to its restricted habitat in an inaccessible region, few of us may ever expect to see it. As its

[1] As this species was formerly called.

wanderings carry it over a wide area in Arctic regions, a few specimens have been picked up by Arctic explorers. For nearly all that we know of its habits we are indebted to the Russian explorer and good ornithologist, Dr. Sergius A. Buturlin (1906), who, during his visit to the Kolyma delta, on the Arctic coast of eastern Siberia, in 1905, collected thirty-eight skins and thirty-six eggs of this beautiful bird. Fortunately he has given us a very full and interesting life history of this species, from which I shall quote freely.

On the morning of May 31 one of my men saw a pair, and during the day I went on the river, where the fathom-thick ice was still quite safe, and came across several dozens. The sun was shining brightly, and in the distance each pair appeared like so many roseate points on the bluish ice of the great stream. I say "pair," as from their first arrival the birds were constantly seen in pairs. They had evidently just finished their migration and were tired after their exertions, for they sat very quietly on the ice. [We] found the rosy gull nesting in little colonies of from 2 or 3 to 10 or 15 pairs, in company with the common black-capped tern of the delta.

One of the colonies was on a piece of wet tundra near two lakes, a square kilometer in extent, covered with a labyrinth of pools of snow water from 2 to 6 or even 10 inches deep, but practicable in wading boots, thanks to its floor of everlasting ice beneath the underlying mud. Between these pools, which were from 15 to 50 feet in diameter, were pieces of very wet ground covered with *Carices*,[1] damp mossy spots, and even tiny patches of comparatively dry bog covered with lichens or *Betula nana* [dwarf birch].

In this colony I found 10 nests of *Rhodostethia*, placed, among those of the tern, on little mossy swamps almost bare of grass, evidently because the more grassy places were too wet and unsafe.

Later on (July 6 and 7) he discovered two more colonies, which he describes as follows:

Here we were clear of the *Salix* [willow] and *Alnus* [alder] thickets and were on the true tundra, which afforded a welcome relief to both eyes and limbs. After the delay caused by a long and heavy snowstorm I discovered two new breeding colonies of this gull—one on the wet grassy border of a lake about a kilometer in diameter, the other in the middle of a somewhat larger lake, furnished with many tiny islands, spacious bogs, and shallow grassy areas. Both colonies contained from 10 to 12 pairs of *Rhodostethia*.

Although he first noted the flight of this species as "more Fulmarlike," Buturlin (1906) finally concluded that it

[1] Sedges.

was really much more tern-like. . . . The rosy gull swims easily, and sometimes I saw it taking a regular bath. It dipped its head under, while sitting deep in the ice-cold lake, and, throwing the water over its back, moved its wings quickly below the surface, holding itself almost clear, and threw itself forcibly head downward into the water. Once a rosy gull flew over the surface of the lake with a cry of "*carvac-wa*" and took up water with its beak on the wing, as swallows do, but subsequently it settled on the surface for some two or three seconds without folding its wings, which were elevated over the back, and drank after the usual fashion.

The note of *Rhodostethia* is peculiar, being high and more melodious than that of gulls in general, and very variable. 1921

SABINE'S GULL   *Xema sabini*

This beautiful little gull was named for its discoverer, Capt. Edward Sabine, who first saw it on its breeding grounds on some low rocky islands off the west coast of Greenland, where it was associated and breeding with a number of Arctic terns. It is not an abundant bird, however, on the Greenland coast, but it has been found breeding at widely scattered points in the Arctic regions of both hemispheres. Its center of abundance during the breeding season seems to be in the vicinity of Bering Sea. Dr. E. W. Nelson (1887) says:

On June 13, 1880, about 20 miles from St. Michael [Alaska], while egging in company with some Eskimo, we found a pond, some 200 yards across, in the middle of which were two small islands. A gunshot caused at least 100 of these gulls to rise like a white cloud over the islet, and showed us that we had found a breeding place. As we stood on the shore a few birds came off, and circling close about us for a few moments, but rarely making any outcry, returned to the island, where the others had already settled again and appeared to be sitting upon the ground. The water of the lake we found to be about waist-deep, under which lay a solid bed of ice of unknown depth.

The smallest island lay nearest, and sending one of my men out to it he found a set of two eggs of the black-throated loon,[1] one set of the arctic tern's eggs, and two of Sabine's gull. Proceeding to the next island he found a set of *Aythya marila nearctica* [Greater Scaup] eggs as he stepped ashore, and a moment later cried out that the ground was covered with gulls' eggs. At the same time he answered with chattering teeth that the water in the lake was very cold. Having never seen the nest of this gull I called my man back and he transported me upon his back to the island after narrowly escaping several falls on the way. The island was very low, and the driest spots were but little above the water. Built on the driest

[1] As the subspecies *pacifica* of the Arctic Loon was formerly called.

places were 27 nests, containing from one to three eggs each, and as many others just ready for occupancy. Four or five nests were frequently placed within two or three feet of each other. In about one-half the cases the eggs were laid upon a few grass blades the spot afforded with no alteration save a slight depression made by the bird's body. In the majority of the other nests a few grass blades and stems had been arranged circularly about the eggs, and in the remainder only enough material had been added to afford the merest apology for a nest.

While I was securing my prizes the birds hovered overhead in great anxiety, although they rarely uttered their grating cry, and in the very few instances when a bird darted down at us it was in perfect silence. While we were on the island several glaucous gulls and jaegers passed by, and in every case they were attacked by several of the Xemas and driven hastily away. Two nests had been despoiled either by these birds or a muskrat, as the broken shells showed. When the eggs were secured a large and fine lot of gulls were obtained, and we then made our way back to camp heavily laden with spoils. Solitary nests were afterwards found either on islands like the last or on the border of a pond. In one instance the female left her eggs when I was over 100 yards away and flew directly away until she was lost to sight. 1921

GULL-BILLED TERN *Gelochelidon nilotica*

This species was referred to by the earlier writers as the marsh tern, on account of its preference for the salt marshes as a feeding ground, and in many places as a breeding ground also; but, based on my limited experience with it on the Atlantic coast, I should say that it hardly deserves that name, for, at the present time, on the coasts of Virginia and the Carolinas, it seems to prefer to nest on the sandy beaches. But, as it is a cosmopolitan species of wide distribution, its habits differ in different localities. It was formerly much more abundant and more widely distributed on our Atlantic coast than it is to-day.

On the Virginia coast Doctor Rives (1890) referred to it as "common at Cobb's Island, and breeds, formerly in great abundance," indicating that, even at that date, it had begun to decrease. He says further:

I have been informed that great numbers of the eggs have formerly been taken from the north end of Hog Island, adjoining Cobb's.

Ten years later, in 1900, Captain Andrews reported to Mr. Dutcher (1901) that the gull-billed terns on Cobb's Island had been reduced to about a thousand. The following year, according to the same authority, their number had been reduced to three hundred. In 1903, Doctor Chapman (1903) found only eight pairs there; and when Doctor Bishop and I visited Virginia in 1907 we saw only two pairs on Cobb's Island, and perhaps eight or ten pairs on Wreck Island, a few miles distant. Mr. A. B. Howell (1911) visited Cobb's Island in 1909 and recorded eight pairs.[1] This record shows clearly the results of the same causes which annihilated the least terns in this region—the demands of the millinery trade for the decoration of women's hats and the zeal with which a lucrative trade was pushed by local gunners.   1921

FORSTER'S TERN   *Sterna forsteri*

I first found this species breeding on Wreck Island, off the coast of Virginia, on June 28, 1907, where we discovered a colony of about fifty pairs. This and the other large islands in the group are much like Cobb's Island, consisting of long, wide beaches on the outer, or ocean, side, flat and sandy in some places or piled high with accumulated oyster shells in others. Back of the beaches, on the shore side, are extensive salt meadows or marshes, intersected by numerous creeks and dotted with small ponds or mud holes.

Our attention was first attracted to the Forster's terns by their harsh grating cries, as they flew out to meet us while exploring one of the creeks in our skiff. We finally located the colony, by the actions of the birds, just beyond the long grass, which grew thickly along the banks of the creek, and found the nests thickly scattered along the drifted piles of dead sedges, which the high tides had floated off the marsh and deposited in long rows close to the tall-growing sedges. The nests were so close together that I counted twelve nests in a space about ten yards long by three yards wide. One nest was placed within three feet of a clapper rail's nest. The nests were mostly large and elaborate structures, remarkably well built, and reminding me of the nests of Franklin's gulls. They consisted of large piles of dead sedges and grasses, surmounted by neat little nests, deeply hollowed, with well-rounded and compactly woven rims. [These] looked like works of art when compared with the slovenly nests built by other species of terns. Most of the nests contained three or four eggs, but many sets of five were found and a few nests held newly hatched young.   1921

COMMON TERN   *Sterna hirundo*

One of the most charming features of our eastern seacoast is this graceful little "sea swallow." The most attractive combination of

[1] "It still is rare"—Murray, J. J. *The Birds of Virginia*, 1952.

summer sea, sky, and sandy beach would be but an empty, lifeless scene without the little "mackerel gull," such a fitting accompaniment of its gentle surroundings and so suggestive of summer sunshine and cooling sea breezes. One can not help admiring such an elegant and dainty creature, its spotless and delicate plumage and its buoyant, graceful flight, as it flies listlessly up the beach until the discovery of some school of small fry, on which it feeds, causes it to pause, hover for an instant, and plunge headlong into the water for some tiny minnow.

We came near losing this beautiful bird a few years ago, because its exquisite plumage was so much in demand for feminine decoration that, before we realized it, collectors for the millinery trade had alarmingly reduced its numbers. Stringent laws, however, were passed for its protection and it has now practically regained its former abundance.

A visit to Muskeget Island [Massachusetts] in June or July, the height of the breeding season, is an experience never to be forgotten. As we approach it in our little sailboat a cloud of minute white specks is seen hovering over it and the air is full of birds coming and going, for not all of this vast multitude can find food enough in the immediate vicinity; hence they wander far to the shores of Martha's Vineyard and Cape Cod.

As we land and walk out among the sand hills the terns rise from the ground on all sides and circle about us overhead in an ever-increasing cloud. Some are darting down at our heads with harsh and grating cries of protest, others are drifting around us closely at hand. If we look up into the air we are made fairly dizzy; for as far as we can see, extending up into the deep blue sky, is a bewildering maze of whirling birds, flying in every direction and at varying heights in countless thousands. Their plaintive notes when heard singly are nearly musical, but the combined din of such a multitude of voices is almost deafening in its effect, and for days afterwards we can hear the rhythmic chorus ringing in our ears. If we shoot down one of them every voice is hushed; the silence is appalling as they come gliding in from every side in sympathetic horror to hover over their fallen companion and try to encourage him to rise again.

Now is the greedy murderer's chance, as the plume hunters have learned to their advantage, for as fast as the terns are shot down others will hurry in, and, as if at a given signal, all will burst out again into an excited chorus of angry cries of protest, hovering over and darting down at their dead companions in confusion and despair; but if no more are shot they seem soon to forget, the crowd gradually disperses and all goes on as if nothing had happened. 1921

ARCTIC TERN   *Sterna paradisaea*   (Townsend)

The Arctic tern breeds throughout the entire circumpolar regions as far north as it can find land, and south in this country to northern British Columbia, Great Slave Lake[1], Central Keewatin[2], Maine, and Muskeget Island, Massachusetts. It is credited by Cooke (1911) with being "the world's migration champion." After the breeding season is over the bird repairs from the Arctic to the Antarctic regions. "What their track is over that 11,000 miles of intervening space no one knows," says Cooke (1911).[3]

A few scattered individuals have been noted along the United States coast south to Long Island, but the great flocks of thousands and thousands of these terns which alternate from one pole to the other have never been met by any trained ornithologist competent to learn their preferred path and their time schedule. The Arctic terns arrive in the far north about June 15 and leave about August 25, thus staying 14 weeks at the nesting site. They probably spend a few weeks longer in the winter than in the summer home and, if so, this leaves them scarcely 20 weeks for the round trip of 22,000 miles. Not less than 150 miles in a straight line must be their daily task, and this is undoubtedly multiplied several times by their zigzag twisting and turning in pursuit of food.

The Arctic terns have more hours of daylight and sunlight than any other animal on the globe. At their most northern nesting site the midnight sun has already appeared before their arrival, and it never sets during their entire stay at the breeding grounds. During two months of their sojourn in the Antarctic they do not see a sunset, and for the rest of the time the sun dips only a little way below the horizon and broad daylight continues all night. The birds therefore, have 24 hours of daylight for at least eight months in the year, and during the other four months have considerably more daylight than darkness. 1921

ROSEATE TERN   *Sterna dougallii*

I shall never forget the thrill of pleasure I experienced when I held in my hand, for the first time, a freshly killed roseate tern and admired with deepest reverence the delicate refinement of one of

[1] District of Mackenzie, Northwest Territories.

[2] Northwest Territories.

[3] Banding has now shown that birds breeding in eastern Canada and the United States migrate in fall east across the Atlantic to Europe and then south, some reaching the Antarctic via the African coast and the Cape of Good Hope, others recrossing the Atlantic to Brazil and flying down the east coast of South America. Birds that breed in western Canada and Alaska migrate along the Pacific coast to the Antarctic.

nature's loveliest productions. The softest colors of the summer sky were reflected on its back and pointed wings, while its breast glowed with the faint blush of some rare seashell. The graceful outlines, the spotless purity of its delicate plumage, and the long tapering tail feathers made it seem like some ethereal spirit of the heavens which it was sacrilege for human hands to touch.

Having been always intimately associated on our Atlantic coast with the common tern, it has suffered with that species in the persecution inflicted on these birds by hunters for the millinery trade. It was everywhere threatened with extermination, and became extirpated in many localities until its range was much restricted.[1]

The flight of the roseate tern is exceedingly light and graceful; it is the greyhound of its tribe, the longest, slenderest, and most highly specialized of the terns. As it floats along, with its long tail feathers streaming out behind, it seems to cleave the air with the greatest ease and swiftness, like a slender-pointed arrow. Its downward plunges into the water for its prey are swift and accurate; it often goes beneath the surface and generally emerges with a tiny minnow in its bill. Its shape and movements will generally serve to identify it, and if near enough, its black bill is a good field mark.

Its voice, however, is the surest means of identification, for it is entirely unlike that of the other terns with which it associates. Its alarm note seems entirely out of keeping with its grace and beauty of form and color, for it is harsh and grating, a prolonged rasping cry, like the syllables *"kreck"* or *"crack"* or *"kraak,"* louder and on a lower key than the cries of other terns. Mr. Brewster (1879) has likened this note of excitement or anger to the sound made "by forcibly tearing a strong piece of cotton cloth."

During the last week in May, while the countless hordes of terns are gathering on these breeding grounds, the roseate terns may be seen flying about in pairs or chasing each other in the air, with their long slender tail feathers streaming behind; or, in the dense flocks, resting and sunning themselves on the beach, their simple courtship may be seen. Both birds show their interest in each other by stretching their necks upward and strutting about with drooping wings and elevated tails; or standing side by side they exchange greetings. Finally the accepted suitor mounts his mate and stands squarely upon her back for a long time, with frequent interlocking of bills. The nuptial caress is most deliberate; and after it is over they stand close together, billing and cooing and preening each other's plumage. 1921

[1] Fortunately, under protection, it has now come back.

ALEUTIAN TERN   *Sterna aleutica*

According to Doctor Nelson (1887), the Aleutian terns reach St. Michael[1] from May 20 to 30, rarely earlier than the first date, and are found scattered along the coast, in company with the Arctic tern, for a short time, but early in June they gather about the islands where they nest. One of these islands is about a mile from St. Michael[1], in the mouth of a tide channel known as the "canal." This island is nearly half a mile across, rises about 30 feet from the beach in a sharp incline, and has a rather level top, covered with a thick mat of grass, moss, and other vegetation. The upland is dry, and here the birds breed, laying their eggs directly upon the moss, with no attempt at a lining, which would be entirely unnecessary there. Some 18 miles to the eastward, along the coast, and less than a mile from the Eskimo village of Kegikhtowik, is another island in a bay, presenting almost the same characteristics as the one first described, and upon the higher portions the birds nest even more commonly, for, as against the 20 pairs or so nesting on the first island, some 30 or 40 pairs occupied the latter island both seasons when it was visited by the writer.   1921

SOOTY TERN   *Sterna fuscata*

This wide ranging species, represented by different races in the two hemispheres, gathers for the purpose of breeding into numerous vast colonies on remote islands in the tropical waters of both oceans, where it is one of the best known sea birds and one of the most popular as a producer of eggs for food. Its most famous resort is probably Bird Key in the Dry Tortugas.[2]

From Prof. John B. Watson's (1908) careful observations of this species and the noddy, made in this colony, we have learned much regarding their habits and characteristics. Some of this information I shall attempt to give in concise form or in exact quotations from his excellent paper, to which I would refer the reader for details. Regarding the nest-building activities he says:

The building of the sooty nest is quickly accomplished. The obtaining of a nest site is the difficult part of the reaction. As has been said, the sooties build their nests very near one another. For this reason it is extremely difficult to make complete observations. My observations began late one afternoon, before any eggs had been laid. Hundreds of the birds were grouped together, incessantly fighting and screaming. It quickly became apparent that most of them had chosen a nest site and were

[1] Central western Alaska, on Norton Sound.
[2] Florida, now Fort Jefferson National Monument.

defending it against all late comers. Both male and female were present. Each pair in this particular locality defended a circular territory, roughly 14 inches to 2 feet in diameter. Other birds in wandering around would stumble into this sacred territory and a fight would ensue. The fights would often lead to encroachments upon the territory of still other birds. The number of those fighting would thus be constantly increased. I have seen as many as 14 sooties thus engaging in a fight. Birds 10 to 15 feet away would rush into the fight and the noise and confusion beggared description. Sometimes as many as 10 or 15 such fighting groups could be observed in the area of 1,000 square feet. Quiet would momentarily ensue and then be broken by another series of fights. During the choice of the nesting site the fights continue day and night, with only intermittent periods of quiet.

Within this charmed circle the two mated birds remain relatively quiet. At this time sexual activity is at its height. It frequently happened in the sexual process that the two birds would step outside of their own territory and a general fight would ensue. When the sexual reaction is in progress it is a signal for the surrounding males to encroach. Coition is thus completed only after much fighting. I have seen the male attempt to mount the female 12 to 15 times, and at each attempt be interfered with by neighboring males.

The colony on Laysan Island[1] is probably the largest, and it certainly is a wonder among wonders. Prof. Homer R. Dill (1912), reporting on the condition of this colony, states:

The first day of June we measured the rookeries of these birds and two days later we went over the same ground again. We found that in two days the rookeries on the west side had increased in area 3,600 square yards. The final estimate of the number of sooty terns was made June 4—333,900 for both rookeries. This species outnumbers any other on the island.   1921

BRIDLED TERN   *Sterna anaethetus*

[A tropical species that ranges casually off our southern coasts.]

The bridled tern so closely resembles its near relative, the sooty tern, that it can hardly be distinguished from it in life by the casual observer. Both species are known to the island natives as "egg birds," about which Dr. Frank M. Chapman (1908) says:

Throughout the Bahamas the name "Egg bird" is applied to the sooty, bridled, and noddy terns. The latter part of April these birds come in large numbers to certain regularly frequented keys to breed. If their resort be near a settlement, they are robbed of their eggs by its inhabitants. In Nassau I have seen many of them offered for sale on the street, each one with the shell punctured as a guarantee that one was not buying a

[1] Nine hundred fifty miles west of Honolulu, Hawaii. Now part of the Hawaiian Islands National Wildlife Refuge.

tern. If they are remote from human habitation, they are generally preyed upon by the cruising spongers, to whose scanty bill of fare fresh eggs are an eagerly sought addition. Doubtless there are but few colonies of terns in the Bahamas that do not contribute to the food supply of the usually hungry native, hence the current name egg bird. Efforts to secure the passage of a law prohibiting the taking of the eggs of these birds has failed, and, sentiment aside, provided they are permitted to breed and their numbers therefore not decreased, there seems to be no reason why, in a country of such limited food products, this source of supply should not be drawn upon.   1921

LEAST TERN   *Sterna albifrons*

Clearly impressed upon my mind is a vivid picture of a peaceful summer scene in a remote corner of Cape Cod; a broad, flat sandy point stretched for a mile or more out into the sea; the deep blue ocean with its cooling breezes made a pleasing contrast to the glaring white sands which reflected the heat of the midday sun; scattered about on the sandy plain around me were the little hollows containing the eggs of the least tern, almost invisible among the pebbles, bits of shells, and small stones, which they resemble so closely; and overhead the air was full of the graceful, flitting forms of this little "sea swallow," darting down at me, with sharp cries of anxiety, or soaring far aloft until they were lost to sight in the ethereal blue of a cloudless sky. Such a picture as this was a common sight, in those days, anywhere along the Atlantic coast from Massachusetts to Florida, where the least tern was widely distributed and very abundant in all suitable localities. But its graceful form and delicate plumage was so much in demand for the millinery trade that it was practically extirpated in nearly all places where it was easily accessible, leaving only a delightful memory of a joy that had passed.[1] It was never particularly shy and was easily killed on its breeding grounds, its social and sympathetic habits making it a simple matter to practically annihilate a whole colony in a single season.

The most pitiful tale of destruction is the story of the Cobbs' Island and other colonies on the coast of Virginia. Mr. H. B. Bailey (1876), in writing of the nesting habits of the least tern, or "little striker," on Cobb's Island in 1875, says:

Colonies of about 50 pairs each of this species extend the whole length of the island at about a distance of 1 mile apart.

Least terns were astonishingly abundant all along the Virginia coast at that time, but during the next decade their destruction was

[1] Fortunately, under protection, this species has come back well.

appalling. Professional collectors for the millinery trade spent the greater part of the breeding season on the islands and killed the innocent birds in almost incredible numbers. The resident fishermen and oystermen also found it a lucrative occupation. As many as twelve hundred birds were often killed in a day, and one of the residents, who had taken part in the slaughter himself, told me that as many as one hundred thousand terns were sometimes killed in a season. Mr. William H. Fisher (1897), writing of conditions in 1891, says:

When I first went to [Cobb's] island 28 years ago the least, common, and Forster's tern nested there in colonies of thousands, but now few of them breed and the least is seldom seen. During four days on the island in May, 1891, I only saw one of the latter, and it was as wild as an oystercatcher, which is a very wild bird. The royal tern also nested on the island at one time.

The least terns disappeared entirely during the next ten years. Dr. Frank M. Chapman (1903) visited Cobb's Island in 1902 to gather material for his habitat group, and found them entirely gone. He says of their destruction:

The former captain of the life-saving station told me of 1,400 least terns being killed in one day; while the present captain of the station and Mr. E. B. Cobb, owner of the island, informed me that when terns were first killed for millinery purposes they, with another man, killed 2,800 birds in three days on and near Cobb's Island. The birds were packed in cracked ice and shipped to New York for skinning, 10 cents being paid for each one. 1921

ROYAL TERN   *Thalasseus maximus*

My own experience with the nesting habits of the royal tern was gained in the large protected colonies of the Breton Island reservation, off the coast of Louisiana.

On June 18, 1910, with Warden W. M. Sprinkle, in his patrol boat, I visited one of these colonies.

As I approached, over the level sandy plain on which it was spread out, the birds all arose at once, as if impelled by a common impulse, with a great roar of thousands of wings, a dense cloud of screaming birds, and a bewildering moving picture of flashing black and white.

I counted the nests in a measured area and then roughly measured the whole colony, from which I estimated that it contained, at least, thirty-five hundred nests. There were a hundred nests in a space four yards square; certainly this was a densely packed colony of a highly gregarious species.

The colony described above may be considered as typical of the species, which almost always nests in similar situations in closely populated colonies. The nest is nothing more than a slight hollow in the sand, without any attempt at a lining. I believe that the normal set consists of two eggs.   1921

ELEGANT TERN   *Thalasseus elegans*

This beautiful tern well deserves its name, for in color, form, and behavior it is certainly one of the most elegant of our sea birds, the most exquisite member of the charming group of "sea swallows." Unfortunately, owing to its remote habitat, it has been seen in life by very few ornithologists. Many handsome specimens have found their way into collections, but the dried skin can give but a faint impression of the grace and beauty of the living bird. Not all of the few collectors who have explored the coasts of the peninsula of Lower California have succeeded in finding it, and still fewer have seen it on its breeding grounds. Consequently very little is known of its life history and habits. Probably Mr. Wilmot W. Brown, Jr., has been more successful than anyone else in the pursuit of this rare species, and we are indebted to him for practically all that we know in regard to its nesting habits.

Mr. Brown obtained a fine series of the eggs of this species for Col. John E. Thayer (1911*a*), who published a brief account of its nesting habits on Cerralvo Island, Lower California. He says:

The nests were slight depressions in the sand on the beach about 20 yards from the surf on the protected or land side of the island.

[The eggs] were taken April 9 and 15, 1910. Most of the eggs were slightly incubated. One egg is generally what they lay, sometimes two, but only rarely.   1921

SANDWICH TERN   *Thalasseus sandvicensis*

Among the sandy islands and shoals of our southern Atlantic and Gulf coasts we find this fine tern, everywhere intimately associated with its larger relative, the royal tern; like Damon and Pythias, they are always together and seldom is one found without the other. The same resorts seem to be congenial to both, but there is probably some stronger bond of friendship which we do not understand.

Mr. Stanley C. Arthur writes me:

At this time I made an experiment, contemplated for the past several years. I had often wondered why it is, where there are several thousand single speckled eggs, such as the Cabot terns[1] deposit on the beaches, one

[1] As this species was formerly called.

particular egg can be singled out by the parent as her own private and individual property, and have often wondered whether or not they can, with certainty, know their own egg. I have often been asked: "How does the tern know its own eggs?" and have always facetiously answered: "By counting the spots." As I was studying the birds I selected two Cabots, one on the left and the other on my right, that were marked quite distinctly—one having a wholly black crest and one having its crest speckled with a few white feathers which heralded the coming of the winter plumage.

At 11:15 I left the blind, which naturally scared off the birds, and changed the egg on my left, which had been covered by the pure black-headed tern, and moved it several feet away, exchanging it for the egg that had been covered by the Cabot with white feathers in its crest. This egg was placed on the spot belonging to the black-headed tern. At 11.18 the circling and frantically crying birds commenced resettling on their eggs, and showing not the slightest concern each tern sought its own egg despite the fact that it had been moved several feet and placed in a different nest. After allowing each bird to remain on its egg for 15 minutes, I again left the blind and retransferred the eggs with the same result as before. Each parent bird settled on its own egg without hesitation, and, as before, not evidencing any surprise over the change of the location.

1921

CASPIAN TERN   *Hydroprogne caspia*

Among the vast hordes of sea birds nesting in the great colonies of the southern Atlantic and Gulf coasts, this king of all the terns may be seen climbing into the air on its long, strong wings, its big red bill wide open, yelling out its loud raucous cry of defiance. As the dominant, ruling spirit in the colonies it scorns the companionship of humbler fowl, holds itself aloof, and lives a little apart from the others. The largest, the strongest, and the fiercest of the terns, it well deserves the name, imperial tern. It was christened Caspian tern by Pallas, because it was first described from a specimen taken near the Caspian Sea. It is a cosmopolitan species of wide palaearctic and nearctic distribution.

On the Texas coast large colonies are found. Capt. B. F. Goss, in a letter to Major Bendire, says:

We found the Caspian tern breeding only in Nueces Bay, and, although we examined 150 miles of coast, did not see a bird of this species more than a mile or two from the mouth of the bay. They breed on some small, low sandy islands near the middle of the bay. We took about 60 sets of eggs in all, mostly on one island not larger than 4 by 6 rods. As we approached this spot in a boat the birds rose about 8 feet and hovered a few moments, looking like a white cloud; then commenced circling, doubling, and turning in the most remarkable manner. It was a beautiful sight. As we approached they began plunging at the ground in great apparent excitement. My companion shouted, "They are breaking their eggs," and we hastened with all speed to the spot; found about 40 sets, a few of one, but mostly of two eggs. These lay on the bare sand without any attempt at a nest. At least one-quarter of the eggs had been broken by the birds in their frantic plunges, some only marked, in others the bill had passed clear through the egg. My companion said they had done the same thing in former years when he was collecting the eggs for culinary purposes, and thought they did it to prevent the eggs falling into our hands. It seemed to me like a frantic attempt to remove or conceal the eggs, but will not attempt to account for the actions of the birds, but deem the fact worth recording.   1921

BLACK TERN   *Chlidonias niger*

A prairie slough, teeming with bird life is one of the most fascinating spots for an ornithologist, for nowhere else can he come in close touch with such a variety of species of interesting birds, with such a multitude of individuals crowded into a narrow space and under such favorable conditions for observation. I have never enjoyed anything more keenly than the long drives we used to take over the virgin prairies of North Dakota, drawn by a lively pair of unshod bronchos, unconfined by fences or roads, with nothing to guide us but the narrow wagon ruts which marked the section lines and served as the only highways. In those days the prairies were like a sea of grass, as boundless as the ocean and nearly as level, where only the distant horizon marked the limit of our view.

We seemed to be driving on and on into limitless space until suddenly we came to a depression in the prairie marked by a steep embankment, and there, ten feet below the level of the prairie, lay a great slough spread out before us. Various ducks—mallards, pintails, shovellers, and blue-winged teal—began rising from the surface as we appeared, and way out in the open water in the center of the slough we could see redheads, canvasbacks, and ruddy ducks swimming about in scattered flocks. [There] among all this great concourse of bird life, was the subject of this sketch, the black tern, one of the most active and the most restless of the throng flitting about hither and thither with a wayward, desultory flight, light and buoyant as a butterfly. Its darting zigzag flight as it mounts into the air to chase a fluttering moth is suggestive of a flycatcher or a nighthawk; as it skims swiftly over the surface of the water it reminds me of a swallow; and its true relationship to the terns is shown as it hovers along over the billowy tops of a great sea of tall waving grass, dipping down occasionally to snatch an insect from the slender, swaying tops. When looking for food the bill is usually pointed downward, but in ordinary flight it points forward.

Among all the water birds of the middle west I suppose the black tern is the most widely distributed, the most universally common and the most characteristic summer resident of the sloughs, marshes, and wet meadows of the plains. The center of its abundance seems to be in the great, flat marsh country of Manitoba, where we found it everywhere the commonest and most conspicuous water bird in the extensive cane swamps about Lake Winnipegosis and Waterhen Lake, breeding anywhere in wet marshy situations. 1921

NODDY TERN   *Anous stolidus*

This dusky tropical species enjoys a wide distribution on both sides of the Equator in both of our great oceans.

It resorts to many different islands throughout its range to breed [including the Dry Tortugas, Florida], and its nesting habits vary considerably in different localities.

Mr. W. E. D. Scott (1891) has published some interesting notes by Mr. Charles B. Taylor, regarding the arrival of the noddies on Morant Cays, near Jamaica, from which I quote, as follows:

At the time of my arrival at the Cays (2d of April) there were no sooty terns there and very few noddies, but these latter increased in numbers daily, until by the 19th of April, the date of my departure, they had assembled in hundreds and were evidently preparing to lay, yet in two females taken two or three days after my arrival the eggs in the ovaries were very small.

Soon after sunset the birds came in to roost among the low bushes fringing the shore, and up to a late hour many kept arriving. They flew very swiftly, just skimming the surface of the water, and standing on the shore at dusk (the time they began to arrive) it was rarely possible to see the birds coming until they were actually on the island. They alighted noiselessly and instantly on gaining the fringing bushes; later in the month, however, as their numbers increased, belated birds found difficulty in effecting an easy landing among the branches, those already in possession pecking right and left at all newcomers and croaking harshly. Each day, as their numbers increased, they became more vociferous, until at last the melancholy wail of those flying overhead and the croak of the sitting birds was kept up without intermission all through the night. On moonlight nights they appeared unusually abundant and restless.

I have watched them there until far into the night, as in scores they kept flying to and from the bushes. Although up and about before dawn on most mornings, I was seldom in time to watch the noddies leave their roost. One morning, however, I got a good idea of their numbers. It wanted about an hour or so of daybreak, and the moon was still bright, when someone walking along the shore appeared to give a general alarm. Scores of birds got up and went swiftly out to sea, and for some little time a constant stream poured out from the bushes along the shores in every direction, as far as it was possible to see; flying before the wind, they went out of sight in an instant. They left the land always in the same manner in which they came in to roost, dropping to the surface of the water immediately on clearing the shore. Notwithstanding their apparent abundance, the noddies, in point of numbers, sink into comparative insignificance after the arrival of the sooty terns.

The birds are said to be mated before they arrive on the island,[1] and, as he did not arrive until five days later than the birds, Prof. Watson was unable to observe their earlier actions; but he tentatively presents the following account of what is probably a mating performance:

One day I observed several noddies "sunning" upon the wire covering of one of my large experimental cages. Suddenly, one of the birds (male) began nodding and bowing to a bird standing near (female). The female gave immediate attention and began efforts to extract fish from the throat of the male. The male would first make efforts to disgorge, then put the tip of the beak almost to the ground and incline it to the angle most suitable to admit her beak. She would then thrust her beak into his (the ordinary feeding reaction). The feeding reaction was alternated with the nodding. After this series of acts had been repeated 20 times the male flew off and brought a stick. He deposited this near the female and then again offered to feed her. She again tried to feed; then the male attempted sexual relations. She immediately flew away, but almost immediately returned and alighted at a slightly different place. The male again brought the stick and again bowed and offered to feed her. She accepted the food, but again flew away when the male attempted to mount her. At this juncture the island was disturbed and my observations could not continue.

1921

SKIMMERS   Family Rynchopidae

BLACK SKIMMER   *Rynchops nigra*

The coasts of Virginia and the Carolinas are fringed with chains of low, sandy islands, many of them lying far out from the shores, with broad, flat, sandy beaches on the ocean side, and often on the

[1] Dry Tortugas, Florida.

inner side with extensive salt marshes which are intersected by numerous creeks and shallow estuaries. Although practically worthless for human occupancy, these islands form ideal resorts for several species of water birds and shore birds. Cobb's Island [Virginia], the most famous and perhaps the most typical of this class of islands, has for many years been a popular resort for sportsmen and bird lovers, though its bird population has been sadly depleted during recent years.

When the rising tide flows in around the island, covering the outer sand bars, driving the birds from their low-tide roosting and feeding places and flooding the shallow estuaries, then the "flood gulls," as they are called, may be seen skimming over the muddy shallows, about the mouths of the creeks, or up into the narrow inlets, gracefully gliding on their long, slender wings close to the surface in search of their finny prey, the tiny minnows, which have followed the advancing tide into the protecting, grassy shallows.

Their mating performances show off their marvelous powers of flight to advantage and are most exciting as two or more males give chase to the coveted female.

The coy one, shooting aslant to either side, dashes along with marvelous speed, flying hither and thither, upward, downward, in all directions. Her suitors strive to overtake her; they emit their love cries with vehemence; you are gladdened by their softly and tenderly enunciated *ha, ha,* or the *hack, hack, cae, cae,* of the last in the chase. Like the female, they all perform the most curious zigzags as they follow in close pursuit, and as each beau at length passes her in succession he extends his wings for an instant, and in a manner struts by her side. (Audubon, 1840.)

The food of the black skimmer consists mainly of small fish, and to some extent shrimps and other small crustaceans. It feeds largely on the wing by skimming close to the smooth water, cutting with its long, rigid lower mandible the surface, from which it scoops into the small mouth the animal food to be found there. The upper mandible, which is movable, can plainly be seen to close down upon any morsel of food which is picked up. That it feeds largely at night everyone knows who has lain at anchor among the shoals of the South Atlantic coast and seen the shadowy forms flitting by in the gloom, but it does not do so exclusively, as has been stated. I have frequently seen it feeding in broad daylight, and think that it is more influenced by the tides than by anything else, for these at certain stages make its food more accessible. It is never seen to dive for its food, and its bill is not adapted for picking it up on the shore.

1921

AUKS, MURRES, AND PUFFINS
Family Alcidae

GREAT AUK   *Pinguinus impennis*   (Townsend)

The great auk is extinct. So thoroughly and suddenly did its extinction come about that at one time the bird was considered to be a myth, yet a comparatively few years ago it existed in great numbers.

The following description is by M. Martin (1753), who lived for three weeks on St. Kilda[1] in June 1697:

The sea fowl are first gairfowl,[2] being the stateliest as well as the largest sort, and above the size of a solan goose,[3] of a black color, red about the eyes, a large spot under each, a long broad bill; it stands stately, its whole body erected, its wings short, flies not at all; lays its egg upon the bare rock, which if taken away, she lays no more for that year; she is whole footed, and has the hatching spot upon her breast, i.e., a bare spot from which the feathers have fallen off with the heat in hatching; its egg is twice as big as that of a solan goose, and is variously spotted, black, green, and dark; it comes without regard to any wind, appears the first of May, and goes away about the middle of June.

Professor Newton (1861), writing on Mr. J. Wolley's "Researches in Iceland" respecting the garefowl,[2] says:

They swam with their heads much lifted up, but their necks drawn in; they never tried to flap along the water, but dived as soon as alarmed. On the rocks they sat more upright than either guillemots or razorbills, and their station was further removed from the sea. They were easily frightened by noise, but not by what they saw. They sometimes uttered a few low croaks. They have never been known to defend their eggs, but would bite fiercely if they had the chance when caught. They walk or run with little short steps and go straight like a man. One has been known to drop down some two fathoms off the rock into the water. Finally, I may add that the color of the inside of their mouths is said to have been yellow, as in the allied species.

Cartwright (1792) in his journal under date of July 5, 1785 prophesies the speedy extermination of the great auk. He says:

A boat came in from Funk Island[4] laden with birds, chiefly penguins.[2] Funk Island is a small flat island rock about 20 leagues east of the island of Fogo[4] in the latitude of 50° north. Innumerable flocks of sea fowl breed

[1] Island in North Atlantic, fifty miles west of Hebrides, Scotland.
[2] As this species was then called.
[3] As the Gannet was sometimes called.
[4] Off north coast of Newfoundland.

upon it every summer, which are of great service to the poor inhabitants of Fogo, who make voyages there to load with birds and eggs. When the water is smooth, they make their shallop fast to the shore, lay their gang-boards from the gunwale of the boat to the rocks, and then drive as many penguins on board as she will hold; for, the wings of those birds being remarkably short, they can not fly; but it has been customary of late years for several crews of men to live all summer on that island for the sole purpose of killing birds for the sake of their feathers; the destruction which they have made is incredible. If a stop is not soon put to that practice, the whole breed will be diminished to almost nothing, particularly the penguins; for this is now the only island they have left to breed upon; all others lying so near to the shores of Newfoundland, they are con-tinually robbed. The birds which the people bring from thence they salt and eat, in lieu of salted pork.

The following note by J. A. Allen (1876) describes more in detail the horrible slaughter for the feathers:

Mr. Michael Carrol, of Bonavista, Newfoundland, has recently given me the following very interesting facts respecting the extermination of the great auk (*Alca impennis*) at the Funk Islands. In early life he was often a visitor to these islands, and a witness of what he here describes. He says these birds were formerly very numerous on the Funk Islands, and 45 to 50 years ago were hunted for their feathers, soon after which time they were wholly exterminated. As the auks could not fly, the fishermen would surround them in small boats and drive them ashore into pounds previously constructed of stones. The birds were then easily killed, and their feathers removed by immersing the birds in scalding water, which was ready at hand in large kettles set for this purpose. The bodies were used as fuel for boiling the water.

The remains of the huts and pounds are still on the island, but the birds are no more! The quantity of great auk's bones and even of mummified remains found on Funk Island by [F. A.] Lucas and others all testify to the destruction that went on there.

The last of these birds, two individuals, were taken alive on June 3, 1844, at Eldey, a skerry or rocky islet off the southwest point of Iceland. Their viscera are now preserved in the Royal University Museum, Copenhagen, but it is not known what became of the skins and bones. The narrative by Grieve (1885) of this capture is of such a tragically historic character, it is quoted here:

As the men clambered up they saw two garefowls sitting among number-less other rock-birds (*Uria troile*[1] and *Alca torda*[2]), and at once gave chase. The garefowls showed not the slightest disposition to repel the invaders, but immediately ran along under the high cliff, their heads erect, their

[1] Common Murre.
[2] Razorbill.

little wings somewhat extended. They uttered no cry of alarm, and moved, with their short steps, about as quickly as a man could walk. Jon (Brandsson) with outstretched arms, drove one into a corner, where he soon had it fast. Siguror (Islefsson) and Ketil pursued the second, and the former seized it close to the edge of the rock here risen to a precipice some fathoms high, the water being directly below it. Ketil (Ketilsm) then returned to the sloping shelf whence the birds had started, and saw an egg lying on the lava slab, which he knew to be a garefowl's. Whether there was not another egg is uncertain. All this took place in much less time than it takes to tell it.

Grieve (1885) listed seventy-nine or eighty-one skins of the great auk, two or three physiological preparations, ten skeletons, one hundred and twenty-one or one hundred and thirty-one birds represented by detached bones and sixty-eight or seventy eggs still in existence. The numbers of these have slightly increased, especially in the list of detached bones, which would bring the number of individuals up to many thousands. The value of the skins and of the eggs has increased many fold and has reached fabulous sums.   1919

RAZORBILL   *Alca torda*

On Funk Island, off the coast of Newfoundland, the razor-billed auk, together with several other species of sea birds, once bred abundantly, but frequent and persistent raids, at which the birds were killed for their feathers or for bait and their eggs gathered in large numbers for food, finally reduced these populous colonies to a pitiful remnant. Mr. William Palmer (1890), who visited Funk Island in 1887, writes of it as follows:

It is easy to imagine what must have been the abundance of these birds in former years on this lonely, almost inaccessible ocean island. Great auks, murres, razorbills, puffins, Arctic terns, gannets, and perhaps other species undoubtedly swarmed, each species having its own nesting ground, and never molested except by an occasional visit from the now extinct Newfoundland red man; but now, since the white fisherman began to plunder this, to them, food and feather giving rock, how changed: To-day, but for the Arctic terns (which are useless for food or feathers) and the puffins (which are in most cases impossible to dig out), the island may be said to be deserted by birds. Only bones of the great auk, a few murres, still fewer razorbills, and a few birds of other species are all that now breed on the island. Sixteen barrels of murre and razorbill eggs have been known to be gathered at one time, and taken to St. John's. On July 23 and 24, aside from those of the Arctic tern, we did not see a dozen eggs.

[Devin A. Garrity reported 200 Razorbills and 250,000 Common Murres on Funk Island in 1958].

When we visited Bird Rock[1] in 1904 we estimated that the total population was about ten thousand birds, of which about one thousand eight hundred were razor-billed auks; the auks apparently outnumbered either one species of murre, but not the two species combined, and were exceeded in abundance only by the gannets and the kittiwakes. The strongholds of the auks were mainly on the upper ledges, near the top of the rock, where they had crawled into every available crevice or cavity and under every overhanging rock to lay their single eggs. Occasionally a razorbill's egg could be found on the open ledges with the murres, or in the entrance to a puffin burrow, but, as a rule, they were more or less concealed or under cover. The razorbills were the tamest, the least suspicious, and the most sociable, or perhaps, I should say inquisitive, of all the birds on the rock; I need only sit still for a few moments in the vicinity of their nests, when they would begin to gather on all the surrounding rocks in small parties, eyeing me with curiosity, waddling awkwardly about and making a faint guttural sound. They certainly looked very attractive in their sleek coats of dark seal brown and pure white breasts; occasionally one would open its mouth, showing the rich yellow interior, a marked color contrast which adds brilliancy to its courtship display. I noticed that whereas both the auks and murres usually sit in an upright position, while perched on the ledges, they assume the normal horizontal position, as other birds do, while incubating on their eggs; moreover, there is a bare space in the center of the breast of an incubating bird in which the egg is held horizontally and lengthwise.

1919

COMMON MURRE   *Uria aalge*

U. a. aalge (Atlantic Murre)

As we approached Bird Rock[1] on June 23, 1904, the setting sun shone full upon the tall, red sandstone cliffs, roughly sculptured by the elements into broad shelves, narrow ledges, and deep crevices, which offered lodging room for countless sea fowl, domiciled in their summer homes to rear their young. I estimated that the common murres numbered about 1,400.

Between the bands of gannets we could see, as we drew near, row upon row of smaller, black birds standing in serried ranks, shoulder to shoulder, on the narrow ledges scattered over the face of the cliff. These were the murres and the Brünnich's murres[2] standing on or

[1] Gulf of St. Lawrence (see Gannet).
[2] As the Thick-billed Murre was then called.

near their eggs in their customary attitude, facing the cliff, and with their backs to the sea.

The Bird Rock colonies have been so often described that any lengthy account of them would be unnecessary repetition. At the time of our visit, June 23 to 25, 1904, the total population of the rock was estimated at about ten thousand birds.

The eggs were generally inaccessible, except with the aid of a rope, and were mostly on the lower or middle sections of the cliffs, but there were some which we could reach by going down the ladders and climbing around on the broader ledges. Here the eggs were laid on the bare rock or on the loose soil accumulated by disintegrating rock; they were laid in rows, about as close as the birds could sit, and usually with the smaller end pointing outward. Nearly every one who has written about the eggs of the murres has called attention to their pyriform shape, which is supposed to cause them to roll in a circle, when disturbed, instead of rolling off the ledges; but anyone who has had much experience in murre rookeries knows that any sudden disturbance, which frightens the birds off their nests, generally results in a shower of eggs, showing that this theory does not always work out in practice.

Various writers have stated that the young birds are transported to the water on the backs of their parents or that the old bird carries the young one in its bill, seizing it by the neck or the wing. Both of these methods seem improbable, and I can not find an authentic account of anyone who has seen it done. Where it is possible to do so, the young birds probably scramble or climb down to the water's edge; but where they breed on steep cliffs overhanging the water, the following method, described by Gätke (1895), is probably the one usually employed; he writes:

In Heligoland[1] this descent of the young birds from the cliff to the sea is accomplished in the following manner: On very fine calm evenings at the end of June or the beginning of July one may hear soon after sunset, from a distance of more than a mile, the confused noise of a thousand voices, the calls of the parent birds, *arr-r-r-r—orr-r-r-r—errr-r-r-r*, and mingled with these the countless tiny voices of their young offspring on the face of the cliff, *irrr-r-r-idd—irrr-r-r-idd*, uttered in timid and anxious accents. The old birds swim about quite close to the foot of the cliff, and the tone of their incessant calls has in it something really persuasive and reasoning, as though they were saying in their language, "Now, do come down, don't be afraid, it is not so hard as it looks," whilst the little timorous voices from above seem to reply quite distinctly, "I can not, I am so afraid, it is so

[1] Island in the North Sea, off Germany.

dreadfully high." Nevertheless, in its distress, the little chick tries to get as near as possible to the mother waiting for it below, and keeps tripping about on the outermost ledge of rock, often of no more than a finger's breadth, until it ends by slipping off, and, turning two or three somersaults, lands with a faint splash on the surface of the water; both parents at once take charge of it between them, and swim off with it toward the open sea.

The murre's flight is swift, direct, strong, and protracted, accomplished by steady, rapid wing beats. When traveling long distances it flies in flocks high in the air, but when moving about near its feeding or breeding grounds it flies close to the water with frequent turnings from side to side. It is so heavy-bodied and small-winged that it can not rise off the water without pattering along the surface. In flying from a cliff, it glides rapidly downward at a steep angle, sweeping in a long curve outward and into a level course. Its momentum is so great in proportion to its wing area that, in alighting on a ledge, it has to approach it in a long upward curve and check its speed by flattening its body, spreading its feet and "back peddling" vigorously with its wings; even then it alights far from gracefully.

U. a. californica (California Murre)

Mr. Milton S. Ray (1904) gives a very good account of the main breeding colonies on the Farallones[1] as follows:

Great Murre Cave, which runs in from the ocean on Shulbrick Point, with its vast bird population, is a wonder to behold. All ledges and projections, as well as the cave floor, were murre covered, and on our approach the great colony became a scene of animation, with a vast nodding of dusky heads and a ringing concert of gurgling cries. The birds, at first in tens and then in twenties, flew out, or by sprawling and flapping over the rocks and into the foaming surf, thus gained the open sea. Some were terribly thrown about in the breakers but apparently received little injury. On our entrance the main body took flight, with a mighty roar of wings, and so close did they fill the cave that it behooved us to get behind bowlders to prevent being struck by them. Many birds still remained in the cave, retreating deep into the branching recesses or, sheeplike, huddled into the corners, where they could be picked up by the hand. The multitudes which took wing would wait, scattered over the water about a quarter of a mile from shore, until the commotion was over and would then come trooping back to the cave.

The chief cause of egg destruction on the Farallones has been the depredations of the professional eggers; the results of their work in

---

[1] Islands in the Pacific Ocean thirty miles west of San Francisco, California.

the past have been astounding, but fortunately for the murres this has long ago been stopped. Mr. Bryant (1888) says:

Between 1850 and 1856 there was reported to have been brought to San Francisco between three and four millions of eggs. For the last few years the number of eggs marketed has averaged from 180,000 to 228,000. In 1886 two men who were left on Sugar Loaf collected 108,000 eggs.

The eggs were considered a delicacy and sold in the markets at from twelve to twenty cents a dozen.   1919

THICK-BILLED MURRE   *Uria lomvia*

U. l. lomvia   (Brunnich's Murre)

All along the bold rocky shores of the Atlantic Ocean, from the Gulf of St. Lawrence northward to Greenland and Ellesmere Land [Canadian Arctic], the thick-billed murre is one of the commonest sea birds, a characteristic bird of the rough, cold, northern ocean, following the first advance of spring among the breaking fields of ice to its summer breeding grounds on the rugged cliffs of our Arctic coasts.

Mr. Ekblaw has sent me the following account of the Saunders Island colony [northern Greenland]:

To attempt to paint an adequate picture of the rookery on Saunders Island would almost be futile; to succeed in doing so, would be to convict one's self of wild exaggeration. Literally millions of the birds make the west end of the island their home, and with them are associated hundreds of glaucous gulls and guillemots and thousands of kittiwakes and fulmars; every niche, every ledge, furnishes nesting places; I believe the number of birds on the cliffs is limited only by the number of possible nesting or perching places. The ledges formed by the harder, projecting strata are covered with birds; by the files of birds ranged upon them, one may trace the ledges with one's eyes as far as one can see.

The millions of birds fringing the ledges of these cliffs leave them for periods of several days in the early part of the season, but when the brooding season begins they sally out in the morning in long lines and files to the open water where they feed, to return to the cliffs in the evening. Though large numbers are constantly coming and going throughout the 24-hour day, the greatest exodus is at about 6 or 7 o'clock in the morning. Upon alighting on the ledges when they return, the birds face toward the cliff, give their wings a flutter or two, shake out their feathers vigorously, and preen them carefully. After a glance or two around to see which of their neighbors are at home and a friendly exchange of greetings with those nearest them, they face about and make a careful and critical examination of the prospect.

The birds begin mating about the last week in May, the birds in their best years being probably the first to begin. The mating season is at its height, however, about the fifteenth or twentieth of June. Mating takes place both on the ice and on the ledges of the cliff. Their courting and nuptial struggles are grotesque. The male is very aggressive and persistent, the female apparently most indifferent to all the male's blandishments or reluctant to assume the task of incubation and brooding. Sometimes she so effectively resists the attentions of the male by pecking and striking him that he gives up in despair and neglects her. Then she usually squats seductively before him. The sexual act seems to be of great interest to the birds upon the same and neighboring ledges, for they crane their necks to watch it, and chatter volubly, as if commenting caustically upon such open and flagrant misconduct, even at home. Often a pair, in their nuptial struggles on the cliff, tumble precipitately off like balls of black-and-white yarn. The male does not for a moment release his hold upon the female's crest, apparently determined to do or die, even though both he and she be dashed to death upon the ice or rocks below. But always, just as an awful bump seems inevitable, they separate, flying congenially out across the ice or over the open sea.

U. l. arra (Pallas's Murre)

The largest breeding colony of Pallas's murres, probably the largest breeding colony of any kind, that I have ever seen was on the most famous volcanic island of Bering Sea, Bogoslof Island, about seventy miles northwest of Unalaska.[1] The violent eruptions of the summer of 1910 threw up enough material to join together the three little islands forming the Bogoslof group. In 1911 the volcano had subsided and the towering peaks of Castle Rock, from two hundred to three hundred feet high, were literally covered with nesting murres. I could hardly hazard a guess as to how many hundred thousand murres were breeding on this and on other portions of the island. On the steep sides of the rocky peaks every available ledge, shelf, or cavity was occupied by murres, sitting as close as they could, in long rows on the narrow ledges and in dense masses on the flat places and on the sloping piles of volcanic dust, sand, and loose rocks below the cliffs. As we walked up these slopes the murres began pouring off the rocks above us, sweeping down by us in steady streams, stumbling, scrambling, and bounding along over the rocks and stones, in their frantic efforts to get awing, a ludicrous performance; and down with them came a shower of eggs, dislodged in their haste, rolling or bounding along to smash on the first rock they struck. 1919

---

[1] One of the Aleutian Islands.

DOVEKIE   *Plautus alle*

Nearly all Arctic explorers have referred to the astonishing abundance of the little "rotche," as this species is called, on its breeding grounds. The following two quotations by Morris (1903) will serve as illustrations:

Captain Beechey says [at Magdalen Bay, western Greenland]:

They are so numerous that we have often seen an uninterrupted line of them extending full halfway over the bay, or to a distance of more than 3 miles. This column, on the average, might have been about 6 yards broad and as many deep. There must have been nearly four millions of birds on the wing at one time.

Mr. W. Elmer Ekblaw contributes the following excellent account of the nesting habits of the dovekie:

The nesting sites are determined probably by several factors, perhaps of equal significance. These sites are always along cliffs with rather steep talus slopes, of rather large fragments, among which the birds can find entrances, and cavities well enough within shelter to be safe from winds and weather and predatory animals. In suitable talus slopes its nests extend from near the high tide water mark to the top of the slope, in every possible place. Because of the slow disintegration of the rocks, as compared with the breaking off of the fragments from the cliffs, the talus slopes are piles of coarse rocks with cavities, passages, crevices, and tunnels everywhere among them. In these cavities and passages at various distances from the outside, according to the convenience and safety of the place, the nests are placed. Frequently a mat of grass grows over the surface of the rocks, but since it is only a superficial mat, and as long as openings are left for the ingress of the birds, this does not detract in the least from the desirability of the site. Along Foulke Fjord, on the cliffs south of Cape Alexander [northwest Greenland] and near Sonntag Bay I have found thousands nesting on what was apparently only a grass slope with an occasional projecting rock, but examination revealed the fact that it was only a concealed talus slope after all. Where the breaking down of the cliff above, or where there is considerable rolling of the surface rocks, the grass does not form, though upon the margins of the talus tongues, and in a semicircle about their terminations when they do not reach the sea the grass mat encroaches. In a few cases the grass mat has so deeply covered the talus that the auklets have abandoned it, because they could not enter. Not only in the talus piles does the dovekie nest, but also in crevices—almost without exception in horizontal crevices—it makes its home as well; but this only when talus slopes near at hand have nests too, for this little bird is most socially inclined, nesting, feeding, swimming, flying, and migrating in great gregarious flocks.

It builds no nest. Its one egg, or rarely two, is laid on a rock or shelf in a passageway or cavity, usually in a niche along, or at the end of, a passageway. This rock, after many generations of auks[1] have nested there, is covered with more or less damp dung, upon which the egg or eggs are laid. Several nests may be very close together, or a considerable interval may occur between a nest and its neighbor. The entrance to a nest is usually marked by a white patch on the rock, where more than the usual amount of dung is deposited, for whenever one of the old birds alights at the entrance, he, or she, almost invariably defecates. The earliest eggs are laid in the last week of June, but it is during the first week of July that laying is at its height, at Etah [Greenland]. In the last week in June the Eskimo women begin gathering the eggs, but they are not so plentiful as they become a week later. Each female lays one egg and this is the usual number. Rarely two eggs are laid, and in four cases of this that I saw the eggs were slightly smaller than the normal egg.

The dovekie is preeminently a social bird. Its vast colonies on these northwest Greenland shores form one of the most striking features of the coast and play an important part in the ecology and human economy of the region. They furnish the food for the many foxes of this region; without these birds the foxes would be so few that the natives could not secure adequate clothing, and these "Arctic Highlanders" could not have persisted here as the most northern people of the world. No trading station would have been established by the Danes; one of the chief incentives to some of Peary's and other expeditions of the coast would have been missing. The grass slopes about the rookeries, the luxuriant herbage being due to their dung, support the largest numbers of hare and ptarmigan, and probably afforded the richest pastures for the caribou before the introduction of firearms effected their extermination from some of the areas along the coast. The burgomaster gull[2] and the gyrfalcon feed upon the dovekie throughout the summer and rear their young upon them too. The fox, burgomaster gull, and gyrfalcon are the chief natural enemies of the dovekie; in addition, the Eskimo, the raven, and perhaps some of the water animals prey upon the birdlets; the white whale, so the Eskimo say, catches and eats many.   1919

BLACK GUILLEMOT   *Cepphus grylle*

C. g. atlantis   (Black Guillemot)

The picturesque coast of Maine is deeply cut by numerous rock-bound bays and harbors, protected by rugged promontories, and dotted with many attractive islands, where forests of pointed firs and spruces grow almost down to the water's edge. It well deserves

---

[1] This species was sometimes called the Little Auk.
[2] Glaucous Gull.

its popularity, for I can not imagine a more delightful coast for a summer cruise. Not the least of its attractions is this beautiful little "sea pigeon," so common about all the rocky islands and harbors, where it skims away in front of us in a wide circle, flying close to the water, with its trim, little, black body swiftly propelled by the rapid movements of its wings, the white wing patches flashing in the sunlight and the bright red feet showing behind. It is interesting to watch it as it rises from the water ahead of the boat, flying forward at first until well ahead of us, then swinging in a long curve to one side, and finally dropping into the water again far astern; every bird seems to fly in exactly the same course, almost never flying straight away to one side, as other birds do.

Its flight is strong, swift, and direct. In diving it flops under the surface with open wings, using them regularly in subaqueous flight. Dr. Charles W. Townsend writes to me:

The habit possessed by the black guillemot of dabbling with its bill at the water may have arisen in attempts to obtain food or to sip the water, but it has apparently degenerated into a nervous trick devoid of useful purpose, like the tail wagging of pipits and other birds. When disturbed by the approach of a boat, black guillemots often dab frequently at the water as if in nervous trepidation before taking flight. In rising from the water the feet are used as an aid, and strike back the water one after the other alternately. Black guillemots often chase one another in play or in passion, and make the water boil as they dodge in and out above and below the surface with much flapping of wings and spreading of tails as they thrust with their pointed bills.

C. g. *ultimus* (Short-billed Black Guillemot)

[This] northern "sea pigeon" is essentially a bird of the Arctic Ocean. It has been seen as far north as 84° in summer, and apparently pushes northwards in the spring as fast and as far as the leads open in the ice.

Mr. W. Elmer Ekblaw writes to me as follows:

If any water bird in the Smith Sound region [Canadian Arctic] merits the adjective ubiquitous, the guillemot certainly does. Throughout the entire extent of the northwest Greenland coast and along the shores of Ellesmereland this active, pigeonlike bird is found throughout the open season; in the open water of the sound it finds sustenance even in the dark of winter. There is no fjord so deep that the guillemot does not enter into its head; there is no promontory so stormy or so steep that the guillemot does not frequent it. As there is hardly a rock ledge on land that does not form the home or hunting ground of the snow bunting so along the coast there is no ledge or cliff that does not afford a home and nesting site to one or many guillemots.

When resting idle and unalarmed on the water, it floats high so that much white of its under parts shows, but when alarmed or ready for a dive it sinks itself and rides low, only its black head and back showing. From this low position it dives most easily, like a flash, and with but very little commotion. It dives readily and fast, using its wings to help its feet in propelling itself; it dives so quickly at gunfire that it seems often to evade the shot fired at it from a distance, in this respect resembling the murre, which seems even quicker, however. While swimming about it has the peculiar habit of nervously moving its head backward and forward. It is less shy than most other sea birds, both on the cliffs and in the leads or pools, or on the open sea, apparently trusting and unafraid, undisturbed by the proximity of man. This apparent confidence is quite different from the shyness of the guillemot[1] farther south in Danish Greenland where it is practically unapproachable.

A flock of guillemots contentedly feeding in a pool or lead is a pleasant sight; sometimes they dive as individuals, sometimes as a flock. When satisfied with food, or when tired of the water, they crawl out on the edge of the ice to bask or sleep, often in dense flocks.

When resting on the ice, the guillemot is likely to take flight if suddenly startled, but if more gradually alarmed, it prefers to take to the water to dive. Either from the edge of the ice or in the water, one bird more shy takes the lead in diving, then a few follow, and in a moment the whole flock, leaving trails of bubbles behind. They soon come to the surface, but if the source of their alarm has come nearer them, they dive again at once, remaining submerged for a longer time. It can stay under the water for some little time, either when frightened or feeding—up to a minute and a quarter. [But] when repeatedly frightened it can not continue submerging itself and finally takes flight.

Rising against the wind, the guillemot takes to its wings rather quickly and easily; but with the wind, or when there is no wind at all, it has considerable difficulty. Under either of these conditions the bird must make a determined effort; it flutters along the surface partly flying, partly paddling with its little red feet, to develop enough initial velocity to raise it, often for long distances before it trusts to its wings alone. Once in the air, it sways from side to side as it rises, resembling a quail or partridge. Its flight is exceedingly rapid, yet it can turn most abruptly in flight, and likewise most abruptly check its flight—apparently by assuming a sudden vertical position of the body—to drop hoveringly into the water, in a manner quite different from its usual "shoot-the-chute" slide into a pool, like a ship slipping uncontrolled into the sea from her ways. Often the bird stoops so sharply from considerable heights that it drops like a meteor; the noise a flock of such dropping birds makes is like that of a little hurricane. 1919

---

[1] *C.g. arcticus* (Northern Black Guillemot).

PIGEON GUILLEMOT   *Cepphus columba*

In flight or on the water the pigeon guillemot closely resembles the black guillemot, the only distinguishing mark being the black wedge in the white wing patch, which is not very conspicuous at a distance. It flies swiftly and strongly, usually close to the water, and seems to prefer to fly out and around an approaching boat in a circle. It is a good diver and "flies" under water, using only its wings for propulsion, with its conspicuous red feet held straight out behind, probably to help it in steering. It swims buoyantly and gracefully, frequently with its head below the surface, as if feeding or looking for food. It congregates in small parties on the low rocks near the shore, to bask in the sun or to rest, where it stands nearly upright with its tail resting on the rock or sits upon its breast in a more restful attitude. Its feet are strong enough for it to stand upon and it can walk about quite freely.

Throughout the whole length of the Aleutian chain the pigeon guillemot was one of the common birds, sitting in little groups on the kelp-fringed rocks about the harbors or flying out around us in circles to satisfy its curiosity. We found it nesting during the latter half of June under the piles of loose rocks and boulders along the shores, at the bases of rocky cliffs, as well as in the crevices in the rocks above. Farther north, on the rugged headlands of St. Matthew[1] and Hall Islands,[1] we saw a few pigeon guillemots flying out from the crevices in the lofty cliffs or sitting in little groups on the ledges among the puffins, auklets, and fulmars. They were undoubtedly nesting here in the inaccessible crevices in the rocks, where the nests of all these species were beyond our reach.

Much has been written about the nesting habits of the pigeon guillemot on the Farallone Islands[2] but the following extracts from Mr. Chester Barlow's (1894) writings will suffice to give an idea of its normal nesting habits here and elsewhere:

The "sea pigeons," or pigeon guillemots, are among the most interesting of the birds. They are lovers of the sea and prefer the rocks near the surf, when not incubating their eggs. We were fortunate in discovering a rookery of these birds, and had it not been late for fresh eggs, a splendid series could have been secured. The hill, at the summit of which is the lighthouse, is very steep, and the cliffs at the top are more or less honeycombed with burrows in which the puffins and auklets nest. Farther down

[1] Bering Sea, now part of the Bering Sea Wildlife Refuge.
[2] Pacific Ocean, thirty miles west of San Francisco.

is a stretch of loose, shifting chips of rock, while near the bottom are numerous bowlders, some of gigantic proportions, under and between which are cavities in which the guillemots nest. As one approaches this rookery many of the birds are seen sitting upright, softly "whistling," but upon close approach those on the rocks take wing, while their mates flutter from among the rocks and join them. Then, by a careful search of promising-looking cavities, one may secure a nice series.

No nest is constructed in which to deposit the eggs, but almost invariably the eggs repose upon a collection of small granite chips or pebbles gathered by the birds. Both birds assist at incubation, and I have a male bird taken with a set of two eggs. The rookery described is not near the ocean, but many of the guillemots nest in holes in the cliffs above the sea. At any time groups of birds may be seen gathered on the rocks near the surf. I have noticed young ones so close to the water that the spent force of a "roller" would almost wash them away.   1919

MARBLED MURRELET   *Brachyramphus marmoratum*

While cruising northward through the picturesque inside passages which extend from Puget Sound to Alaska, where the heavily timbered hills rise abruptly from the water, range after range up to the snow-capped mountain tops, and where frequent waterfalls come tumbling down over the cliffs into the placid waters of the bays and channels, we frequently saw these little sea birds skimming over the surface of the water. This is their chosen summer home.

The flight of this species is very swift, direct, and strong, usually close to the water when on its feeding grounds, but at a great height in the air when flying inland. Its wings are small but very stiff and powerful, and they vibrate very rapidly. Like most of the Alcidae it is equipped with wings as small as it can use to propel it through the air and as large as it can use to advantage under water; they are a compromise between the requirements of the two media, but enable it to actually fly, and swiftly, too, in either. The marbled murrelet rises quickly and easily from the surface of smooth water and dashes away, gaining full speed very quickly. Doctor Grinnell (1897*b*) estimated the speed as "not less than 100 miles an hour," and says:

The murrelets have a peculiar habit when rising from the surface of the water of falling back and touching the water two or three times in rapid succession before gaining full headway. These same birds have another strange habit of flying at great heights over the ocean and even across large islands. They become active and fly in this manner at dusk, and may be seen leaving the water in pairs, and starting upward uttering their wild, weird cries.

It is particularly abundant in winter about Puget Sound and the straits and channels around Vancouver Island [British Columbia]. Mr. Dawson (1909) has sketched a vivid picture of it in its winter home, from which I quote as follows:

To be sure it is a bit chilly out and there are spiteful dabs of rain between whiles, but the forward deck is clear, for the helpless ones are crowded in the cabin. We may have the bow to ourselves and what a glorious company of sights and sounds there are about us. Above the whining of the waters and the crashing of the prow come shrill exultant cries, *Meer-meer-meer-meer*. The murrelets are in their element, and they shriek to each other across the dancing waters like Tritons at play. Perhaps association will partly account for it, but somehow the note of the marbled murrelet seems of itself to suggest piping gales and rugged cliffs beset by pounding surf. It is the articulate cry of the sea in a royal mood.

1919

KITTLITZ'S MURRELET   *Brachyramphus brevirostre*

For what we know about the breeding habits of Kittlitz's murrelet we are indebted to Col. John E. Thayer (1914), who has what are probably the only authentic eggs of this rare species in existence. The eggs were collected by Mr. Frank E. Kleinschmidt in May and June 1913, in the vicinity of Pavloff Bay, which "is near the west end and on the south side of the Alaska Peninsula, a little northwest of the Shumagin Islands." He publishes Mr. Kleinschmidt's notes in full, from which I quote the following:

Eight years ago when I shot my first Kittlitz murrelet in the ice pack of Bering Sea, an Eskimo, looking at the bird, said, "Him lay egg way up in snow on mountain." I ridiculed the idea then of this bird laying its egg in the snow far from the sea on the mountain side, but, keeping a constant lookout, expected to find its breeding place on the rocky islands of Alaska or Siberia, perhaps in company with the auks and murres. Now, however, I found the Eskimo's words corroborated and the murrelet's solitary egg laid in just such a strange place as he described. I inclose a photograph marking the spot where I found it, and this egg also.

During my recent expedition I spent the time between the first and middle of May cruising in Chatham Strait,[1] Icy Strait,[1] and Glacier Bay.[1] Among other specimens we collected quite a few marbled murrelets and also several Kittlitz murrelets. It was the height of the breeding season of these two species, for we found in every specimen fully or partly formed eggs, most of which, however, were broken in the collecting. However, I preserved, of the Kittlitz murrelet, one fully formed and colored egg, besides several broken ones.

[1] Southern Alaska.

On June 5, while lying at anchor off Pavloff Bay, Alaska Peninsula, a trapper and miner came aboard, who saw me preparing skins of the Kittlitz and marbled murrelets. He recognized the Kittlitz immediately, and said it was strange that a water bird should lay its egg far inland, high on the mountain sides, in the snow. Upon closer questioning he said he meant that the egg was laid, not on the snow, but far above timber line on the mountain, in bare spots, amid the snow. In the 16 years he had been there he had found but two eggs, but he remembered well the eggs and bird. I had him describe the egg carefully before I showed him the one I possessed, and it tallied with his description.

On June 6 I was hunting brown bear for the Carnegie Museum, in company with this man, and while crossing a high divide, a Kittlitz murrelet flew past us. "There is your bird," called the trapper immediately; "it has a nest here somewhere." On June 10 I saw with my glasses a she-bear and two cubs far up in the snow of Mount Pavloff. To reach them I had to climb several miles inside the snow line, with only here and there a few bare spots to give me a much-desired walking ground, when close to my feet rose a Kittlitz murrelet. There on the bare lava, without even the pretension of a hollow, lay a single egg.

XANTUS' MURRELET   *Endomychura hypoleuca*

This white-breasted murrelet is now well known as a fairly common bird about the rocky islands from southern California along the west coast of Lower California at least as far as Magdalena Bay.

The favorite nesting site is a cranny among loose bowlders, but nearly as frequently one finds them back under a rock where it was necessary for them to scratch away a little of the loose dirt in order to gain entrance.

(A. B. Howell)

When first hatched the young murrelet remains in the nesting site for perhaps two or three days, never more than four days, according to several good observers. As soon as the young bird is strong enough, perhaps soon after its down is thoroughly dry, it is conducted by its parents to the water and led away to sea. It seems remarkable that such tender young can stand the buffeting that they must endure in a rough sea and many of them must lose their lives in finding their way through the breakers which surround their rocky birthplace, but perhaps they are safer at sea than on land. Mr. Howell writes me, on this subject, as follows:

When the eggs are once pipped they show amazing vitality. A set that was rescued by A. van Rossem and me after having been deserted by the parents among the cold rocks for 36 hours hatched out two lusty young-sters and these we succeeded in keeping alive for several days on a diet of hardboiled egg. When we substituted bits of fish for this, one died. The other crawled out of the tent, tumbled down a cliff, and when discovered, was making his way out to sea with all speed. They are surely made for swimming for the tarsus when one day old is equal to that of the adults. When in the downy stage they present the most attractive appearance of any bird that I know and are truly full of life, hopping up and down and flapping their little wings from pure joy of life. Upon being placed in the water at the age of two days they at once made themselves thoroughly at home. They can then swim as fast as a man usually walks and dive at the slightest suspicion of danger, swimming for several yards beneath the surface. A large fish rose to one of them twice and the little fellow cleverly dodged him. No one as far as I know has ever taken a young *hypoleucus* on land that was more than a few days old. Twelve that I kept under observation were taken out to sea before they were 4 days old. H. Wright shot a downy young beside an adult several miles from land, and others have observed them. How they reach the water is a question, for a murrelet's bill is not made to carry anything so bulky and they could not be carried on the old bird's back. Many must fall a prey to large fish during the first couple of weeks of their life and many more die of exposure during heavy winds. Their down, although very dense, soon becomes water-soaked and it seems that their only salvation would be to climb upon their parent's back and dry themselves in the sun. . . .

In flight the wing beats are very rapid, almost a buzz, and they are capable of great speed. When attacked by a duck hawk while flying they will suffer themselves to be caught rather than take to the water. Shortly after dark large numbers of the birds make their way into the coves and shallow water near the islands. From then until dawn they can be heard giving their characteristic cry, which can best be described as a shrill slow twitter, about four notes to the second. At night, especially when hunting a nesting site, they are sometimes attracted by a light on shore. Doubtless they make several trips to the burrows throughout the night. During the day they keep well out to sea and are usually to be found in pairs or family parties. When pressed too closely they rise to the wind and fly into the distance, but refuse to dive unless wounded.   1919

CRAVERI'S MURRELET   *Endomychura craveri*

Col. John E. Thayer (1909) published a letter from Mr. Wilmot W. Brown, Jr., giving an interesting account of the nesting and other habits of this species, from which I quote, as follows:

The object of the expedition to the islands was to make a search for the eggs of *Brachyramphus craveri*, the Craveri murrelet. I am pleased to write you that I took over 40 eggs of this species on a rock that lies about 2 miles from San Jose Island [Gulf of California]. I also took a series of 35 skins. We found the murrelets nesting in the crevices among the rocks of the bluff. The nest in all instances was a slight depression in the earth at the end of the crevice and generally contained two eggs, but some nests only contained one. The young take to the sea two days after being hatched. Twenty-two days is the period of incubation. The males help in the act of incubation, many males being taken on the eggs in the day time.

In the early morning hours, particularly about an hour before dawn, there was much activity among the murrelets, they at this time being seen in pairs chasing each other, and making much noise among the rocks. Our tent was at the foot of the bluff and it was impossible to sleep, the murrelets made so much noise; for when they fly there is a loud whirring sound. Toward the end of our stay they learned that the walls of our tent were soft and seemed to take delight in butting into it in their amorous frolics. One pair in the excitement must have hit it head onward, for they dropped to the ground with a thud and fluttered together under the side of the tent into my bed, where I was trying to sleep. I caught them by throwing my blanket over them. This is the first collecting I have ever done in bed. They proved to be male and female. In the daytime I did not observe any in the waters around the island. They seem to feed far out to sea, for with the exception of the setting birds in the crevices, I did not see any in the vicinity of the islands in the daytime. But in the early hours of the morning the rocks of the bluff seemed alive with them; they all disappeared on the approach of dawn. This species has three distinct notes, the one of displeasure being very harsh. According to Mr. Brewster's book, it seems only one set of eggs of this species has been taken and that was on the island of Raza [Gulf of California] in 1875, and was taken by Doctor Streets. The island of Raza is over 300 miles north of San Jose Island.   1919

ANCIENT MURRELET   *Synthliboramphus antiquum*

In the large deep-water bays of the Aleutian Islands, protected from the furious storms of Bering Sea by towering cliffs and lofty snow-laden mountains which rise abruptly from the shores, these curious and dainty little sea birds find congenial summer homes on tranquil inland seas. Here we never failed to find them, in every harbor we visited in June, floating quietly in little parties of from four to six birds on the smooth waters of sheltered bays and often close to the shores. Although at other seasons this species frequents the open sea and is generally seen on migrations farther from land than others of its tribe, in the summer it seems to love to frequent protected harbors where it can find deep water, leaving its winter companions, the auklets, far outside.

Mr. Chase Littlejohn, who spent the spring and summer of 1894

on different islands south of the Alaska Peninsula, furnished Major
Bendire (1895) with some very full and interesting notes on the
breeding habits of this species on Sanak Island.

On June 23 our party returned to the island on which we first landed, and
found to our great satisfaction that the murrelets' eggs were more plentiful
than on our former visit, and a few of them were taken. We also soon discovered that they were not especially particular in the selection of a nesting site. An abandoned burrow of Cassin's auklet, a dark crevice in cliffs,
under large broken rocks which had fallen from the latter, or under large
tussocks of rank grass, with which the higher portion of the island was
covered, would answer equally well. Under these almost solid bunches
(the grass remaining from several previous years), the murrelets would
force their way, leaving only a slight hole in the mass, which usually was
very hard to detect. After once gaining an entrance into this matted vegetation and working their way in for 2 or 3 feet, a shallow cavity about 5
inches in diameter and 2 or 3 inches deep, was scratched out and this
was nicely lined with blades of dry grass of last year's growth, carried
in from the outside, making a very neat and snug home, in which the two
beautiful eggs, comprising a set, were deposited. Some of their nests were
found fully 200 yards from the water. In the other situations mentioned
little and often no nest is made, and the eggs are deposited on the bare
rocks, in the soft sand, or on the wet, muddy soil. I even took several sets
on the bare ice at the bottom of some auklet's burrow, the ground being
still frozen, immediately beneath the grass and moss on July 3, when I
left the island.   1919

CASSIN'S AUKLET   *Ptychoramphus aleutica*

One of the most populous colonies of this species is to be found on
the Farallone Islands,[1] of which Mr. W. Leon Dawson (1911) writes:

The Cassin auklets are everywhere. Burrows predominate, but there is
not a cleft, nook, crack, cranny, fissure, aperture, retreat, niche, cave, re-
ceptacle, or hidey-hole from the water's edge to the summit of the light
tower which is not likely to harbor this ubiquitous bird. The interstices of
the stone walls contain them to the number of thousands. Every cavity not
definitely occupied by puffin, petrel, or rabbit is tenanted by an auklet, and
in many cases quarters are shared. If one's imagination is not sufficiently
stimulated by regular occurrences, it will be jogged by appearances in unexpected places—an old nest of rock wren or pigeon guillemot, an inner
recess of a murre cave, an abandoned spur of puffin burrow, an overturned
wheelbarrow or neglected board lying on the ground, driftwood on the
beach—anything affording the slightest prospect of protection or cover.
A pile of coal, sacked up and awaiting transfer from landing to siren, was

[1] Pacific Ocean, thirty miles west of San Francisco.

found to be full of them. Since this was the rule from center to circumference of this magic isle, we conclude that the Cassin auklet is the commonest bird on the Farallones, and estimates of population anywhere short of one or two hundred thousand do not take account of the facts.

The Cassin auklet seems incapable of controlling the force of its flight, and the wonder is that the birds are not every one of them dashed to pieces in a single night. In this respect they remind one of nothing else so much as beetles or moths, which come hurtling into the region of candlelight, crash against the candlestick, and without an instant's pause begin an animated search afoot. This crash-and-crawl method seems not exceptional but characteristic in the auklet. It was especially noticeable in the paved area just outside our workroom door. Crash! announced the arrival of another food-laden messenger from the unknown deeps. The impact of collision with the building invariably stunned the bird so that it fell to the ground, but it immediately began a frantic search, and as likely as not, before you could lay hands on it, disappeared in a crack under the doorstep.   1919

PARAKEET AUKLET   *Cyclorrhynchus psittacula*

The auklets, like the fur seals, of the Pribilof Islands spend the greater part of their lives at sea and return to these lonely fog-bound islands in Bering Sea to rear their young, where they are wholly engrossed with the cares of reproduction. My short visit to these islands in the summer of 1911 served only as an introduction and gave me but a slight glimpse into their life histories. Our introduction to the famous fur-seal islands was characteristic of that dismal climate. We had been sailing by compass all night from Bogoslof Island,[1] and morning found us still groping in the prevailing thick fog, which serves to keep the seals' coats cool and moist, but is a menace to mariners. At last, when we had about concluded that we had missed our reckoning and had passed the islands, we began to see a few of these large white-breasted auklets flying past us to the eastward. Turning, we followed them, and before long we could hear the barking, roaring, and bellowing of the fur seals in their rookeries on St. Paul Island.[2] Feeling our way carefully toward them until we could dimly see the outline of the cliffs, we crept along the shore into Village Cove.

On July 7, 1911, I spent one of the most eventful afternoons of my life studying the nesting habits of this and the hosts of other sea birds that make their summer home on the wonderful, little, rocky islet of

---

[1] Now a National Wildlife Refuge.
[2] One of the Pribilof Islands.

the Pribilof group, Walrus Island. Here we found the paroquet,[1] crested, and least auklets, together with the tufted puffin, nesting under the loose piles of water-worn boulders which were piled up in a great ridge in the beachlike center of the island, connecting the higher extremities. By rolling away such of the boulders as we could move, we succeeded in uncovering some two dozen nests. Compared with the other auklets, which were very lively and noisy, the paroquet auklets were very gentle and tame; they did not seem to be greatly disturbed or alarmed by our rock moving operations; we usually found the female, and occasionally the male, sitting quietly on its single egg, serenely looking at us with its big white eyes. The curious up-turned red bill and the white under parts were easily recognized even in the dark recesses of its nesting caverns. There was only a single egg in each case, which was lying on the bare rock or soil or on a bed of loose pebbles; no nesting material had been brought in.

The flight of the paroquet auklet is very much like that of the smaller auklets—swift, direct, and strong, with frequent turnings from side to side as its course is altered. It can be easily recognized by its large size and white breast; it also usually flies at a higher elevation above the water than the other species. It travels long distances in search of food. It swims buoyantly and rapidly and it is a very good diver.   1919

CRESTED AUKLET   *Aethia cristatella*

The following account by Mr. C. H. Townsend (1913) would seem to indicate that the center of abundance of the crested auklet lies south of the Alaska Peninsula. He writes:

On the evening of August 1 the *Albatross* came to anchor in Yukon Harbor at Big Koniushi Island, of the Shumagin group. While the ship was working her way into this wild and uninhabited bay everyone noticed the increasing numbers of crested auklets. The farther in we went the more numerous they became, until the captain called me to the bridge to tell him what I could about them.

The birds were nearly all of the crested species and were present in myriads. The surface of the water was covered with them and the air was filled with them. Large, compact flocks launched themselves into the air from the lofty cliffs and careened toward the vessel with great speed and whirring of wings. The crested auklets were here more numerous than were the "choochkies" (least auklets) at St. George, in the Pribilofs, cele-brated as the center of abundance for that species.

---

[1] As the name of this species was formerly spelled.

Twilight did not come until after 9 o'clock, and during the long evening the birds were amazingly active. Flocks of them continued to come in rapid succession from the cliffs, many passing close to the ship at high speed and swinging about the harbor. After the anchor was dropped near the cliffs a loud blast of the whistle made the auklets still more abundant. The bird legions started from the cliffs, until the misty air and the water about the ship was alive with them. It was a memorable ornithological display, and when darkness came the birds were still moving actively.

These birds appeared to be nesting chiefly in crevices in the cliffs, although they could be heard under the boulders near the beaches.

The flight of the crested auklet is more direct and business-like than that of the others. They usually fly in small, dense flocks close to the water. They are active swimmers and can rise easily from the surface.   1919

LEAST AUKLET   *Aethia pusilla*

I first met this diminutive sea bird, the smallest of the Alcidae, in 1911 while passing through Unimak Pass, the main entrance into Bering Sea, where a few small flocks were seen among the thousands of puffins, murres, and other auklets scattered over the smooth surface of the water. But it was not until we reached Kiska Island, in the Aleutian chain, that I began to realize its abundance and learn something of its habits. One smooth, foggy afternoon Mr. R. H. Beck and I took a small skiff and rowed out of the harbor to collect sea birds. Large flocks of harlequin ducks, scoters, and Pacific eiders[1] flew past us along the rocky shore; numerous pigeon guillemots skimmed along the surface ahead of us, and several pelagic cormorants flew out from the cliffs to meet us, circling about our boat to satisfy their curiosity. But we left them all behind us as the rocky shores faded out of sight in the fog, and we found ourselves at sea among the auklets. Immense flocks of those curious little birds surrounded us on all sides, countless thousands of them, sitting in dense masses on the water, disappearing beneath the surface as if by magic, and as suddenly reappearing or swirling about us in great swarms, reminding us more of bees than of birds, as their chunky little bodies bounded along over the waves, their small wings vibrating at high speed. They would rise readily from the surface and would dive like lightning, so quickly that we could not see how it was done; but we could frequently see them swimming under water, using their wings. When one or more of their number were shot, others would come and alight

---

[1] *Somateria mollissima v. nigra,* a subspecies of the Common Eider.

near them, showing a sympathetic interest between what were per-haps mated pairs.

The "choochkies," as they are called by the natives, begin to arrive to their breeding grounds in hundreds about the first of May, increasing to thousands during that month and reaching the height of their abundance early in June, when they swarm in millions about the rocky beaches of the Pribilof Islands, outnumbering any other species in Bering Sea. It is difficult for one who has not seen them to appreciate their abundance and one is not likely to overestimate their numbers. One of their greatest breeding grounds is on the Diomede Islands, in Bering Straits, which Mr. E. W. Nelson (1887) has thus aptly described:

As we lay at anchor close under the Big Diomede the cliffs arose almost sheer for hundreds of feet. Gazing up toward one of these banks we could see the air filled with minute black specks, which seemed to be floating by in an endless stream. The roar from the rush of waves against the base of the cliffs was deadened by the strange humming chorus of faint cries from myriads of small throats, and as we landed, a glance upward showed the island standing out in bold, jagged relief against the sky and surrounded by such inconceivable numbers of flying birds that it could only be likened to a vast beehive, with the swarm of bees hovering about it. The mazy flight of the birds had the effect several times of making me dizzy as I watched them. Breeding there were several species of auks and guillemots. Our first visit was made about the middle of July, and most of the birds, including the present species, had fresh eggs.   1919

WHISKERED AUKLET   *Aethia pygmaea*

We are indebted to Dr. Leonhard Stejneger (1885) for nearly all we know about the life history of this curious and obscure species, the rarest and the least known of the auklets. He says of its breeding habits:

This little auk, certainly the prettiest species of the whole family, has apparently the center of its distribution on the islands visited by me. On Bering Island[1] it is rather rare, however, though it breeds in the crevices of the outlying islet Arij Kamen, in a precipice near the fishing place Saranna, and probably in several places on the southern part of the island, for instance, at Kikij Mys. Copper Island,[1] with its steep rocky shores, is the favorite home of this bird, however. It may be found breeding all around the coast where suitable holes and crevices occur. I know of nesting places near the main village, at Karabelnij,[1] and on Tschornij Mys.[1] At the latter place it occupied holes in the basaltic cliff alongside those of

[1] Commander Islands, Soviet Far East.

Oceanodroma furcata [Fork-tailed Petrel], the latter inhabiting the deeper ones. It could be told at once by the peculiar smell emanating from the caverns of the latter bird, which species was to be found inside.

They are early breeders, in that respect being considerably ahead of their allies, for instance, *Lunda cirrhata* [Tufted Puffin], so early in fact, that no eggs could be procured in the latter part of June, when I had the opportunity to go in search of them. The nests at that time already contained young ones. These remain in the nest until full fledged. A specimen having left the nest only a few days previous, was taken alive on board the steamer when at anchor at Glinka, Copper Island, July 18. This bird was found early in the morning, concealed in a fold of one of the sails, the inexperienced youth having probably mistaken it for the crevice of a rock. This would indicate that they pass the nights in holes as long as they stay near land.   1919

RHINOCEROS AUKLET   *Cerorhinca monocerata*

Mr. Dawson (1909) has given us the following attractive account of the arrival of these auklets on the island.[1]

Late in April the auklets, stirred by a common impulse, muster from the wide seas and move upon Destruction by night. If there has been any scouting or premature development work, it has been carried on by night only and has escaped observation. In fact, it is a point of honor among the auklets never to appear in the vicinity of the great rookery—or aukery— by day. At the tribal home-coming, the keepers tell us, there is a great hubbub. If the location be a brushy hillside, the birds upon arrival crash into the bushes like meteors and take chances of a braining. Upon the ground, they first argue with old neighbors about boundaries. If growls and barks and parrot-like shrieks mean anything, there are some differences of opinion discovered. Perhaps also the details of matrimony have not all been arranged, and there is much screaming avowal.

Doctor Grinnell (1899) gives an interesting account of his efforts to get within gunshot of a rhinoceros auklet swimming on the water, which well illustrates its power of diving and swimming for long distances under water. He also says:

The manner and pose of the rhinoceros auklet, resting or swimming on the water are quite different from those of any other sea bird met with around Catalina.[2] It is short and chunky, with head drawn in close to the body, leaving scarcely any tract that might be called a neck. The water line comes up to about the lower edge of the wings when closed against the body, so that the bird does not rest lightly on the water, like a gull or phalarope. The head is held on the same line as the body, directly out

[1] Destruction Island, Washington.
[2] Island off southern California.

in front, so that the top of the head and back are on the same level. The whole bird at a little distance looks most like a block of wood floating on the water. We did not once see one flying. They all preferred to dive. One which was shot at and probably slightly wounded, attempted to take flight but failed to get clear of the water, and after dragging along the surface for several feet, instantly dove. The great ease and rapidity which is shown in diving and traveling under water is remarkable. We heard no note, and there was never but one in sight at a time. They were mostly seen about a quarter of a mile from shore.

Professor Heath (1915) writes [of Forrester Island, Alaska]:

In former times the rhinoceros auklet was far more numerous than it is at the present time, according to the reports of the [Haidah] Indians. As late as 50 years ago many of the slopes now untenanted afforded nesting sites for these and other birds, and the hills now occupied had a far greater population than one finds to-day. In those earlier times the sky was literally darkened as they put out to sea, and the sound of their cries was a veritable babel. The diminution might naturally be ascribed to the activity of the natives, who relish this species above all others, but the natives themselves meet such a claim with the evidence of many scores of years when, with a much larger tribe than at present, they gathered eggs and birds in vastly greater numbers without any appreciable decline in the bird colony. Their explanation rests solely upon the belief that the decrease is due entirely to the rank growth of underbrush and ferns which form a tangled mat too dense to permit of ready flight to and from the burrows. In former times, even within the memory of some of the older men of the tribe, the country was much more open; and it is certainly a readily observed fact that this species avoids the thickets and seeks out more open ground. Occasional nests are found in salmonberry patches, but well-worn runways invariably lead into the open.   1919

COMMON PUFFIN   *Fratercula arctica*   (Townsend)

At the present time the most southerly breeding station is Matinicus Rock off the middle coast of Maine. Here only two pairs are left.[1] The only other breeding place left on the coast of the United States is at Machias Seal Island [Maine]. Here in 1904, according to Dutcher (1904), there was a colony of three hundred of these birds.[2] It is probable that the coast of Maine was formerly the resort of large numbers of this species. According to Knight (1908) a few pairs probably bred on Seal Island not far from Matinicus as recently as 1888. Audubon (1840), who visited the Bay of Fundy in 1833, says

[1] B. B. Cadbury counted one hundred seventy-four in late July 1957.
[2] 500 pairs were estimated in 1958.

it bred commonly on the islands in the bay "although not one perhaps now for a hundred that bred there 20 years ago." Now, they are nearly if not entirely extirpated. Macoun (1909) gives only one breeding locality for Nova Scotia, namely, Seal Island, Yarmouth County; but it is probable that a century ago the coast swarmed with these interesting birds. Along the Newfoundland coast the puffin is still to be found breeding, but in much diminished numbers. At Byron Island in the Magdalen group[1] and at Bird Rock[1] puffins still breed, as well as at Wreck Bay, Anticosti,[2] and elsewhere on this island. On the Labrador coast their numbers are rapidly diminishing.

In 1860 Coues (1861) thus describes the island at the mouth of Hamilton Inlet on the eastern Labrador coast:

The Parrakeet Islands are three in number, lying along the western shore of Esquimau Bay, just at its mouth. The one I visited is the innermost, as well as the largest, though the others are equally crammed with birds. It is about a mile in circumference. As we rounded the island close to the shore they came tumbling out of their holes by hundreds and, with the thousands we disturbed from the surface of the water, soon made a perfect cloud above and around us, no longer flying in flocks, but forming one dense continuous mass.[3]

He also records them in numbers in the bay near Rigolet. Forty-six years later, in 1906, Townsend and Allen saw only thirteen puffins on a steamer trip from Battle Harbor to Nain, stopping at Rigolet, and only forty-three on the return trip. Six years later, in 1912, Bent (1913) "did not see a single puffin north of the Straits [of Belle Isle]."[4]

Puffins are as a rule unsuspicious and generally allow a close approach. As one approaches in a steamer or other boat, the swimming bird shows its anxiety by nervously dipping its head into the water from time to time. Then it is apt to show the greatest indecision as to which action to adopt—flight below the water or above. Both actions—aerial as well as subaqueous—can be described as flight, for the wings, although held somewhat differently, are as vigorously used below the water as in the air. In the former as in the latter case the feet are not used but trail behind. One can easily observe the beginning of the subaqueous flight, for the wings are flapped out for their first stroke as the bird enters the water.   1919

---

[1] Gulf of St. Lawrence.

[2] Island in the Gulf of St. Lawrence.

[3] 1926 population of this (Puffin) Island was 500 birds.

[4] According to Oliver Austin Jr. this simply means that none of these observers was ever fortunate enough to get near any of the main Puffin colonies; ". . . a locally abundant summer resident . . . breeds . . . as far north as the Nain region."

HORNED PUFFIN *Fratercula corniculata*

The horned puffin is essentially an Alaskan and a Bering Sea bird, being found breeding throughout the whole length of the Alaskan coast, and on all the coasts and islands of Bering Sea.

Mr. B. J. Bretherton (1896) gives an unique account of the nesting habits of this species on Kodiak Island [Alaska]; he writes:

On first arriving, these birds do a great deal of flying; they gather in bands, and sit perched on the rocky face of some high bluff, and keep up a continuous whistling call; at irregular intervals the whole band will leave the bluff and fly a short distance out to sea and return.

The eggs of this species are laid in a tunnel, or burrow, dug in the ground by the bird, and a few handfuls of dry grass and feathers constitute the nest.

The construction of the tunnel is unique; it always has an opening at both ends. The nesting site is some high rocky bluff overhanging the sea, and near the top where the soil lies on the rock, the bird commences its excavations, first constructing a sort of runway for a few feet along the face of the bluff, then going directly inward, sometimes in a straight line, while others are crooked. In the same way, the length of the tunnel is very variable, and the nest may be at most any distance from 2 to 10 feet from the face of the bluff. From the nest, the tunnel passes on inland, making a sharp upward turn to the surface of the ground.

The same burrows are used year after year, but whether by the same birds or not was not ascertained. Some burrows have by long usage become as large as rabbit holes, while newly made ones are only just large enough to admit the birds. Both entrances are used indiscriminately by the bird, and it is surprising to see with what accuracy they can fly directly into the holes in the ground.

Mr. Turner (1886) gives us another chapter in the story, as follows:

The young leave the nest before being able to fly. The parent assists them to the water; and, should they have been reared on the face of a high bluff, the old bird catches the young one by the wing and they flutter at a long angle to the water. The old bird endeavors to keep under the young one. I have seen them drop their young accidentally and cause great consternation of the parent, which could not check her flight immediately, but returned and showed great solicitude by turning the young one over and over in the water to see if it was injured. During severe storms the young are taken to the lee of some reef or islet until the waves become quiet.   1919

TUFTED PUFFIN   *Lunda cirrhata*

We hailed with delight our first glimpse of the Aleutian Islands, as the rugged peaks of the Krenitzin group, Tigalda, Avatinak, and Ugamak, loomed up in the horizon, dimly outlined in the foggy distance. They are the sturdy sentinels of rock that guard the entrance to Bering Sea, shrouded in perpetual mist, their snow-capped summits enveloped in heavy banks of cloud. Such is the gateway to this interesting region and here we were introduced to its wonderful bird life. We had seen a few tufted puffins at sea, migrating toward their summer home, but it was not until we reached the entrance to Unimak Pass that we began to realize the astonishing abundance of this species in that region. The sea was smooth, and scattered over its surface for miles, as far as we could see, were thousands and thousands of tufted puffins. We stood in the bow and watched them in their ludicrous attempts to escape as we passed through them. The wind was very light and was behind us, which made it almost impossible for them to rise from the water; they flopped along the surface in the most helpless manner; they barely managed to avoid being run over, but almost never succeeded in flying and only occasionally did they have sense enough to escape by diving, at which they were very skillful. They had probably only recently arrived and were congregating in the vicinity of their breeding grounds. The tufted puffin is largely pelagic in its habits, during the great part of the year migrating well out at sea, almost out of sight of land, and gradually working in toward shore, as the breeding season approaches. They are usually in pairs when they arrive.

The arrival of the "Toporkie," as they are called, is a cause of great rejoicing among the Aleuts, for it heralds the approach of summer and means an abundant supply of good food, for both birds and eggs are a welcome relief from salted and dried seal meat on which they have been living. As soon as the puffins are sufficiently abundant about the islands where they breed, the natives organize merry hunting parties to capture them. On certain days they frequent their breeding grounds in immense numbers, flying back and forth in straight lines, crossing and recrossing the small grassed-topped island, just high enough to clear it. The birds are swift fliers and seem unable to change their course quickly. The Aleuts take advantage of this peculiarity and catch them in large, long-handled nets, which are suddenly raised in front of the birds and which they can not dodge. It is a simple process when the birds are flying thickly, and large numbers are taken in this way. The birds are killed by biting the head or breaking the back. Besides furnishing a welcome supply of fresh meat, the birds are skinned and the skins are cured and used for clothing. A parka made of puffin skins is not only a very warm but a very light and serviceable garment. About forty-five skins are required to make one parka, which is made like a shirt with a hood and is worn with the feathers on the inside.   1919

BIBLIOGRAPHY

ABBOTT, CLINTON GILBERT
1911   *The Home Life of the Osprey.*

ALFORD, CHARLES E.
1921   "Diving Ducks: Some Notes on Their Habits and Courtship,"
British Birds, vol. 15, pp. 33-38.

ALLEN, ARTHUR AUGUSTUS
1913   "Stilt Sandpipers" (*Micropalama himantopus*) at Ithaca, New
York, *The Auk,* vol. 30, pp. 430-432.
1915   "The Behavior of the Least Bittern," *Bird-Lore,* vol. 17, pp.
425-430.

ALLEN, JOEL ASAPH
1876   "The Extinction of the Great Auk at the Funk Islands,"
American Naturalist, vol. 10, p. 48.

ANDERSON, RUDOLPH MARIA
1913   "Report on the Natural History Collections of the Expedition,"
in *My Life with the Eskimo,* by Vilhjalmur Stefansson.

ANTHONY, ALFRED WEBSTER
1896a   "Eggs of the Black, Socorro and Least Petrels," *The Nidologist,*
vol. 4, p. 16.
1896b   "The Black-vented Shearwater (*Puffinus opisthomelas*),"
The Auk, vol. 13, p. 223.
1898b   "Petrels of Southern California," *The Auk,* vol. 15, p. 140.
1898e   "The Boobys of the Revillagigedo Islands," *The Osprey,* vol.
3, p. 4.
1900a   "A Night on Land," *The Condor,* vol. 2, p. 28.
1903   "Migration of Richardson's Grouse," *The Auk,* vol. 20, No. 1,
pp. 24-27, January.
1906   "Random Notes on Pacific Coast Gulls," *The Auk,* vol. 23, p.
129.

AUDUBON, JOHN JAMES
1840-1844   *The Birds of America.*

AUDUBON, MARIA REBECCA
1897   *Audubon and His Journals.*

BAILEY, ALFRED MARSHALL
1925-26   "A Report on the Birds of Northwestern Alaska and Regions
Adjacent to Bering Strait," Part 6. *The Condor,* vol. 27, pp. 232-238.
1927   "Notes on the Birds of Southeastern Alaska," *The Auk,* vol.
44, Nos. 1-3, pp. 1-23, 184-205, 351-367, January-July.

BAILEY, FLORENCE MERRIAM (Mrs. Vernon)
1916   "A Populous Shore," *The Condor,* vol. 18, pp. 100-110.
1918   *Wild Animals of Glacier National Park.* The Birds, pp. 103-
199, plates 22-37, figs. 19-94. Washington.
1928   *Birds of New Mexico.*

BAILEY, HAROLD HARRIS
1913   *The Birds of Virginia.*

BAILEY, HARRY BALCH
1876   "Notes on Birds Found Breeding on Cobb's Island, Virginia,
between May 25 and May 29, 1875," *Quarterly Bulletin of the Nuttall
Ornithological Club,* vol. 1, p. 24.

BAILEY, VERNON
1902   Notes in *Handbook of Birds of the Western United States* by
Florence Merriam Bailey.

BAIRD, SPENCER FULLERTON, BREWER, THOMAS MAYO, and RIDGWAY,
ROBERT
1884   *The Water Birds of North America.*

BARLOW, CHESTER
1894   "An Ornithological Paradise," *The Museum,* vol. 1, p. 37.

BARROWS, WALTER BRADFORD
1913   "Concealing Action of the Bittern (*Botaurus lentiginosus*),"
The Auk, vol. 30, p. 187.

BAYNARD, OSCAR E.
1913   "Home Life of the Glossy Ibis (*Plegadis autumnalis,* Linn.),"
The Wilson Bulletin, vol. 25, pp. 103-117.

BECK, ROLLO HOWARD
1904   "Bird Life Among the Galapagos Islands," *The Condor,* vol.
6, p. 5.

BENDIRE, CHARLES EMIL
1892   *Life Histories of North American Birds,* United States National
Museum Special Bulletin.
1895   "Notes on the Ancient Murrelet, by Chase Littlejohn, with
Annotations," *The Auk,* vol. 12, p. 270.

BENT, ARTHUR CLEVELAND
1912   "A New Subspecies of Ptarmigan from the Aleutian Islands,"
Smithsonian Miscellaneous Collection, vol. 56, No. 30, 2 pp., January 6.
1913   "Notes from Labrador," *Bird Lore,* vol. 15, p. 11.

BEWICK, THOMAS
    1847   *A History of British Birds.*

BLAAUW, FRANS ERNST
    1903   "Notes on the Breeding of Ross's Snow-Goose in Captivity," *The Ibis,* 1903, pp. 245-247.

BLANCHAN, NELTJE
    1898-1908   *Birds that Hunt and are Hunted.*

BOND, FRANK
    1900   "A Nuptial Performance of the Sage Cock," *The Auk,* vol. 17, No. 4, pp. 325-327, illus., October.

BOWDISH, BEECHER SCOVILLE
    1891   "Notes on the Virginia Rail," *The Ornithologist and Botanist,* vol. 1, pp. 73-74.
    1902   "Birds of Porto Rico," *The Auk,* vol. 19, pp. 356-366.
    1909   "Ornithological Miscellany from Audubon Wardens," *The Auk,* vol. 26, p. 116.

BOWLES, JOHN HOOPER
    1909   *The Birds of Washington.*

BRADBURY, WILLIAM CHASE
    1918   "Notes on the Nesting of the Mountain Plover," *The Condor,* vol. 20, pp. 157-163.

BRANDT, HERBERT WILLIAM
    1924   "The Nesting of the Short-tailed Hawk," *The Auk,* vol. 41, pp. 59-64.

BRETHERTON, BERNARD J.
    1896   "Kadiak Island. A Contribution to the Avifauna of Alaska," *The Oregon Naturalist,* vol. 3, p. 45.

BREWSTER, WILLIAM
    1879   "The Terns of the New England Coast," *Bulletin of the Nuttall Ornithological Club,* vol. 4, p. 13.
    1881   "With the Birds on a Florida River," *Bulletin of the Nuttall Ornithological Club,* vol. 6, pp. 38-44.
    1883   "Notes on the Birds Observed During a Summer Cruise in the Gulf of St. Lawrence," *Proceedings of the Boston Society of Natural History,* vol. 22, p. 364.
    1890   "The Heath Hen: Notes on the Heath Hen (*Tympanuchus cupido*) of Massachusetts," *Forest and Stream,* vol. 35, No. 10, p. 188, September 25.
    1906   "The Birds of the Cambridge Region of Massachusetts," *Memoirs of the Nuttall Ornithological Club,* No. 4.
    1912   "Notes on the Flight of Gulls," *The Auk,* vol. 29, p. 85.
    1925   "The Birds of the Lake Umbagog Region of Maine," *Bulletin of the M.C.Z. at Harvard College,* vol. 66, Part 2.

BROWN, HERBERT
    1900   "The Conditions Governing Bird Life in Arizona," *The Auk,* vol. 17, No. 1, pp. 31-34, January.

BRYAN, WILLIAM ALANSON
   1912   "Report on Conditions on Laysan, with Recommendations for Protecting the Hawaiian Islands Reservation," *Department of Agriculture, Biological Survey, Bulletin No. 42.*

BRYANT, WALTER E.
   1888   "Birds and Eggs from the Farallone Islands," *Proceedings of the California Academy of Sciences,* ser. 2, vol. 1, p. 25.
   1890   "An Ornithological Retrospect," *Zoe,* vol. 1, pp. 289-293.

BURROWS, D. B.
   1917   "White-tailed Hawk," *The Oologist,* vol. 34, pp. 78-81.

BURTCH, VERDI
   1917   "Nesting of the Florida Gallinule," *The Auk,* vol. 34, pp. 319-321.

BUTURLIN, SERGIUS ALEKSANDROVICH
   1906   "The Breeding Grounds of the Rosy Gull," *The Ibis,* 1906, p. 131.

CAHN, ALVIN R.
   1912   "The Freezing of Cayuga Lake in its Relation to Bird Life," *The Auk,* vol. 29, p. 437.
   1923   "Louisiana Herons and Reddish Egrets at Home," *Natural History,* vol. 23, pp. 471-479.

CAHOON, JOHN CYRUS
   1888   "The Shore Birds of Cape Cod," *Ornithologist and Oologist,* vol. 13, pp. 121-124, 129-132, 153-156.

CAMPBELL, ARCHIBALD JAMES
   1901   *Nests and Eggs of Australian Birds.*

CARTWRIGHT, GEORGE
   1792   *A Journal of Transactions and Events During a Residence of Nearly Sixteen Years on the Coast of Labrador.*

CHAPMAN, ABEL
   1924   *The Borders and Beyond.*

CHAPMAN, FRANK MICHLER
   1903   "The Bird Life of Cobb's Island," *Bird-Lore,* vol. 5, p. 109.
   1908   *Camps and Cruises of an Ornithologist.*
   1914   "The Roseate Spoonbill," *Bird-Lore,* vol. 16, pp. 214-217.

CLARKE, WILLIAM EAGLE
   1898   "On the Avifauna of Franz Josef Land," *The Ibis,* 1898, p. 249.
   1906   "On the Birds of the South Orkney Islands: Ornithological Results of the Scottish National Antarctic Expedition," *The Ibis,* 1906, p. 145.

CLAY, CHARLES IRVIN
   1911   "Some Diving Notes on Cormorants," *The Condor,* vol. 13, p. 138.

COLLINS, JOSEPH WILLIAM
   1884   "Notes on the Habits and Methods of Capture of Various

Species of Sea-birds that Occur on the Fishing Banks off the Eastern Coast of North America, and Which Are Used as Bait for Catching Codfish by New England Fishermen," *Commission of Fish and Fisheries. Report of the Commissioner for 1882*, p. 311.

COLVIN, WALTER
    1914   "The Lesser Prairie Hen," *Outing*, vol. 63, pp. 608-614, illus., February.

COOKE, WELLES WOODBRIDGE
    1906   "Distribution and Migration of North American Ducks, Geese, and Swans," *United States Department of Agriculture, Biological Survey, Bulletin No. 26.*
    1911   "Our Greatest Travelers," *The National Geographic*, vol. 22, p. 346.
    1912   "Distribution and Migration of North American Shore Birds," *United States Department of Agriculture, Biological Survey, Bulletin No. 35, Rev.*

CORDEAUX, JOHN
    1898   *British Birds with their Nest and Eggs, Order Anseres*, vol. 4, pp. 52-203.

CORDIER, ALBERT HAWES
    1923   *Birds, their Photographs, and Home Life.*

CORY, CHARLES BARNEY
    1881   "Description of a New Species of the Family Procellariidae," *Bulletin of the Nuttall Ornithological Club*, vol. 6, p. 84.

COUES, ELLIOTT
    1861   "Notes on the Ornithology of Labrador," *Proceedings of the Philadelphia Academy of Natural Sciences*, 1861, p. 215.
    1874   *Birds of the Northwest.*
    1877   *Birds of the Northwest.*

DALL, WILLIAM HEALEY
    1873   *Notes on the Avifauna of the Aleutian Islands, from Unalaska, Eastward.*

DANFORTH, STUART T.
    1925   "Birds of the Cartagena Lagoon, Porto Rico," *Journal of the Department of Agriculture of Porto Rico*, vol. 10, No. 1.

DAWSON, WILLIAM LEON
    1908   "The New Reserves on the Washington Coast," *The Condor*, vol. 10, p. 45.
    1909   *The Birds of Washington.*
    1911   "Another Fortnight on the Farallones," *The Condor*, vol. 13, p. 171.
    1923   *The Birds of California*, 3 vols.

DILL, HOMER R., and BRYAN, WILLIAM ALANSON
    1912   "Report on Conditions on the Hawaiian Bird Reservation with List of the Birds Found on Laysan," *United States Department of*

Agriculture, Biological Survey, Bulletin No. 42.

DIXON, JOSEPH SCATTERGOOD

1916   "Migration of the Yellow-billed Loon," *The Auk,* vol. 33, p. 370.

1917   "The Home Life of the Baird Sandpiper," *The Condor,* vol. 19, pp. 77-84.

1927   "The Surf-Bird's Secret," *The Condor,* vol. 29, pp. 3-16.

DUTCHER, WILLIAM

1891   "The Labrador Duck—A Revised List of the Extant Specimens in North America, with Some Historical Notes," *The Auk,* vol. 8, pp. 201-216.

1901   "Results of Special Protection to Gulls and Terns Obtained Through the Thayer Fund," *The Auk,* vol. 18, p. 76.

1904   "Report of the A.O.U. Committee on the Protection of North American Birds, for the Year 1903," *The Auk,* vol. 21, p. 97.

1905   "Report of the National Association of Audubon Societies," *Bird-Lore,* vol. 7, p. 43.

ELLIOT, DANIEL GIRAUD

1897   *The Gallinaceous Game Birds of North America,* 220 pp., 46 plates, New York.

1898   *The Wild Fowl of North America.*

ELLIOTT, HENRY WOOD

1875   *A Report Upon the Condition of Affairs in the Territory of Alaska.*

FARREN, WILLIAM

1910   In the *British Bird Book,* edited by F. B. Kirkman, pp. 340-356.

FINLEY, WILLIAM LOVELL

1907   "Among the Pelicans," *The Condor,* vol. 9, p. 35.

FISHER, ALBERT KENRICK

1893   "The Hawks and Owls of the United States in Their Relation to Agriculture," *United States Department of Agriculture, Division of Ornithology and Mammalogy, Bulletin No. 3.*

FISHER, WALTER KENRICK

1904   "On the Habits of the Laysan Albatross," *The Auk,* vol. 21, p. 8.

1906   "Birds of Laysan and the Leeward Islands, Hawaiian Group," *Bulletin of the United States Fish Commission,* vol. 23, Part 3, p. 769.

FISHER, WILLIAM HARMANUS

1897   "Cobb's Island, Virginia," *The Osprey,* vol. 1, p. 107.

FORBUSH, EDWARD HOWE

1912   *A History of the Game Birds, Wild-fowl, and Shore Birds of Massachusetts and Adjacent States.*

GABRIELSON, IRA NOEL

1922   "Short Notes on the Life Histories of Various Species of Birds," *Wilson Bulletin,* vol. 34, No. 4, pp. 193-210, December.

GANIER, ALBERT FRANKLIN
 1902   "The Mississippi Kite (*Ictinia misisippiensis*)," *The Osprey*,
        vol. 6, pp. 85-90.
GÄTKE, HEINRICH
 1895   *Heligoland as an Ornithological Observatory.*
GIBSON, ERNEST
 1920   "Further Ornithological Notes from the Neighborhood of Cape
        San Antonio, Province of Buenos Ayres," *The Ibis*, 1920, pp. 1-97.
GODMAN, FREDERICK DUCANE
 1907   *A Monograph of the Petrels*, 1907-1910.
GOODWIN, S. H.
 1904   "About the Utah Gulls," *The Condor*, vol. 6, p. 99.
 1904   "Pelicans Nesting at Utah Lake," *The Condor*, vol. 6, p. 126.
GORDON, SETON PAUL
 1915   *Hill Birds of Scotland.*
GOSS, NATHANIEL STICKNEY
 1891   *History of the Birds of Kansas.*
GOSSE, PHILIP HENRY
 1847   *The Birds of Jamaica.*
GRAYSON, ANDREW JACKSON
 1871   "Natural History of the Tres Marias and Socorro," *Proceedings
        of the Boston Society of Natural History*, June 7, 1871.
GRIEVE, SYMINGTON
 1885   *The Great Auk, or Garefowl.*
GRINNELL, GEORGE BIRD
 1916   "Willets in Migration," *The Auk*, vol. 33, pp. 198-199.
GRINNELL, JOSEPH
 1897   "Petrels of Sitka, Alaska," *The Nidologist*, vol. 4, p. 76
 1897*b*   "Notes on the Marbled Murrelet," *The Osprey*, vol. 1, p. 115.
 1899   "The Rhinoceros Auklet at Catalina Island," *Bulletin of the
        Cooper Ornithological Club*, vol. 1, p. 17.
 1900   "Birds of the Kotzebue Sound Region," *Pacific Coast Avifauna*,
        No. 1.
GRINNELL, JOSEPH, BRYANT, HAROLD CHILD, and STORER, TRACY IRWIN
 1918   *The Game Birds of California.*
GRISCOM, LUDLOW
 1915   "The Little Black Rail on Long Island, New York," *The Auk*,
        vol. 32, p. 227, and p. 228.
GROSS, ALFRED O.
 1912   "Observations on the Yellow-billed Tropic-Bird (*Phaethon
        americanus* Grant), at the Bermuda Islands," *The Auk*, vol. 29, p. 49.
GURNEY, JOHN HENRY
 1913   *The Gannet.*
HAGERUP, ANDREAS THOMSEN
 1891   *The Birds of Greenland.*

HALL, ROBERT
  1900   "Field Notes on the Birds of Kerguelen Island," *The Ibis,*
           1900, p. 1.
HANNA, G. DALLAS
  1921   "The Pribilof Sandpiper," *The Condor,* vol. 26, pp. 50-57.
HARTLEY, GEORGE INNESS
  1922   *The Importance of Bird Life.*
HATCH, PHILO LOUIS
  1892   *Notes on the Birds of Minnesota.*
HEADLEY, FREDERICK WEBB
  1907   *Life and Evolution.*
  1912   *The Flight of Birds.*
HEATH, HAROLD
  1915   "Birds Observed on Forrester Island, Alaska, During the Sum-
           mer of 1913," *The Condor,* vol. 17, p. 20.
HOLLAND, ARTHUR H.
  1892   "Short Notes on the Birds of Estancia Espartella, Argentine
           Republic," *The Ibis,* 1892, pp. 193-214.
HOWE, REGINALD HEBER, JR.
  1902   "Notes on Various Florida Birds," *Contributions to North
           American Ornithology,* vol. 1, pp. 25-32.
HOWELL, ALFRED BRAZIER
  1911   "A Comparative Study at Cobb's Island, Virginia," *The Auk,*
           vol. 28, p. 449.
HOWELL, ARTHUR HOLMES
  1911   "Birds of Arkansas," *United States Department of Agriculture,
           Biological Survey, Bulletin No. 38.*
HUBBARD, SAMUEL, JR.
  1893   "A Tragedy in Bird Life," *Zoe,* vol. 3, pp. 361-362.
HUDSON, WILLIAM HENRY
  1920   *Birds of La Plata.*
  1922   *A Hind in Richmond Park.*
HUNTINGTON, DWIGHT WILLIAMS
  1903   *Our Feathered Game.*
INGERSOLL, ALBERT M.
  1909   "The Only Known Breeding Ground of *Creciscus coturniculus,"
           The Condor,* vol. 11, pp. 123-127.
JOB, HERBERT KEIGHTLEY
  1898   "The Enchanted Isles," *The Osprey,* vol. 3, p. 37.
  1905   *Wild Wings.*
JONES, LYNDS (with Dawson, William Leon)
  1903   *The Birds of Ohio.*
JUDD, SYLVESTER DWIGHT
  1905a   "The Grouse and Wild Turkeys of the United States and
           Their Economic Value." *United States Department of Agriculture,
           Biological Survey, Bulletin 24.*

KENTWOOD
1896 "Martha's Vineyard Heath Hen," *Forest and Stream,* vol. 47, No. 18, p. 343 and p. 344, October 31.

KINGSFORD, E. G.
1917 "Wood Duck Removing Young from the Nest," *The Auk,* vol. 34, pp. 335-336.

KNIGHT, CHARLES WILLIAM ROBERT
1932 "Photographing the Nest Life of the Osprey," *The National Geographic,* vol. 62, pp. 247-260.

KNIGHT, ORA WILLIS
1908 *The Birds of Maine.*

KUMLEIN, LUDWIG
1879 "Contributions to the Natural History of Arctic America," *Bulletin of the United States National Museum, No. 15.*

LACEY, HOWARD
1911 "The Birds of Kerrville, Texas, and Vicinity," *The Auk,* vol. 28, p. 200-219.

LANG, HERBERT
1924 "*Ampullarius* and *Rostrhamus* at Georgetown, British Guiana," *The Nautilus,* vol. 37, pp. 73-77.

LAWRENCE, GEORGE NEWBOLD
1874 "Birds of Western and Northwestern Mexico," *Memoirs of the Boston Society of Natural History,* vol. 2, pp. 265-319.

LEWIS, EVAN
1904 "The Nesting Habits of the White-Tailed Ptarmigan in Colorado," *Bird Lore,* vol. 6, No. 4, pp. 117-121, illus., July-August.

LOOMIS, LEVERETT MILLS
1895 "California Water Birds," No. 1. *Proceedings of the California Academy of Sciences,* Second Series, vol. 5, p. 177.
1896 "California Water Birds," Nos. 2 and 3. *Proceedings of the California Academy of Sciences,* Second Series, vol. 6, p. 1 and p. 353.
1900 "California Water Birds," Nos. 4 and 5. *Proceedings of the California Academy of Sciences,* Third Series, Zoology, vol. 2, p. 277 and p. 349.
1918 *Expedition of the California Academy of Sciences to the Galapagos Islands, 1905-1906. A Review of the Albatrosses, Petrels and Diving Petrels.*

MACFARLANE, RODERICK ROSS
1891 "Notes on and List of Birds and Eggs Collected in Arctic America, 1861-1866," *Proceedings of the United States National Museum,* vol. 14, pp. 413-446.

MACGILLIVRAY, WILLIAM
1852 *A History of British Birds.*

MACKAY, GEORGE HENRY
1892 "Habits of the Oldsquaw (*Clangula hyemalis*) in New England," *The Auk,* vol. 9, pp. 330-337.

1893 "Observations on the Knot (*Tringa canutus*)," *The Auk*, vol. 10, pp. 25-35.

MacMillan, Donald Baxter
1918 *Four Years in the White North.*

Macoun, John
1909 *Catalogue of Canadian Birds. Second edition.*

Manniche, A. L. V.
1910 "The Terrestrial Mammals and Birds of Northeast Greenland," *Medelelser om Grønland*, vol. 45.

Mars, F. St.
1912 "The Eagle Guard," *The Outing Magazine*, vol. 59, p. 676, No. 6, March 1912.

Martin, Martin
1753 *A Voyage to St. Kilda.*

May, John Bichard
1935 *The Hawks of North America.*

Maynard, Charles Johnson
1896 *The Birds of Eastern North America.*

McAtee, Waldo Lee
1910 "Notes on *Chen coerulescens, Chen rossi,* and Other Waterfowl in Louisiana," *The Auk*, vol. 27, pp. 337-339.
1929 "Game Birds Suitable for Naturalizing in the United States," *United States Department of Agriculture Circular 96*, pp. 1-23, figs. 1-14, November.

Merriam, Clinton Hart
1883 "Breeding of the Harlequin Duck," *Bulletin of the Nuttall Ornithological Club*, vol. 8, p. 220.

Millais, John Guille
1902 *The Natural History of the British Surface-Feeding Ducks.*
1913 *British Diving Ducks.*

Montgomery, Henry Hutchinson
1898 "On the Habits of the Mutton-bird of Bass Strait, Australia (*Puffinus tenuirostris*)," *The Ibis*, 1898, p. 209.

Moore, Dr. Robert Thomas
1912 "The Least Sandpiper During the Nesting Season in the Magdalen Islands," *The Auk*, vol. 29, pp. 210-223.

Morris, F. O.
1903 *A History of British Birds.* Fifth edition.

Murdoch, John
1885 "Report of the International Polar Expedition to Point Barrow, Alaska," Part 4. *Natural History*, p. 91.

Murie, Dr. Olaus Johan
1924 "Nesting Records of the Wandering Tattler and Surf-Bird in Alaska," *The Auk*, vol. 41, pp. 231-237.

NELSON, EDWARD WILLIAM

1877*b* "Notes Upon Birds Observed in Southern Illinois, Between July 17 and September 4, 1875," *Bulletin of Essex Institute*, vol. 9, pp. 32-65.

1881 "Habits of the Black Brant in the Vicinity of St. Michaels, Alaska," *Bulletin of the Nuttall Ornithological Club*, vol. 6, pp. 131-138.

1883 *The Birds of Bering Sea and the Arctic Ocean. Cruise of the Revenue-Steamer Corwin in Alaska and the Northwest Arctic Ocean in 1881.*

1887 *Report Upon Natural History Collections Made in Alaska.*

1899 "Birds of the Tres Marias Islands," *North American Fauna*, No. 14, p. 21.

1903 "Notes on the Mexican Cormorant," *The Condor*, vol. 5, p. 139.

1913 "The Emperor Goose," Educational Leaflet, No. 64. *Bird-Lore*, vol. 15, pp. 129-132.

NEWTON, ALFRED

1861 "Abstract of Mr. J. Wolley's Researches in Iceland Respecting the Gare-Fowl or Great Auk (*Alca impennis* Linn.)," *The Ibis*, vol. 3, p. 374.

NICHOLS, JOHN TREADWELL

1920 "Limicoline Voices," *The Auk*, vol. 37, pp. 519-540.

NOBEL, FRANK T.

1904 "Feeding Habits of the Turnstone," *Journal of Maine Ornithological Society*, vol. 6, pp. 57-59.

NUTTALL, THOMAS

1832 *A Manual of the Ornithology of the United States and of Canada, Land Birds.*

1834 *A Manual of the Ornithology of the United States and Canada, Water Birds.*

OGILVIE-GRANT, WILLIAM ROBERT

1896 "On the Birds Observed at the Salvage Islands, near Madeira," *The Ibis*, 1896, p. 41.

PALMER, WILLIAM

1890 "Notes on the Birds Observed During the Cruise of the United States Fish Commission Schooner *Grampus* in the Summer of 1887," *Proceedings of the United States National Museum*, vol. 13, p. 249.

1899 *The Avifauna of the Pribilof Islands. The Fur-Seals and Fur-Seal Islands of the North Pacific Ocean.* Part 3, p. 355.

PEABODY, PUTNAM BURTON

1922 "Haunts and Breeding Habits of the Yellow Rail," *The Journal of the Museum of Comparative Oology*, vol. 2, pp. 33-44.

PEARSON, THOMAS GILBERT

1912 "The White Egrets," *Bird-Lore*, vol. 14, pp. 62-69.

1916 "The Shoveller," *Bird-Lore*, vol. 18, pp. 56-59.

1922   "Herons of the United States," *Bird-Lore*, vol. 24, pp. 306-314.
PHILIPP, PHILIP BERNARD
1925   "Notes on Some Summer Birds of the Magdalen Islands,"
The Canadian Field Naturalist, vol. 39, pp. 75-78.
PHILLIPS, JOHN CHARLES
1928   "Wild Birds Introduced or Transplanted in North America,"
United States Department of Agriculture Technical Bulletin No. 61.
PICKWELL, GAYLE BENJAMIN
1930   "The White-Tailed Kite," *The Condor*, vol. 32, pp. 221-239.
PLATH, KARL
1913   "The Tropic Birds of Bermuda," *Bird-Lore*, vol. 15, p. 345.
POPHAM, HUGH LEYBOURNE
1898   "Further Notes on Birds Observed on the Yenesei River,
Siberia," *The Ibis*, 1898, pp. 489-520.
POST, WILLIAM S.
1914   "Nesting of the Merganser (*Mergus americanus*) in 1913," *The
Oriole*, vol. 2, pp. 18-23.
PREBLE, EDWARD ALEXANDER
1908   "A Biological Investigation of the Athabasca-Mackenzie Region," *North American Fauna*, No. 27.
QUILLIN, ROY W. and HOLLEMAN, RIDLEY
1916   "The San Domingo Grebe in Bexar County, Texas," *The
Condor*, vol. 18, p. 221.
RAWSON, CALVIN L. (J.M.W.)
1882   "Sharp-Shinned Hawk," *Ornithologist and Oologist*, vol. 6, pp.
89-91.
RAY, MILTON SMITH
1904   "A Fortnight on the Farallones," *The Auk*, vol. 21, p. 425.
RICH, WALTER HERBERT
1907   *Feathered Game of the Northeast.*
RIVES, WILLIAM CABELL
1890   "A Catalogue of the Birds of the Virginias," *Proceedings of
the Newport Natural History Society*, No. 7.
ROCKWELL, ROBERT BLANCHARD
1910   "Nesting Notes on the American Eared Grebe and Pied-Billed
Grebe," *The Condor*, vol. 12, p. 188.
ROSS, JAMES CLARK
1835   *Natural History, in Appendix to the Narrative of a Second
Voyage in Search of a Northwest Passage, by Sir John Ross.*
ROWAN, WILLIAM
1926-27   "Notes on Alberta Waders Included in the British List,"
British Birds, vol. 20, pp. 2-10, 34-42, 82-90, 138-145, 186-192.
SANDYS, EDWYN and VAN DYKE, T. S.
1904   *Upland Game Birds.*
SANFORD, LEONARD CUTLER, BISHOP, LOUIS BENNETT, and VAN DYKE,

THEODORE STRONG
1903   *The Waterfowl Family.*

SASS, HERBERT RAVENEL
1930   "Kings of Winter," *Good Housekeeping,* vol. 90, No. 2, pp. 32-33, 202-216, February.

SCHNEIDER, FREDERICK ALEXANDER, JR.
1893   "Nesting of the Cinnamon Teal," *The Nidiologist,* vol. 1, pp. 20-22.

SCOTT, WILLIAM EARL DODGE
1887   "The Present Condition of Some of the Bird Rookeries of the Gulf Coast of Florida," *The Auk,* vol. 4, pp. 135-144, 213-222, 273-284.
1889   "A Summary of Observations on the Birds of the Gulf Coast of Florida," *The Auk,* vol. 6, pp. 13-18.
1890   "An Account of Flamingos (*Phoenicopterus ruber*) Observed in the Vicinity of Cape Sable, Florida," *The Auk,* vol. 7, pp. 221-226.
1891   "Observations on the Birds of Jamaica, West Indies," *The Auk,* vol. 3, p. 249 and p. 353.

SEEBOHM, HENRY
1901   *The Birds of Siberia.*

SELOUS, EDMUND
1906-1907   "Observations on Sexual Selection in Birds," *Zoologist,* 1906, pp. 201-219, 285-294, 419-428; 1907, pp. 60-65, 161-182, 367-381.

SHAW, WILLIAM THOMAS
1908   *The China or Denny Pheasant in Oregon, with Notes on the Native Grouse of the Pacific Northwest.*

SILLOWAY, PERLEY MILTON
1900   "Notes on the Long-Billed Curlew," *The Condor,* vol. 2, pp. 79-82.

SIMMONS, GEORGE FINLAY
1925   *Birds of the Austin Region.*

STEJNEGER, LEONHARD
1885   "Results of Ornithological Explorations in the Commander Islands and in Kamtschatka," *Bulletin of the United States National Museum,* No. 29.

STODDARD, HERBERT LEE
1931   *The Bobwhite Quail, Its Habits, Preservation, and Increase.*

STONE, WITMER
1909   "The Birds of New Jersey, Their Nests, and Eggs," *Annual Report of the New Jersey State Museum.*

STREET, JOHN FLETCHER
1923   "On the Nesting Grounds of the Solitary Sandpiper and the Lesser Yellow-legs," *The Auk,* vol. 40, pp. 577-583.

SUTTON, GEORGE MIKSCH

1923   "Notes on the Nesting of the Wilson's Snipe in Crawford
County, Pennsylvania," *The Wilson Bulletin*, vol. 35, pp. 191-202.

1925   "Notes on the Nesting of the Goshawk in Potter County, Pennsylvania," *The Wilson Bulletin*, vol. 37, pp. 193-199.

SWALES, BRADSHAW HALL

See TAVERNER, PERCY ALGERNON.

SWARTH, HARRY SCHELWALDT

1926   "Report on a Collection of Birds and Mammals from the Atlin
Region, Northern British Columbia," *University of California Publica-
tions in Zoology*, vol. 30, pp. 51-162.

SWENK, MYRON HARMON

1915   "The Eskimo Curlew and Its Disappearance," *Annual Report
of the Smithsonian Institution for 1915*, pp. 325-340.

TAVERNER, PERCY ALGERNON and SWALES, BRADSHAW HALL

1907   "The Birds of Point Pelee," *The Wilson Bulletin*, No. 60,
pp. 82-99.

TAVERNER, PERCY ALGERNON

1926   "Birds of Western Canada," *Victoria Memorial Museum Bulletin*, 41.

THAYER, JOHN ELIOT

1909   Two Letters from W. W. Brown, Jr., published in *The Condor*,
vol. 11.

1911a   "Eggs of the Elegant Tern (*Sterna elegans*)," *The Oologist*,
vol. 28, p. 171.

1914   "Nesting of the Kittlitz Murrelet," *The Condor*, vol. 16, p. 117.

THOMAS, GERALD BAMBER

1908   "The Mexican Black Hawk," *The Condor*, vol. 10, pp. 116-118.

THOMPSON, ERNEST EVAN (SETON, ERNEST THOMPSON)

1890   "The Birds of Manitoba," *Proceedings of the United States
National Museum*, vol. 13, pp. 457-643, pl. 38.

THURSTON, HENRY

1913   "Wilson's Plover," *The Warbler*, vol. 7, pp. 22-24.

TOWNSEND, CHARLES HASKINS

1890   "Birds from the Coasts of Western North America and Adjacent
Islands, Collected in 1888-1890, with Descriptions of New Species,"
Proceedings of the United States National Museum, vol. 13, p. 131.

1913   "The Crested Auklet," The National Association of Audubon
Societies, Educational Leaflet, No. 65. *Bird Lore*, vol. 15, p. 133.

TOWNSEND, CHARLES WENDELL

1905   "The Birds of Essex County, Massachusetts," *Memoirs of the
Nuttall Ornithological Club*. No. 3.

1910   "The Courtship of the Golden-Eye and Eider Ducks," *The
Auk*, vol. 27, pp. 177-181.

1911   "The Courtship and Migration of the Red-Breasted Merganser
(*Mergus serrator*)," *The Auk*, vol. 28, pp. 341-345.

TURLE, WILLIAM H.
1891   "A Visit to the Blasket Islands and the Skelling Rocks," *The Ibis*, 1891, p. 1.

TURNER, LUCIEN MCSHAN
1886   *Contributions to the Natural History of Alaska.*

TYLER, JOHN GRIPPER
1913   "Some Birds of the Fresno District, California," *Pacific Coast Avifauna*, No. 9.

VERRILL, ADDISON EMORY
1902   "The Bermuda Islands," *Transactions of the Connecticut Academy of Arts and Sciences*, vol. 11, Part 2.

VERRILL, ALPHEUS HYATT
1901   "Notes on the Birds of the Bermudas With Descriptions of Two New Subspecies and Several Additions to the Fauna," *The Osprey*, vol. 5, p. 83.

VISHER, STEPHEN SARGENT
1910   "Notes on the Sandhill Crane," *The Wilson Bulletin*, vol. 22, pp. 115-117.

WATSON, JOHN BROADUS
1908   "The Behavior of Noddy and Sooty Terns," *Papers from the Tortugas Laboratory of the Carnegie Institution of Washington*, vol. 2, p. 187.

WAYNE, ARTHUR TREZEVANT
1910   *Birds of South Carolina. Contributions from the Charleston Museum*, No. 1.

WETMORE, ALEXANDER
1926   "Observations on the Birds of Argentina, Paraguay, Uruguay, and Chile," *United States National Museum, Bulletin 133.*

WHEELOCK, IRENE GROSVENOR
1904   *Birds of California.*

WILLETT, GEORGE
1912   "Report of G. Willett, Agent and Warden, Stationed on St. Lazaria Bird Reservation, Alaska," *Bird Lore*, vol. 14, p. 419.

WILLETT, GEORGE and JAY, ANTONIN
1911   "May Notes from San Jacinto Lake," *The Condor*, vol. 13, pp. 156-160.

WILLIAMS, JOHN J.
1903   "On the Use of Sentinels by Valley Quail," *The Condor*, vol. 5, No. 6, pp. 146-148, illus., November-December.

WILSON, ALEXANDER
1832   *American Ornithology*, Jardine edition.

WOOD, WILLIAM
1635   *New England Prospect*, chap. 8, pp. 22-27. London.

WRIGHT, HOWARD W.
1913   "The Birds of San Martin Island, Lower California," *The Condor*, vol. 15, p. 207.

WURDEMANN, GUSTAVUS
  1861   "Letter Relative to the Obtaining of Specimens of Flamingos
           and Other Birds From South Florida," *Annual Report of the Smith-*
           sonian Institution for 1860, pp. 426-430.
YORKE, F. HENRY
  1891   "Green-Wing Teal Shooting," *The American Field,* vol. 35,
           No. 22, pp. 533-535.
  1899   *Our Ducks.*

GEOGRAPHICAL INDEX

GENERAL INDEX